Concise Guide to the

Moths

of Great Britain and Ireland

Martin Townsend and Paul Waring

Illustrated by Richard Lewington

To my late parents, Denis and Barbara Townsend, whose own love and knowledge of the natural world led to my interest in insects and other wildlife. M T

To my late parents, Doris and Clifford Waring, who encouraged my interest in moths in my formative years; to my wife Rachel Thomas, for her support and understanding during many moth projects, past, present and future; and to my young daughter, Kirsty Mae, who already enjoys looking at the pictures in this guide and the live moths in my traps. P W

Acknowledgements

The authors and artist would like, once again, to thank warmly all the individuals and organisations who provided invaluable help in preparing the *Field Guide to the Moths of Great Britain and Ireland* upon which this *Concise Guide* is based, including Mark Tunmore who assisted with accounts of immigrant noctuid species.

Martin Townsend, Paul Waring and Richard Lewington

British Wildlife Publishing
An imprint of Bloomsbury Publishing Plc

50 Bedford Square
London
WC1B 3DP
UK

1385 Broadway
New York
NY 10018
USA

www.bloomsbury.com

First published 2007
Reprinted 2007, 2009, 2011, 2013, 2014, 2015

A catalogue record for this book is available from the British Library.

ISBN: 978-0-95649-029-2

8 10 9 7

The paper used for this book has been independently certified as coming from well-managed forests and other controlled sources according to the rules of the Forest Stewardship Council.

This book has been printed and bound in Italy by Printer Trento S.r.l., an FSC® accredited company for printing books on FSC® mixed paper in compliance with the chain of custody and on-products labelling standards.

Contents

Introduction

In recent years, more and more people have discovered that identifying moths can be an enjo
able and rewarding pastime. This *Concise Guide* has been produced as a durable, handy and easy-to-use companion to the *Field Guide to the Moths of Great Britain and Ireland* (Waring & Townsend 2003). It illustrates nearly all of the larger or 'macro'-moths (874 species) that have been recorded in the wild in Great Britain and Ireland and the Channels Islands, showing the moths in their natural resting postures. The original *Field Guide* is still the most comprehensiv single volume currently available on the identification, life history, status and distribution of Britain's macro-moths. In producing this *Concise Guide*, we set out to create a robust compan designed as an aide purely to identification for the vast majority of species. While the illustrat retain the clarity of the original, the text has been reduced to enable descriptions to appear o the same spread as the artwork which, together with the wiro-binding, means that the inform tion is quickly accessible, even in the midst of the flurry of activity around a moth-trap.

In cases where there is still uncertainty over the identity of a moth after reference to this book and an accurate determination is required, reference to the *Field Guide* should be ma This is especially important if the species is uncommon, or is previously unknown from the geographical region from which you have recorded it. In these cases, retention of a specim or a good quality photograph (if diagnostic features can be seen) is likely to be required be it can be accepted, since the memory often deceives. The network of county moth recorde (see www.angleps.btinternet.co.uk/recorders.pdf) are always happy to receive and verify records.

Species accounts

Each description begins with the common and scientific name of the species (after the Britis checklist, Bradley 2000), followed by abbreviated information on its status and distribution. The emphasis of the short descriptions is on key identification features and comparisons wit similar species with which confusion is most likely. The usual range of variation in colour and markings of the moth is summarised. Less frequent but regularly occurring forms are describ but rare forms are not generally included. The flight season (FS) of each generation is separa by a semi-colon. Where a second or third generation season is in brackets this means it is on partial or occasional. At the end of each description is a list of abbreviations (see below) indi cating the usual habitats in which the moth may be found; the main habitats are listed first.

There is a brief description of family characteristics, including shape, resting posture and generalised comments on behaviour. Exceptions are noted under the species, and particula habits are mentioned where they may help identification.

For information on larval foodplants, further details of habitat, status and distribution, a information on techniques, similar-looking groups of micro-moths and other insects, conse vation and national statuses, please refer to the *Field Guide*. A short list of publications and entomological societies is given on page 154.

A number of species have been added to the British list since the *Field Guide* was published. They include Splendid Brocade *Lacanobia splendens*, Jersey Mocha *Cyclophora ruficiliaria*, Eastern Nycteoline *Nycteola asiatica*, Beautiful Marbled *Eublemma purpurina* an Minsmere Crimson Underwing *Catocala conjuncta*, and these are described. Doubtfully Brit species are usually not included.

Key to abbreviations of habitat categories

A = lowland acid heathland
Ar = arable fields
AWt = acid wetlands
BWd = broadleaved woodland
C = coastal habitats
CGr = calcareous grassland
Cl = coastal grassland on rocky coastlines, cliffs and slopes
CWd = coniferous woodland
G = gardens, urban parkland and other urban situations
Gr = grassland, dry or damp, acid, calcareous or neutral
H = hedgerows
M = acid moorland (uplands)
O = orchards
Q = disused quarries
R = rough, weedy ground
RSh = river shingle
Sd = sand-dunes
Sc = scrub
Sh = coastal shingle
Sm = saltmarsh
Ub = more or less ubiquitous – ca found in a wide variety of hab
Up = uplands – acid moorland, mountain tops and high past
Wd = woodland, well-wooded hedgerows and old rural park
Wt = wetlands, including riverban ditches and carr

Key to abbreviations of geographical regions

T = throughout Great Britain, Ireland and the Channel Islands
S = southern (south of the Wash)
C = central (from the Wash northwards to Cumbria and Northumberland)
N = northern (from Cumbria and Northumberland to Shetland)
E, W = east/west of a line bisecting the Isle of Wight
Ir = Ireland
( ) = main part of distribution elsewhere, but extends locally or rarely to this area

Key to national status categories

RDB = Red Data Book species. Known from less than 15 10km squares
Na = Nationally Scarce A. Recorded from 16-30 10km squares since 1980
Nb = Nationally Scarce B. Recorded from 31-100 10km squares since 1980
Local = recorded from 101-300 10km squares since 1960
Common = recorded from more than 300 10km squares since 1960
Uncommon on introduced foodplant = recorded from less than 100 10km squares since 1980, but dependent on non-native foodplant(s)
Immigrant = considered to have reached the British Isles by natural flight
Rare immigrant = fewer than ten records
Import = reaching the British Isles with human assistance, by importation with goods, etc.
p = prefix to indicate proposed inclusion in the category given

Moth external anatomy and wing markings

The illustration below shows the Angle Shades moth at rest and with wings spread, as in a cabinet specimen. This shows how some diagnostic features such as resting posture (with furled wings) are lost in the cabinet specimen, while conversely, features of the hindwings are revealed. This, together with illustrations of the Lesser Yellow Underwing, show the anatomical terms used in the guide.

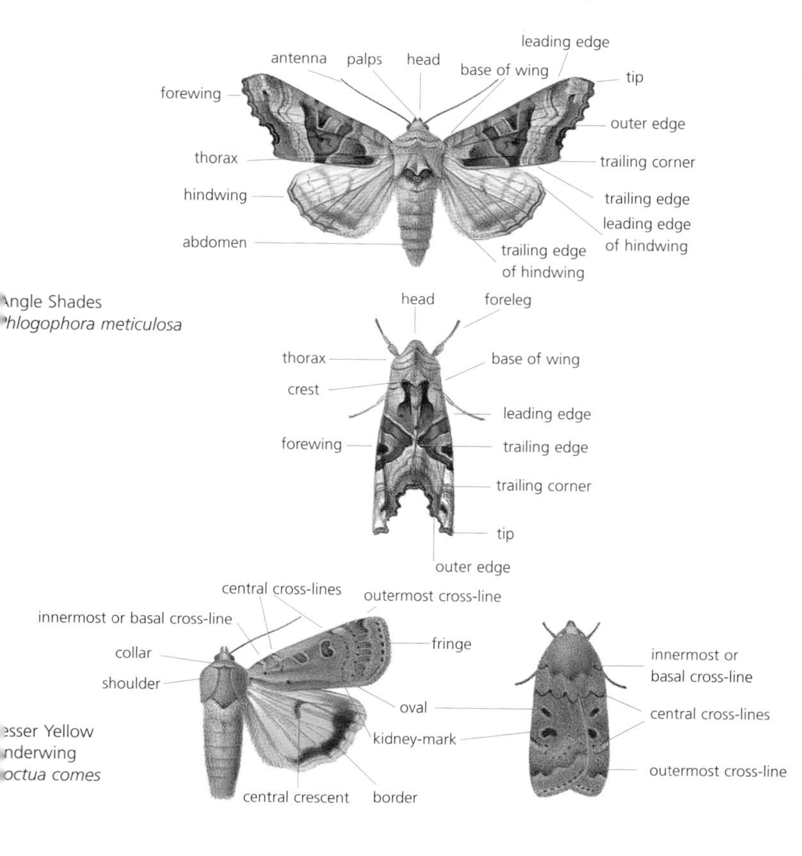

ngle Shades
hlogophora meticulosa

esser Yellow nderwing
octua comes

Hepialidae Swift moths

Primitive moths with elongated wings, held almost vertically against the body when at rest. Main flight is from early dusk until full darkness. All come to light. They do not feed and have very short antennae.

Ghost Moth *Hepialus humuli humuli* Common T; ssp. *thulensis* Shetland **FW** M 21-29mm F 21-35mm. Ssp. *humuli*: Generally the largest of our swift moths. Male has plain white forewing and hindwing (dark grey underneath); female has unmistakable yellowish-orange forewing. Ssp. *thulensis*: Smaller. Male has creamy white or yellowish forewing, variably marked with brown; that of female less yellow than in ssp. *humuli*. Hindwing grey in both sexes. **FS** June-early August. Males have a characteristic 'lekking' flight at dusk, swaying to and fro as if attached to a pendulum. **Hab** Ub.

Orange Swift *Hepialus sylvina* Common T **FW** M 12-18mm F 15-26mm. Male has distinctive bright orange-brown forewing, with two quite narrow, fairly straight, continuous, dark-edged, whitish diagonal lines forming an open V. Duller female is somewhat similar to plainer forms of Map-winged Swift, which has white dot at base and in centre of forewing, and chequered fringes. See also Common Swift. **FS** Late June-early September. **Hab** Ub.

Gold Swift *Hepialus hecta* Local T **FW** M 12-15mm F 13-16mm. Male with golden markings on forewing. Diagonal (sometimes broken) band near base runs roughly parallel to outer markings. Duller female has broad, purplish-grey bands on forewing. Both sexes more slender than Common Swift, banded examples of which have whitish markings, with that near base angled to almost meet outer markings near trailing edge, forming an open V. **FS** Mid June-mid July. **Hab** Wd A Gr.

Common Swift *Hepialus lupulinus* Common T **FW** M 11-16mm F 15-20mm. Forewing markings of male vary greatly in amount and intensity, ranging from whitish to pale brown to grey; entirely plain examples occur. Female slightly larger, with forewing generally much less strongly marked, often plain grey. Orange Swift usually later in the year; forewing broader, brighter in male, with a smooth, finer open white V; female browner than Common Swift, with extensive grey or greyish-white markings. See also Gold Swift. **FS** May-July. **Hab** Ub.

Map-winged Swift *Hepialus fusconebulosa* Local T **FW** 14-26mm. Distinctive, with map-like variegated markings on forewing of the most frequent form. In f. *gallicus*, which occurs throughout the range, forewing more uniformly yellowish brown and whitish markings limited to two small dots, one in centre of wing and one at base. Both forms have chequered fringes, unlike the other swifts. On the sand-dunes of Orkney the moths are small and pale. In Shetland some have particularly bright patterns and have been named f. *shetlandicus*. See also Orange Swift. **FS** Late May-early July or early August in the north. **Hab** M A Wd (CGr Sd).

Cossidae Leopard and goat moths

These are nocturnal moths, and come to light. Wings elongated, held at a steep angle close to the body when at rest. They do not feed.

Zeuzerinae

Reed Leopard *Phragmataecia castaneae* RDB E,S **FW** 15-23mm. Forewing straw-white with fine blackish spotting. Antennae comb-like in male. Abdomen in female very long, usually extending well beyond wing tips. Several wainscot moths are a similar colour and occur in the same habitat, but none have combination of features listed above. **FS** June-July, sometimes late May or early August. **Hab** Wt.

Leopard Moth *Zeuzera pyrina* Common S,E,C,(Ir) **FW** 22-35mm. Thorax big, furry, with six large black spots. Wings whitish, with heavy blackish spotting. Antennae club-like in male. In a rare form central spots of forewing are joined to form stripes. See also Puss Moth. **FS** Late June-early August. **Hab** BWd Sc G.

Cossinae

Goat Moth *Cossus cossus* Nb. T **FW** 32-42mm. Large, very thickset moth. Forewing silvery grey-brown, with many fine, dark, irregular and often branched cross-lines, which resemble cracks in bark. Distinctive upright resting posture. **FS** June-July. **Hab** BWd H Wt.

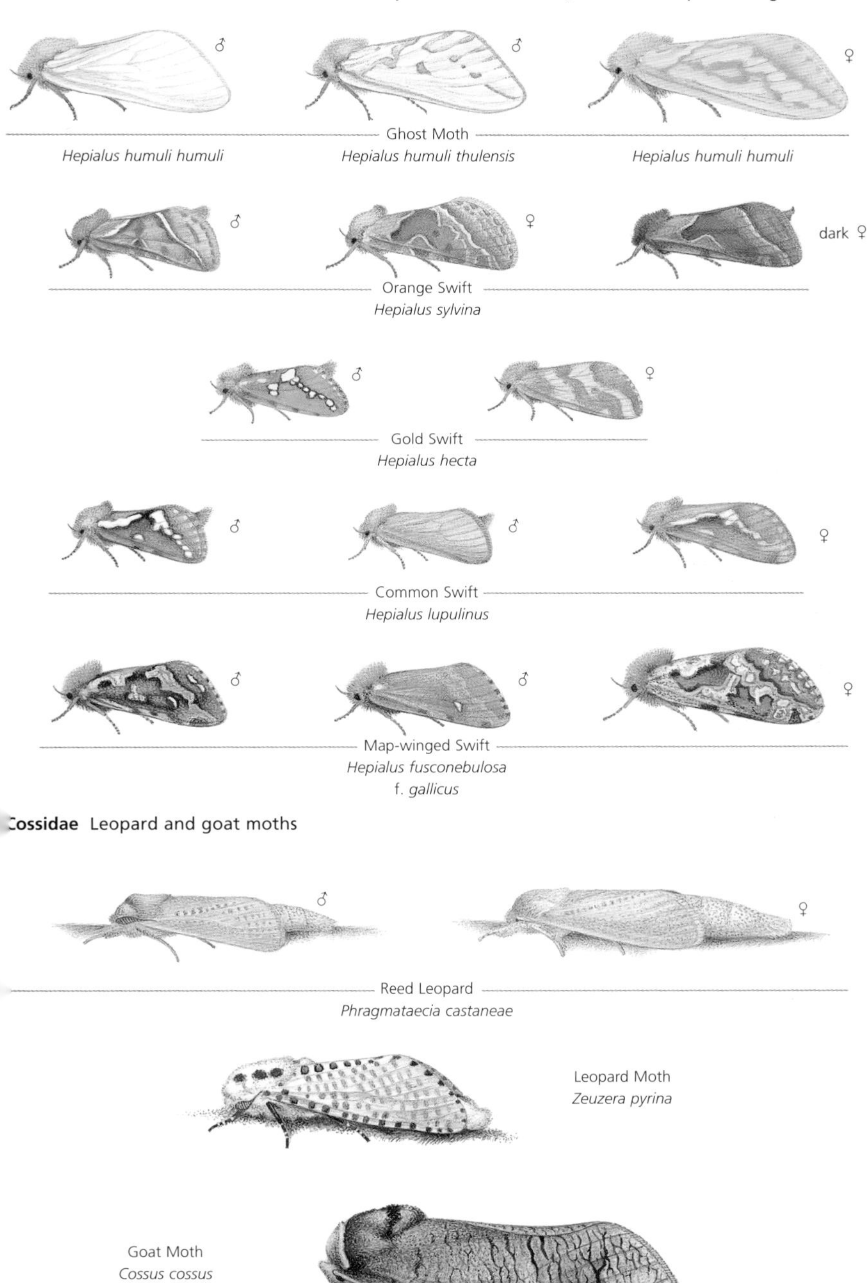

♂
♂
♀
Ghost Moth
Hepialus humuli humuli
Hepialus humuli thulensis
Hepialus humuli humuli
♂
♀
dark ♀
Orange Swift
Hepialus sylvina
♂
♀
Gold Swift
Hepialus hecta
♂
♂
♀
Common Swift
Hepialus lupulinus
♂
♂
♀
Map-winged Swift
Hepialus fusconebulosa
f. gallicus
Cossidae Leopard and goat moths
♂
♀
Reed Leopard
Phragmataecia castaneae
Leopard Moth
Zeuzera pyrina
Goat Moth
Cossus cossus

Zygaenidae

Day-flying moths, often with clubbed antennae.

Procridinae Forester moths

Forester *Adscita statices* Local S,C,Ir **FW** M 12-15mm F 11-13mm. The three British forester moths are superficially almost identical, but can be separated by careful comparison of individuals of the same sex. Males have slightly larger, broader, feathery antennae. When comparing the same sex, Forester and Scarce Forester are about the same size, but Cistus Forester is smaller. Antennae of both sexes of Forester are broader at tip than in Scarce Forester. Moths away from unimproved dry calcareous grassland are unlikely to be Scarce or Cistus Forester. See Scarce Forester for further differences. **FS** Mid May-July, occasionally into August. **Hab** Gr.

Cistus Forester *Adscita geryon* Nb. S,C **FW** M 10-12mm F 9-10mm. Both sexes distinctly smaller than the same sex of Forester and Scarce Forester. See Scarce Forester for differences in antennae. **FS** Late May-early August. **Hab** CGr.

Scarce Forester *Jordanita globulariae* Na. S **FW** M 12-15mm F 10-12mm. Forewing of both sexes generally broader and more rounded at tip than in same sex of Forester. Male antennae tapering and pointed at tip, lacking distinct feather-blade extensions on last three segments. In male Forester and Cistus Forester, not tapering and rather blunt-tipped with ten and seven segments respectively lacking feather-like extensions. In female Scarce Forester antennae longer, very slender, and of almost uniform thickness from tip to base; in the other two species, narrowed towards base. **FS** June-early July. **Hab** CGr.

Antennae ♂ ♀ ♂ ♀

Scarce Forester Forester

Zygaeninae Burnet moths

Scotch Burnet (Mountain Burnet) *Zygaena exulans* ssp. *subochracea* RDB N **FW** 10-16mm. Forewing thinly scaled, with five distinct but sometimes very small red spots. Female with yellow shoulder patches. In Slender Scotch, spot nearest forewing tip is large and hindwing has very narrow dark border. See also Transparent Burnet, which is larger. **FS** Mid June-late July. **Hab** M.

Slender Scotch Burnet *Zygaena loti* ssp. *scotica* RDB (proposed Protected species) NW **FW** 14-16mm. Red spot nearest forewing tip large, formed from merger of two spots. Other four spots distinct and hindwing with very narrow black border. Forelegs yellowish brown in part. Six-spot Burnet may have merged spots near wing tip, but is usually larger, has more thickly-scaled forewing, a less hairy body, and legs are outwardly black. See also Scotch Burnet, Transparent Burnet. **FS** Early June-early July. **Hab** Cl.

New Forest Burnet *Zygaena viciae* ssp. *ytenensis* Extinct; ssp. *argyllensis* RDB (Protected species) NW **FW** 12-14mm. Small, with very round-tipped forewing and five clearly defined red spots, with a broad dark area beyond. Five-spot Burnet is larger and stouter, with more pointed wings. **FS** July. **Hab** Gr.

Six-spot Burnet *Zygaena filipendulae* ssp. *stephensi* Common T **FW** 15-19mm. The only British burnet with six red forewing spots (red patch at base is divided by a vein and counts as two spots). In some forms outermost spots are merged, also sometimes middle pair. Very rarely red is replaced by yellow. See Slender Scotch Burnet. **FS** Late June-August. **Hab** Gr.

Five-spot Burnet *Zygaena trifolii* ssp. *decreta* Local S,WC; ssp. *palustrella* Local S,SE **FW** 14-19mm. Ssp. *decreta* Very difficult to distinguish from much more widespread Narrow-bordered Five-spot Burnet ssp. *latomarginata*, even using features of genitalia. However, habitat, time of year and geographical location may help. Examples with middle pair of spots merged frequent in Five-spot Burnet, rare in Narrow-bordered. Larva has much shorter hairs than that of Narrow-bordered, which has a wider range of foodplants. Also, Narrow-bordered appears earlier. Rarely, red is replaced by yellow. **FS** July-early August. **Hab** Wt Gr. Ssp. *palustrella* has thinner scaling and is usually smaller than ssp. *decreta*. **FS** Late May-June. **Hab** CGr.

Narrow-bordered Five-spot Burnet *Zygaena lonicerae* ssp. *latomarginata* Common S,C,(N); ssp. *jocelynae* RDB (proposed Protected species) NW; ssp. *insularis* Ir **FW** 15-19mm. Differences between this species and Five-spot Burnet (especially ssp. *decreta*) comparative and slight. Generally, in Narrow-bordered forewing longer and more pointed, leading corner of hindwing more pointed with black border narrower, but a number of specimens of each are needed in order to see these differences. Ssp. *jocelynae* is larger than ssp. *latomarginata*, with longer, black fur on head, thorax and abdomen, and larger, sometimes suffused and clouded forewing spots. Ssp. *insularis* has larger spots than ssp. *latomarginata*, with a tendency for middle pair to merge. See also Five-spot Burnet. **FS** Late June-July. **Hab** Gr Wt.

Transparent Burnet *Zygaena purpuralis* ssp. *segontii* RDB presumed extinct WC; ssp. *caledonensis* Na. NW; ssp. *sabulosa* Ir **FW** 14-16mm. Forewing thinly scaled with three blunt red streaks, the outermost hatchet-shaped. The red is sometimes inclined to purplish, more rarely replaced by orange or yellow, and in a rare form blackish. Scotch and Slender Scotch Burnets also have thinly-scaled forewings, but are smaller and thinner, with distinct spots rather than streaks. **FS** Early June-July **Hab** Cl CGr.

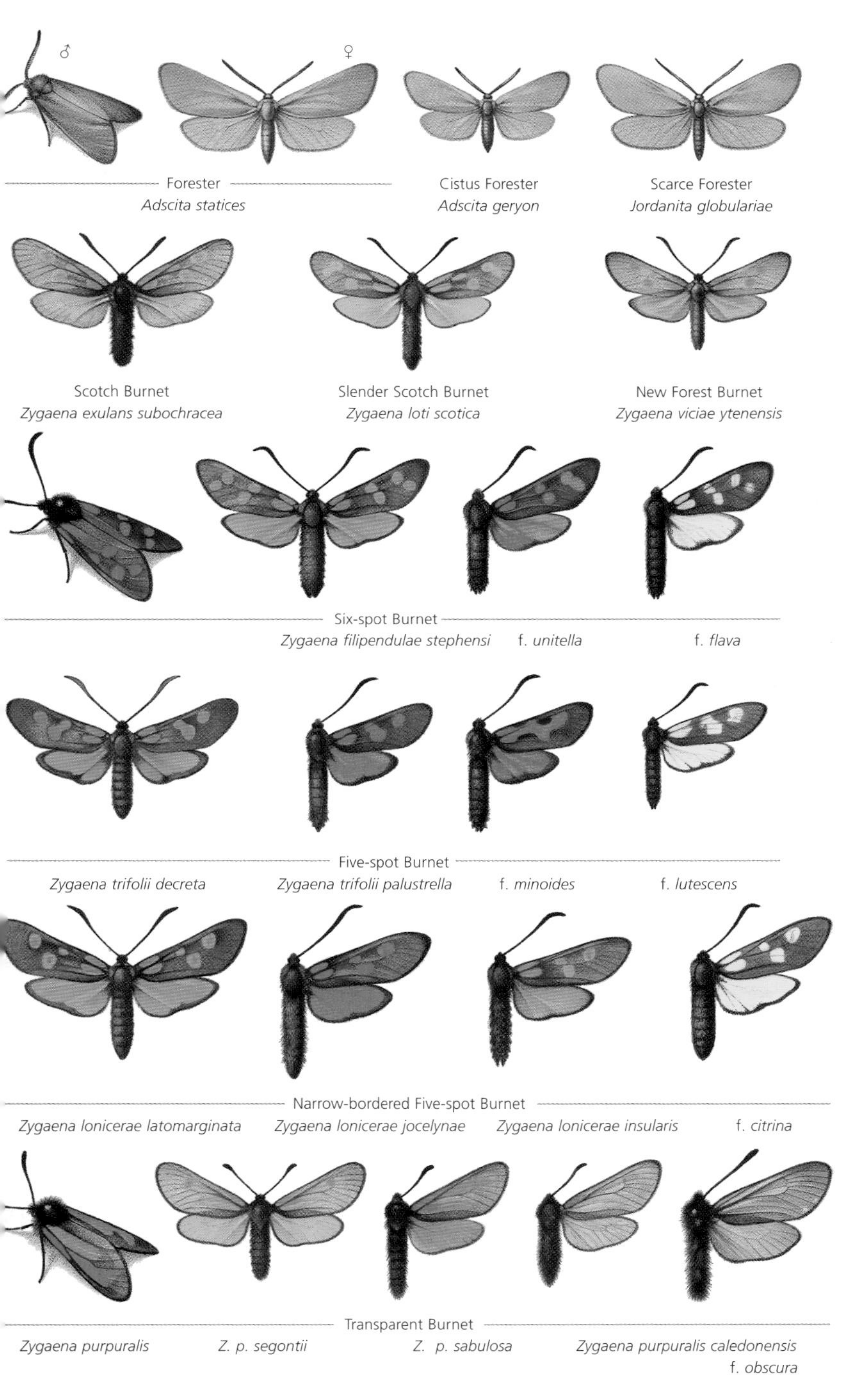
♂
♀
Forester
Adscita statices
Cistus Forester
Adscita geryon
Scarce Forester
Jordanita globulariae
Scotch Burnet
Zygaena exulans subochracea
Slender Scotch Burnet
Zygaena loti scotica
New Forest Burnet
Zygaena viciae ytenensis
Six-spot Burnet
Zygaena filipendulae stephensi
f. *unitella*
f. *flava*
Five-spot Burnet
Zygaena trifolii decreta
Zygaena trifolii palustrella
f. *minoides*
f. *lutescens*
Narrow-bordered Five-spot Burnet
Zygaena lonicerae latomarginata
Zygaena lonicerae jocelynae
Zygaena lonicerae insularis
f. *citrina*
Transparent Burnet
Zygaena purpuralis
Z. p. segontii
Z. p. sabulosa
Zygaena purpuralis caledonensis
f. *obscura*

Limacodidae

Forewings deep, rather rounded. Characteristic tent-like resting posture.

Festoon *Apoda limacodes* Nb. S,E,not SW
FW M 10-12mm F 11-13mm. Forewing broad, orange-brown, with curved cross-lines strongly diverging from leading edge. When fully at rest, forewings held at low angle and creased so that tips are flattened out. Female paler than male, which rests with abdomen upturned. Sometimes area between cross-lines is darker and occasionally male is as pale as female. Rare melanic forms of male have forewing lightly or heavily marked with blackish brown. **FS** June-July. Flies mainly at night, coming to light. Occasionally seen flying in sunshine by day, high in the oak canopy. **Hab** BWd.

Triangle *Heterogenea asella* RDB S,E
FW M 5-7mm F 9-11mm. Small enough to be confused with some microlepidoptera (e.g. Tortricidae). Recognised by combination of rather triangular forewing with leading edge very curved, and tent-like resting posture. Occasionally male is very dark and female is pale yellow. **FS** Mid June-late July. Flies mainly at night, coming to light in small numbers, but also reported flying on sunny afternoons. **Hab** BWd.

Sesiidae Clearwing moths

Day-flying moths, which mimic wasps. Wings with transparent areas. Forewing very narrow. Head much smaller than in wasps. *Sesia*, *Bembecia* and *Pyropteron* species hold the wings quite close to the body when at rest. *Synanthedon* species hold them more widely spread. Usually elusive, but males are attracted to commercially available pheromone lures.

Sesiinae

Hornet Moth *Sesia apiformis* Nb. E,S,Ir
FW 17-21mm. As large and bulky as a true Hornet *Vespa crabro*, and even has jerky, wasp-like movements when disturbed. However, it is yellower, and lacks the wasp-waist. Distinguished from Lunar Hornet Moth by bright yellow head and shoulder patches and black collar. **FS** Mid June-July, sometimes to early August. Adults, including mating pairs, rest on poplar trunks after emergence, usually between 7am and 11am, otherwise seldom seen. **Hab** H G Wt.

Lunar Hornet Moth *Sesia bembeciformis*
Common T **FW** 15-19mm. Similar to Hornet Moth, but smaller with black head and shoulders, and a bright yellow collar. **FS** July-early August. Adults are rarely seen, but rest freshly emerged on willow trunks in the morning. **Hab** Wt BWd A M H Sc.

Paranthreninae

Dusky Clearwing *Paranthrene tabaniformis*
Presumed extinct; former resident **FW** 14mm. Distinguished from all other clearwing moths in Britain by dark clouding over most of forewing. **FS** Late May-mid July. Apparently very elusive, and rarely seen in Britain. **Hab** BWd.

macodidae

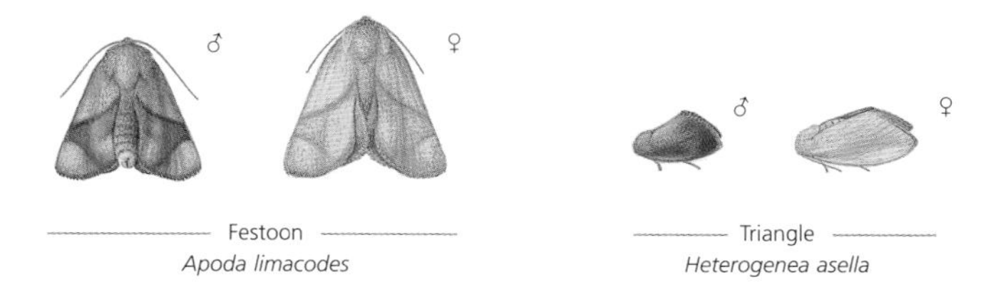

Festoon
Apoda limacodes

Triangle
Heterogenea asella

siidae Clearwing moths

all shown ×1.25

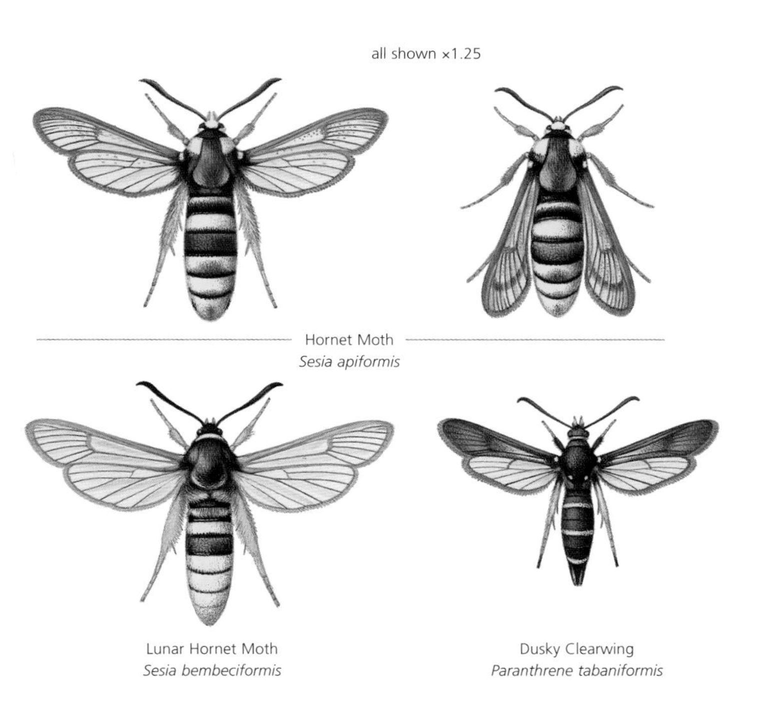

Hornet Moth
Sesia apiformis

Lunar Hornet Moth
Sesia bembeciformis

Dusky Clearwing
Paranthrene tabaniformis

Currant Clearwing *Synanthedon tipuliformis* Nb. S,C,(N,Ir) **FW** 8-10mm. Small clearwing with yellow collar. Usually two fine yellow lines running along thorax. Three (female) or four (male) thin yellow cross-bands on abdomen, which has a black tip. Sallow Clearwing has no yellow lines on thorax. See also Thrift Clearwing. **FS** June-July, usually peaking late June. **Hab** G.

Yellow-legged Clearwing *Synanthedon vespiformis* Nb. S,C **FW** 10-12mm. Central cross-bar on forewing reddish, and easily visible parts of legs largely yellow. Four yellow bands on abdomen. Tail fan yellow above on female (conspicuous in flight); that of male black above, with some yellow underneath. Sometimes leading and trailing edges of forewing bordered with red. Reddish central bar on forewing and yellow legs distinguish this moth from Orange-tailed, Sallow, Currant and Welsh Clearwings. Six-belted Clearwing has six yellow bands and holds wings closer to body at rest. **FS** Late May-mid August. **Hab** BWd.

White-barred Clearwing *Synanthedon spheciformis* Nb. S,C,not SW **FW** 12-14mm. Relatively large, quite dark species. Single yellowish-white band on abdomen, towards base, and whitish band near tip of antenna. Welsh Clearwing has two pale bands on abdomen, a partly or wholly orange tail fan and central band on forewing broader and more rounded. **FS** Mid May-early July, peaking early June. **Hab** A Wt BWd.

Welsh Clearwing *Synanthedon scoliaeformis* RDB N,WC,(Ir) **FW** 12-15mm. Large, broad and roughly heart-shaped central black mark on forewing. Antennae whitish towards tip in female, darker in male, and two narrow yellow bands on abdomen. Tail fan orange in female and brownish orange in male. Orange-tailed Clearwing has two yellow bands on abdomen, but is much smaller with narrower, squarer central forewing mark, and black antennae. See also White-barred Clearwing. **FS** June-early July. **Hab** BWd M.

Sallow Clearwing *Synanthedon flaviventris* Nb. S **FW** 8-9mm. Small clearwing, with dark thorax and three thin yellow bands on otherwise black abdomen. Occasionally a very faint fourth abdominal band. Currant Clearwing similar in size, but has yellow collar and usually yellow lines running along thorax. Yellow-legged Clearwing has largely yellow legs and four distinct yellow bands on abdomen. See also Thrift Clearwing. **FS** Mid June-mid July. **Hab** BWd Wt.

Orange-tailed Clearwing *Synanthedon andrenaeformis* Nb. S **FW** 9-11mm. Distinctive wide orange and black tail fan on slender abdomen of male is visible even in flight. Female tail fan less strongly orange. See Welsh Clearwing and Yellow-legged Clearwing. **FS** Mid May-mid July. **Hab** CGr BWd.

Red-belted Clearwing *Synanthedon myopaeformis* Nb. S **FW** 9-11mm. Single broad red band on abdomen and uniformly black forewing markings. Large Red-belted Clearwing has thin scatter of red scales at base of forewing. Red-tipped Clearwing has dense patch of red scales at tip of forewing. **FS** Mid June-early August. **Hab** G O BWd.

Red-tipped Clearwing *Synanthedon formicaeformis* Nb. S,C,(N),Ir **FW** 9-11mm. Red forewing tip and single broad red band on abdomen. On emergence has two bands of powdery yellow scales on abdomen, lost during early flights. See Red-belted Clearwing, Large Red-belted Clearwing. **FS** Late May-early August, peaking mid-June. **Hab** Wt.

Large Red-belted Clearwing *Synanthedon culiciformis* Nb. T **FW** 12-14mm. Single broad red band on abdomen and scatter of reddish scales at base of forewing. See Red-belted Clearwing, Red-tipped Clearwing. **FS** Mid May-late June. **Hab** BWd A.

Six-belted Clearwing *Bembecia ichneumoniformis* Nb. S,C **FW** 9-12mm. Six yellowish bands on abdomen, frosting of orange scales on tip, and on central bar of forewing. Thrift Clearwing is smaller, with fewer, less obvious bands and lacks orange scales on forewing. See also Yellow-legged Clearwing. **FS** Late June-mid August. Can be obtained using sweep nets and sometimes seen at rest on flowers. **Hab** Gr.

Thrift Clearwing *Synansphecia muscaeformis* Nb. SW,NE,Ir **FW** 6-8mm. Our smallest clearwing, with three (sometimes four) narrow yellowish-white bands on abdomen and no orange scales on forewing. When freshly emerged, wings have a light covering of yellowish-white scales, lost on the first flight. On Currant Clearwing dark outer band on forewing is streaked with orange. Sallow Clearwing has dark thorax. Both are slightly larger, and unlikely to occur in the same habitat as Thrift Clearwing. See also Six-belted Clearwing. **FS** Early June-late July. **Hab** Cl.

Fiery Clearwing *Pyropteron chrysidiformis* RDB (Protected species) SE **FW** 9-12mm. Fiery orange-red scales over most of forewing. Two (female) or three (male) narrow whitish bands on abdomen and orange-red tail fan orange centrally in both sexes. **FS** Mid June-early July. **Hab** Sh Cl.

all shown ×1.25

Currant Clearwing
Synanthedon tipuliformis

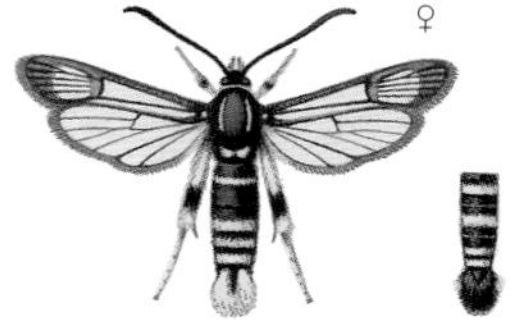

Yellow-legged Clearwing
Synanthedon vespiformis

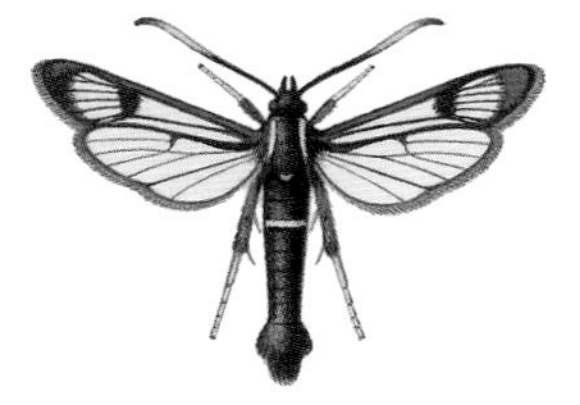

White-barred Clearwing
Synanthedon spheciformis

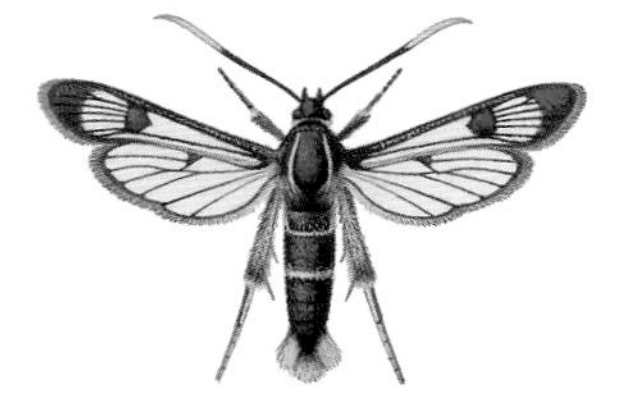

Welsh Clearwing
Synanthedon scoliaeformis

Sallow Clearwing
Synanthedon flaviventris

Orange-tailed Clearwing
Synanthedon andrenaeformis

Red-belted Clearwing
Synanthedon myopaeformis

Red-tipped Clearwing
Synanthedon formicaeformis

Large Red-belted Clearwing
Synanthedon culiciformis

Six-belted Clearwing
Bembecia ichneumoniformis

Thrift Clearwing
Synansphecia muscaeformis

Fiery Clearwing
Pyropteron chrysidiformis

Lasiocampidae Eggar moths

Thickset, large or medium-sized moths. Males with broadly feathered antennae. Wings often very broad. Mainly nocturnal, coming to light. They do not feed. Males of two British species fly by day.

December Moth *Poecilocampa populi* Common T **FW** 15-22mm. Forewing charcoal coloured, with creamy-white markings. **FS** Late October-January. **Hab** BWd H G.

Pale Eggar *Trichiura crataegi* Common T,(Ir) **FW** 14-17mm. Pale grey colour, flight season and wavy black or dark grey outer edge of central band on forewing are diagnostic. See Pine Processionary (p.86). **FS** August-September. **Hab** BWd H A M G.

Small Eggar *Eriogaster lanestris* Nb. S,C,Ir **FW** 15-21mm. Deep reddish-brown colour, whitish spot in centre of forewing and a whitish cross-line. Female larger with large tuft of grey hair at abdomen tip. See December Moth. **FS** January-March. Rarely seen; occasionally comes to light. **Hab** H Sc.

Lackey *Malacosoma neustria* Common S,C,(N),Ir **FW** M 13-16mm F 16-21mm. Straw yellow to reddish brown. Two roughly parallel cross-lines (only rarely weak or absent) on forewing, brown and white chequered fringes with two very distinct reflective white patches (these are duller in Ground Lackey), and hindwing either coloured as forewing, or paler. See Ground Lackey. **FS** July-August. **Hab** Ub.

Ground Lackey *Malacosoma castrensis* Na. SE,SW **FW** M 13-16mm F 17-21mm. Similar to Lackey. Two cross-lines (often weak or absent) on forewing form a waist at centre due to outward-facing kink in inner cross-line, more obviously in male. First cross-line curves strongly towards base in trailing half. Forewing margin chequered brown and buff; hindwing coloured as forewing or darker, with fringes paler than wing (darker in Lackey). **FS** July-August. **Hab** Sm Sh.

Grass Eggar *Lasiocampa trifolii* Na. S,WC; **Pale Grass Eggar** f. *flava* RDB SE **FW** M 21-24mm F 25-30mm. Reddish brown, with curved outer cross-line on forewing and clear white central spot. Darker, sometimes blackish-brown forms occur in more northern and western colonies. Pale Grass Eggar is straw yellow or brownish yellow. The infrequent f. *obsoleta* lacks cross-lines and central spot has no dark ring. Female Pale Grass Eggar is smaller than female Oak Eggar, which has more rounded forewing tip and wider outer cross-band. **FS** August-September. **Hab** C A.

♂
♀
December Moth
Poecilocampa populi
Pale Eggar
Trichiura crataegi
Small Eggar
Eriogaster lanestris
♂
♀
Lackey
Malacosoma neustria
♂
♀
Ground Lackey
Malacosoma castrensis
♂
♀
Grass Eggar
Lasiocampa trifolii
♂
♂
f. *obsoleta*
Pale Grass Eggar
Lasiocampa trifolii f. *flava*

Oak Eggar *Lasiocampa quercus* Common S,C; **Northern Eggar** f. *callunae* Common N,W,Ir **FW** M 25-34mm F 33-40mm. Male rich deep brown, with white central spot and broad pale outer band on forewing. Female buff or light brown, with similar pattern. Northern Eggar is larger; in male pale basal patch on forewing often larger; female darker and browner than Oak Eggar. Blackish-brown f. *olivacea* is found in Oak Eggars on sand-dunes on Cheshire and Lancashire coasts, and in Northern Eggars in Yorkshire and northern Scotland. See Grass Eggar, which is usually smaller. **FS** In south, July-August. In north, late May-July. Male flies by day. Female from early dusk and comes to light. **Hab** A M H BWd Wt C.

Fox Moth *Macrothylacia rubi* Common T **FW** M 22-26mm F 26-31mm. Large, with two narrow, roughly parallel (less so in female) pale cross-bands on otherwise plain forewing with no central white spot. Male red-brown, female grey-brown. In northern and upland areas often darker, less red and greyer. **FS** May-June. Male flies by day and sometimes at night, coming to light. Female flies at night and comes to light. **Hab** A M C Gr.

Pine-tree Lappet *Dendrolimus pini* Rare immigrant S **FW** 31-40mm. Male reddish brown with white central spot on forewing and fine, dark, scalloped central cross-line, jagged outer band and whitish frosting. Female larger, more golden brown, with paler outer band and forewing margin. **FS** In mainland Europe, June-August.

Drinker *Euthrix potatoria* Common S,C,NW,Ir **FW** M 21-25mm F 28-35mm. Distinguished from other large eggars by outer cross-line on forewing which runs diagonally to wing tip, and the two central white spots. Male normally warm reddish brown, with yellowish patches. Female from deep yellow to very pale buff, whitish, or reddish brown. In fens of East Anglia, male is frequently yellowish (f. *pallida*), rarely elsewhere. **FS** July-August. **Hab** Wt Gr BWd H.

Small Lappet *Phyllodesma ilicifolia* Former resident; presumed extinct C,SW **FW** 18-20mm. Like much smaller Lappet in shape, markings and posture, but forewing light brown, greyer towards outer edge. **FS** Late April-May. **Hab** M Wd.

Lappet *Gastropacha quercifolia* Common S,EC **FW** 28-42mm. Large. Purplish-brown coloration, scalloped outer edge of wing, resting posture and prominent snout diagnostic. **FS** Late June-mid August. **Hab** H BWd Sc.

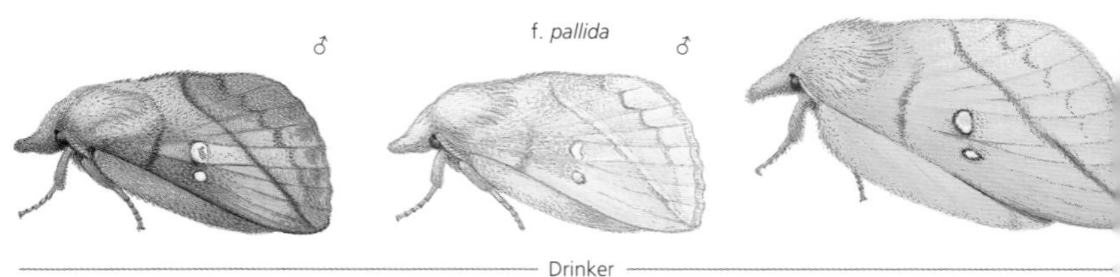

Drinker
Euthrix potatoria

Small Lappet
Phyllodesma ilicifolia

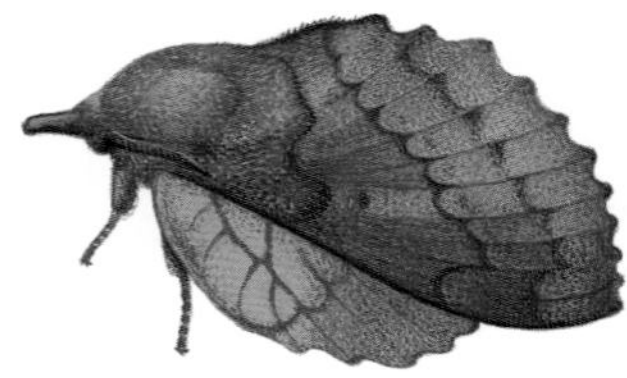

Lappet
Gastropacha quercifolia

Oak Eggar
Lasiocampa quercus

Northern Eggar
Lasiocampa quercus f. *callunae*

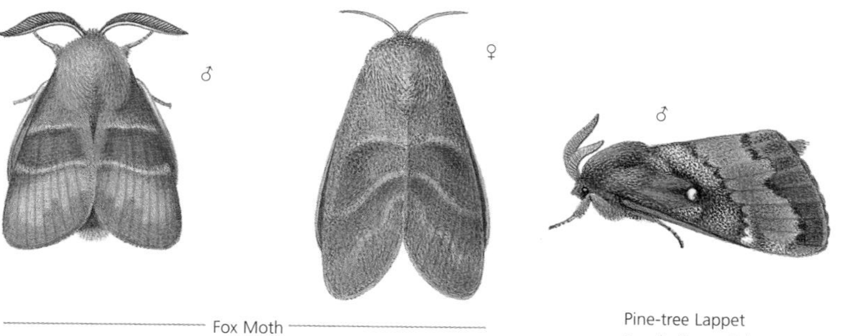

Fox Moth
Macrothylacia rubi

Pine-tree Lappet
Dendrolimus pini

Saturniidae Emperor moths

Emperor Moth *Saturnia pavonia* Common T **FW** M 27-32mm F 35-41mm. Unmistakable. Great Peacock Moth *Saturnia pyri* (occasional accidental, introduction or escape) is darker and much larger. **FS** April-late May. Male flies by day in sunshine. Female nocturnal and comes to light, usually soon after dusk. **Hab** A M BWd Wt Sd H Sc.

Endromidae

Kentish Glory *Endromis versicolora* Na. NE **FW** M 27-30mm F 34-39mm. Unmistakable. Slightly smaller, darker male has orange-brown hindwing; that of female largely brownish white. **FS** Late April-mid May. Male flies by day. Both sexes fly from dusk and come to light. **Hab** BWd M.

Drepanidae Hook-tips

Slender moths with broad wings and often hooked forewings. Some fly naturally or can be disturbed by day. All fly at night and come to light.

Scalloped Hook-tip *Falcaria lacertinaria* Common T **FW** 14-18mm. Outer edge of forewing irregularly scalloped, two dark parallel cross-lines and small dark central dot. Rests with wings raised, tent-like. Second-generation moths are smaller and paler. First-generation moths often with stronger markings and more silvery grey, especially in north. Beautiful Hook-tip (p.150) has only two projections on outer edge of forewing, two dark central dots and rests with wings flat. **FS** Late April-late June; mid July-August. In Scotland, late May-June. Can be disturbed from foodplant (birches) by day. **Hab** BWd A Wt H.

Oak Hook-tip *Watsonalla binaria* Common S,C **FW** 13-18mm. Orange-brown, with two well-defined pale cross-lines on forewing, and lilac tinge when freshly emerged. Two prominent blackish spots in centre of forewing, and two small dots on hindwing. Female has orange hindwing. Rests with wings spread flat, as does Barred Hook-tip, which has more distinct, darker central cross-band on forewing, one brown central spot and no central dots on hindwing. **FS** May-June; late July-mid September. Male occasionally flies high around oaks by day. **Hab** BWd H G.

Barred Hook-tip *Watsonalla cultraria* Local S,C,(Ir) **FW** 12-17mm. Broad, darker central cross-band on orange-brown forewing. Only one (rarely two) often rather faint, brown central dot, and no such dots on hindwing. See Oak Hook-tip. **FS** May-June; mid July-early September. Male flies by day, high around foodplant (Beech). **Hab** BWd.

Pebble Hook-tip *Drepana falcataria falcataria* Common S,C,Ir; ssp. *scotica* Local N **FW** 17-21mm. Ssp. *falcataria*: Central, rather pebble-like spot on forewing and distinct purplish-brown blotch along outer edge, near wing tip. Hindwing paler, especially in leading half. Rests with wings spread flat. F. *pallida*: Very pale, approaching ssp. *scotica*, but less strongly marked. Ssp. *scotica*: Ground-colour of wings straw-white and outer markings darker than in ssp. *falcataria*. See also Dusky Hook-tip and Scarce Hook-tip. **FS** Ssp. *falcataria* late April-June; mid July-early September. Ssp. *scotica* mid May-late July. **Hab** BWd A G.

Dusky Hook-tip *Drepana curvatula* Immigrant S,E **FW** 16-21mm. Brown, with lilac tinge when freshly emerged. Rests with wings spread flat. Forewing central spots smaller than ssp. *falcataria* of Pebble Hook-tip, and hindwing has strong dark cross-line beyond middle. See also Scarce Hook-tip. **FS** In mainland Europe, May-June; late July-August.

Scarce Hook-tip *Sabra harpagula* RDB SW **FW** 17-20mm. Forewing more strongly hooked than in related species, with second projection roughly midway along outer edge. Brown and gold central forewing blotch, and lilac and black outer markings. Rests with wings spread flat. Pebble and Dusky Hook-tips lack large central blotch and extra outer projection. **FS** Early June-mid July. **Hab** BWd.

Chinese Character *Cilix glaucata* Common S,C,(N),Ir **FW** 10-13mm. When at rest, with wings held steeply over the body, closely resembles a bird dropping. **FS** Late April-early June; July-early September. **Hab** Ub.

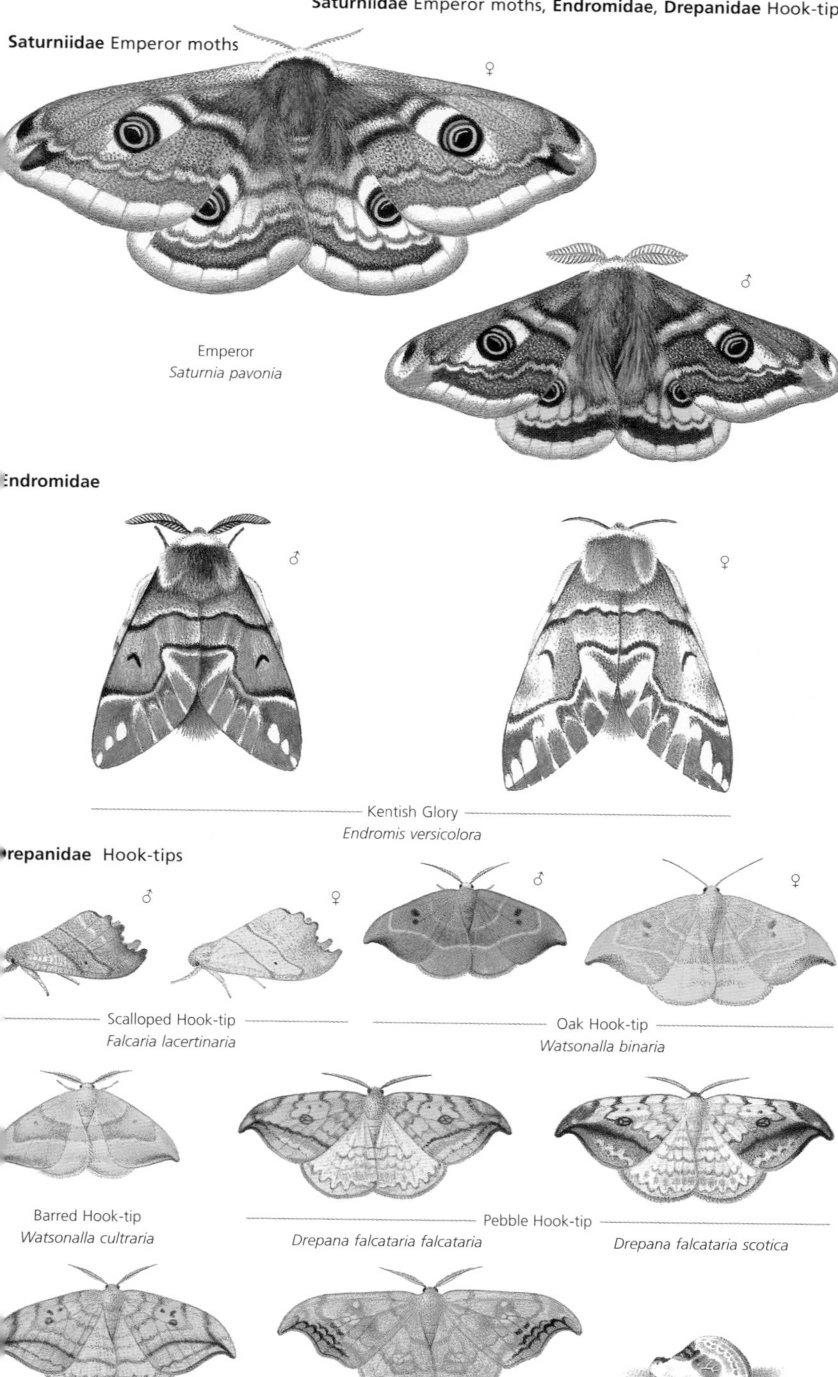
Saturniidae Emperor moths
♀
♂
Emperor
Saturnia pavonia
Endromidae
♂
♀
Kentish Glory
Endromis versicolora
Drepanidae Hook-tips
♂
♀
♂
♀
Scalloped Hook-tip
Falcaria lacertinaria
Oak Hook-tip
Watsonalla binaria
Barred Hook-tip
Watsonalla cultraria
Pebble Hook-tip
Drepana falcataria falcataria
Drepana falcataria scotica
Dusky Hook-tip
Drepana curvatula
Scarce Hook-tip
Sabra harpagula
Chinese Character
Cilix glaucata

Thyatiridae

Superficially similar to the Noctuidae. All rest with wings held close to the body. Thorax often with prominent tufts. They fly at night and are attracted to light, and most come to sugary baits.

Peach Blossom *Thyatira batis* Common T **FW** 16-19mm. Pink and brown petal-like forewing markings. **FS** Late May-late July; (in south, occasionally late August-September). **Hab** Wd Sc H G.

Buff Arches *Habrosyne pyritoides* Common S,C,Ir **FW** 17-20mm. Forewing markings have a flint-like quality, etched with white and orange-brown 'arches'. **FS** Late June-early August; (occasional in autumn). **Hab** Wd Sc H G.

Figure of Eighty *Tethea ocularis* ssp. *octogesimea* Common S,C **FW** 16-20mm. White and rather finely etched number '80' in centre of forewing. Cross-lines generally rather fine; that beyond '80' mark curves more or less around it before reaching leading edge. Forewing light to dark brown, often with purplish sheen. Dark f. *fusca* was first recorded in south and south-east England in 1940s, and has since spread. See Poplar Lutestring, Figure of Eight (p.86). **FS** Late May-July. **Hab** BWd Wt H G.

Poplar Lutestring *Tethea or or* Local S; ssp. *scotica* Local N; ssp. *hibernica* Ir **FW** 16-19mm. Ssp. *or*: Similar to Figure of Eighty but only vaguely numerical central markings on forewing, and more numerous, thicker, dark wavy cross-lines ('lutestrings'); usually three or four in basal half, and that beyond central marks turning toward wing tip before leading edge. Central markings occasionally faint or absent. See also Yellow Horned, Oak Lutestring and Figure of Eight (p.86). Ssp. *scotica*: Usually paler grey with dark markings more sharply defined, sometimes with purplish tinge when freshly emerged. Ssp. *hibernica*: Between ssp. *or* and ssp. *scotica* in colour, but with weaker markings. **FS** In England and Wales, late May-early August. In Scotland and Ireland, June-early July. Nocturnal. **Hab** BWd.

Satin Lutestring *Tetheella fluctuosa* Local SE,W,Ir **FW** 17-21mm. Similar to Common Lutestring but larger. Small dark crescent or central dash on forewing and small dark dash arising on leading edge just inside pale outermost cross-line. Most examples in south have outer part of forewing broadly pale. F. *albilinea* is darker with narrow whitish bands. F. *unicolor* has more uniformly dark greyish-brown forewing. **FS** June-early August. **Hab** BWd.

Common Lutestring *Ochropacha duplaris* Common T **FW** 14-18mm. On forewing, pair of small dark central dots and diagonal black dash arising from tip, visible in all forms. Uniform grey-brown f. *obscura* and melanic forms predominate in many areas. Strongly banded forms are more frequent in north and west, including Ireland, where outer area of forewing is often white. Paired spots and dash remain visible in all forms. See Satin Lutestring. **FS** Mid June-mid August. **Hab** BWd Sc G.

Oak Lutestring *Cymatophorima diluta* ssp. *hartwiegi* Local S,C **FW** 15-17mm. Two strong, black-edged, brown cross-bands on pale grey forewing. In frequent and widespread f. *nubilata* forewing largely brown with darker cross-lines. Rarely forewing grey-brown with broad, blackish central cross-band. Poplar Lutestring has grey cross-bands and different flight season. **FS** Late August-early October. **Hab** BWd.

Yellow Horned *Achlya flavicornis* ssp. *galbanus* Common S,C,Ir; ssp. *scotica* Common N **FW** 17-20mm. Ssp. *galbanus*: Antennae orange. Forewing grey with variable whitish frosting, especially on central portion of leading edge. Ssp. *scotica*: Larger, with darker, mauvish-grey forewing, and more heavily marked. Poplar Lutestring has brown antennae and different flight season. **FS** Late February-mid April. **Hab** BWd A M.

Frosted Green *Polyploca ridens* Local S **FW** 15-17mm. Forewing dark or blackish green, with prominent tufts on thorax and variable mixture of greenish-white marbling. F. *unicolor*, found in Surrey and Hertfordshire, is very dark without markings. Bright forms are more frequent further north and west. **FS** Mid April-mid May. Seldom comes to sugary baits. **Hab** BWd.

Peach Blossom
Thyatira batis

Buff Arches
Habrosyne pyritoides

Figure of Eighty
Tethea ocularis octogesimea f. *fusca*

Poplar Lutestring
Tethea or or *Tethea or scotica*

Satin Lutestring
Tetheella fluctuosa f. *albilinea*

Common Lutestring
Ochropacha duplaris f. *obscura*

Oak Lutestring
Cymatophorima diluta hartwiegi f. *nubilata*

Yellow Horned
Achlya flavicornis galbanus *Achlya flavicornis scotica*

Frosted Green
Polyploca ridens

Geometridae

Mainly slender-bodied (but see Ennominae, p.52), usually with broad forewing and relatively slow flight. Most are active at night (unless stated), and attend light traps and flowers to a varying degree, but are uncommon at sugar. Many are also active by day, or readily fly from their roosting sites if disturbed. May also be found at rest. Only exceptions and notable behaviours are mentioned in the species accounts.

Archiearinae Orange Underwings

Orange Underwing *Archiearis parthenias* Local S,C,N **FW** 16-19mm. Very similar to Light Orange Underwing. On hindwing underside, orange band projects centrally into dark outer band, often reaching outer margin. Forewing generally longer, usually with stronger white central cross-band (especially male). Male antennae finely serrated. In Light Orange Underwing, dark outer band on underside hindwing unbroken; central projection of orange band absent (or at most slight); male antennae slightly feathered. Orange Underwing starts flying two weeks earlier than Light Orange Underwing. Male Vapourer similar in flight, but has later flight season. **FS** March-April. Only active by day, usually flying high. **Hab** (Larva on birches) BWd A.

Light Orange Underwing *Archiearis notha* Nb. S **FW** 15-17mm. See Orange Underwing for differences. **FS** Late March-April, occasionally early May. Only active by day, usually flying high. **Hab** (Larva on Aspen) BWd.

Alsophilinae

March Moth *Alsophila aescularia* Common T **FW** 16-19mm. Male has triangular grey-brown forewing overlapped when at rest and with two jagged, dark-edged whitish cross-bands. Female barrel-shaped, with microscopic wing-stumps and conspicuous brown tuft at abdomen tip. Male Spring Usher (p.62) has dark, wavy cross-lines and (usually) distinct paler central cross-band and forewings not overlapping at rest. **FS** February-April. Female on tree trunks at night and in early morning. **Hab** BWd H Sc G.

Geometrinae Emeralds

Rest Harrow *Aplasta ononaria* RDB Immigrant SE **FW** 13-14mm. Delta-shaped. At rest, hangs from a grass stem. Reddish banding and freckling, heaviest on male, and no sharp markings. **FS** Late June-July; (late August-September). Immigrants mid July-early October. Easily disturbed by day. **Hab** Sd.

Grass Emerald *Pseudoterpna pruinata* ssp. *atropunctaria* Common T **FW** 14-19mm. Bluish green (fading to greyish white) with rather jagged, dark green or blackish central cross-lines on forewing (white in most emeralds), but see Jersey Emerald. **FS** Mid June-August; (occasionally September-October). Easily disturbed by day. **Hab** A H BWd Sc Up.

Jersey Emerald *Pseudoterpna coronillaria* Jerse **FW** 16-20mm. Similar to Grass Emerald in shape and markings, but grey, dusted with darker scales, and central forewing cross-lines dark brown. Cross line beyond middle usually more jagged (but variable in Grass Emerald). **FS** June-July. **Hab** Sc.

Large Emerald *Geometra papilionaria* Commo T **FW** 24-29mm. Large, with butterfly-like resting posture; wings spread and raised at an angle from the horizontal. **FS** June-August. **Hab** BWd Sc G.

Blotched Emerald *Comibaena bajularia* Local S,C **FW** 14-17mm. Cream and fawn blotch in traili corner of forewing. Wings rounded and fringes chequered. Ground-colour often fades to buffish- o pinkish white. **FS** Late June-July. **Hab** BWd.

Essex Emerald *Thetidia smaragdaria* ssp. *maritima* Previously RDB; now presumed extin SE **FW** 14-17mm. Rich velvety green when fresh. Forewing leading edge gold, white central spot ar plain fringes. See Small Emerald. **FS** Mid June-mid July. **Hab** Sm.

Common Emerald *Hemithea aestivaria* Common S,C,Ir **FW** 14-17mm. Forewing pointed, with two pale wavy cross-lines. Single projection o hindwing and chequered fringes. Sussex Emerald has two points on hindwing. **FS** Late June-late July **Hab** BWd H G.

Small Grass Emerald *Chlorissa viridata* Na. S,WC **FW** 11-13mm. Small, dull green (when newly emerged). Forewing leading edge gold, central spot absent, fairly straight cross-lines. See Little Emerald, but Small Grass Emerald does not fade to whitish. **FS** June-early July. **Hab** AWt.

Sussex Emerald *Thalera fimbrialis* RDB (Protected) SE **FW** 15-16mm. Two projections on hindwing distinctive. See Common Emerald. **FS** July-early August. Mainly active at dusk and dawn, coming to light. **Hab** Sh.

Small Emerald *Hemistola chrysoprasaria* Local S,(C) **FW** 17-20mm. Wings rather rounded, rich blue-green (when newly emerged). May fade to white, but curved whitish cross-lines remain visible Light Emerald (p.72) has straighter cross-lines and reddish dash at forewing tip. See Essex Emerald. **FS** Late June-early August. **Hab** BWd H Sc G.

Little Emerald *Jodis lactearia* Common S,C,NW,Ir **FW** 11-13mm. Delicate greenish white when newly emerged, rapidly fading to white, but cross-lines remain visible. Usually two white cross-lines on hindwing, inner one often faint. Male has finely feathered antennae. Small Grass Emerald, even when faded, is duller, with only one cross-lin on hindwing, and antennae of male not feathered Small, whitish wave moths have darker cross-lines. **FS** May-June; in Channel Islands, also August. Mostly seen at dusk. **Hab** H Sc BWd.

Little Emerald
Jodis lactearia

Sterrhinae Mochas and waves

Dingy Mocha *Cyclophora pendularia* RDB S **FW** 12-14mm. Pinkish grey with heavy, rather coarse freckling. Dark forms of Birch Mocha have slightly less hooked forewing tip, trailing corner less curved and inset, and hindwing has less distinct point. **FS** May-early June; July-early August. **Hab** Sc.

Mocha *Cyclophora annularia* Nb. S **FW** 11-14mm. Wavy black markings, on creamy yellow wings. **FS** Mid May-mid June; late July-August. **Hab** BWd H.

Birch Mocha *Cyclophora albipunctata* Local T **FW** 12-14mm. Grey or whitish, sometimes with diffuse, pinkish-red or greyish central cross-band or flush. See Dingy Mocha. **FS** Early May-late June; late July-late August. In north, May-July. **Hab** BWd.

Blair's Mocha *Cyclophora puppillaria* Immigrant S,Ir **FW** 12-15mm. Rather plain or softly-speckled pinkish-brown wings, each with small, central black-edged dots. Clay Triple-lines has forewing more tapered and strongly hooked. False Mocha is more coarsely freckled, usually with dark blotches near forewing outer edge, tip blunter. See also Jersey Mocha. **FS** August-October.

Jersey Mocha *Cyclophora ruficiliaria* Rare immigrant; resident Channel Islands. 1st generation wings light brown, noticeably freckled, fringes reddish. Central spots small, pale. Dark central cross-line. 2nd generation similar, more weakly marked. See Blair's and False Mocha. Reference to genitalia may be necessary. **FS** May-June; July-August. [Not illustrated.]

False Mocha *Cyclophora porata* Nb. S,C **FW** 12-14mm. Wings light pinkish brown, coarsely freckled. Pale central dots strongly dark-ringed. Maiden's Blush lacks central dots. Clay Triple-lines lacks freckling. See also Maiden's Blush, Jersey Mocha, Blair's Mocha. **FS** May-July; July-August. **Hab** BWd.

Maiden's Blush *Cyclophora punctaria* Local S,C,(N,Ir) **FW** 13-16mm. Wings fawn; may have central pink blush; central dots absent. See Clay Triple-lines (lacks freckling). See also False Mocha. **FS** Early May-early July; mid July-late September. **Hab** BWd.

Clay Triple-lines *Cyclophora linearia* Local S,C,(Ir) **FW** 14-16mm. 1st generation with 1-3 strong grey cross-lines on pale orange-brown forewing. 2nd generation moths smaller, pinkish brown, cross-lines weaker; sometimes central spot on hindwing. See False Mocha, Maiden's Blush, Blair's Mocha. **FS** May-July; (mid August-mid October). **Hab** BWd G.

Blood-vein *Timandra comae* Common S,C,(N,Ir) **FW** 15-18mm. Diagonal pink or brownish-red line on creamy buff wings; bright pink fringes. **FS** May-early July; early July-mid September; (in south, mid September-November). **Hab** BWd Wt H G.

Lewes Wave *Scopula immorata* Former resident; presumed extinct **FW** 11-14mm. Wings soft grey-brown with wavy cross-bands, outermost whitish. Fringes chequered. Antennae in male slightly feathered. See Common Heath (p.70). **FS** Early June-mid July; (August-September). **Hab** A.

Sub-angled Wave *Scopula nigropunctata* RDB SE **FW** 14-16mm. Wings brownish white, very fin brown speckling, small black central dot; wavy gre brown cross-lines, central broader, fairly straight and angled at forewing leading edge. Hindwing pointed. Cream Wave and Lesser Cream Wave hav hindwing rounded. See also Rosy Wave. **FS** July-early August. **Hab** Sc(C) BWd.

Lace Border *Scopula ornata* Na. S **FW** 12-13mr Chalky white wings; grey and brown marked oute most area. **FS** May-June; mid July-early September **Hab** CGr.

Tawny Wave *Scopula rubiginata* RDB Immigrant SE **FW** 9-11mm. Deep pinkish brown or dull brow Usually 3 dark cross-lines on forewing. Bright Wav sandy brown; forewing more pointed with tiny da dots in fringes; cross-lines less distinct. Ochraceou Wave has 4 cross-lines, and is more orange. See also Purple-bordered Gold. **FS** Mid June-mid July; mid August-early September. **Hab** Gr Wd Sd.

Mullein Wave *Scopula marginepunctata* Local S,C,(N),Ir **FW** 12-15mm. Usually creamy white. Fi blackish markings and variable blackish dusting, absent in f. *mundata* (Sussex, Dorset and IOW). If heavily-dusted, can appear grey-brown, rarely blackish. Weaver's Wave smaller; usually larger dar blocks on narrower forewing. **FS** June-July; Augus September. In Scotland, June-July. **Hab** C CGr.

Small Blood-vein *Scopula imitaria* Common S,C,Ir **FW** 13-15mm. Wings sandy brown; fine darker wavy cross-lines, central with dark outer shading; black central dots. **FS** July-August; (in south, September-October). **Hab** Ub.

Rosy Wave *Scopula emutaria* Nb. S,E,W **FW** 11-13mm. Milky white, often with a delicate pink tinge, very finely dusted. Central forewing cross-band nearly straight; row of dark dots beyor Hindwing pointed. See Sub-angled Wave, Lesser Cream Wave. **FS** Late June-July. **Hab** Sm AWt.

Lesser Cream Wave *Scopula immutata* Local S,C,Ir **FW** 12-13mm. Wings rather rounded, whitis with fine dusting; curved or slightly wavy pale brow cross-lines. Central dot strongest on hindwing. Cream Wave larger, forewing more pointed, leadin edge more arched near tip; cross-lines more irregul See also Smoky Wave, Rosy Wave, Sub-angled Wav **FS** Late June-early August. **Hab** Wt Gr.

Cream Wave *Scopula floslactata* Local S,C,Ir; f. *scotica* Local NW **FW** 13-16mm. Creamy white with thin darker dusting; brown wavy cross-lines. Forewing with leading edge noticeably arched toward tip. Hindwing rounded. Black central dot very small on hindwing; usually absent on forewir F. *scotica* smaller and darker, with thicker, dark speckling. Smoky Wave lacks dark central dots an cross-lines are straighter and often less distinct. Se also Lesser Cream Wave, Sub-angled Wave. **FS** May-June, to July in Scotland. **Hab** BWd Sc.

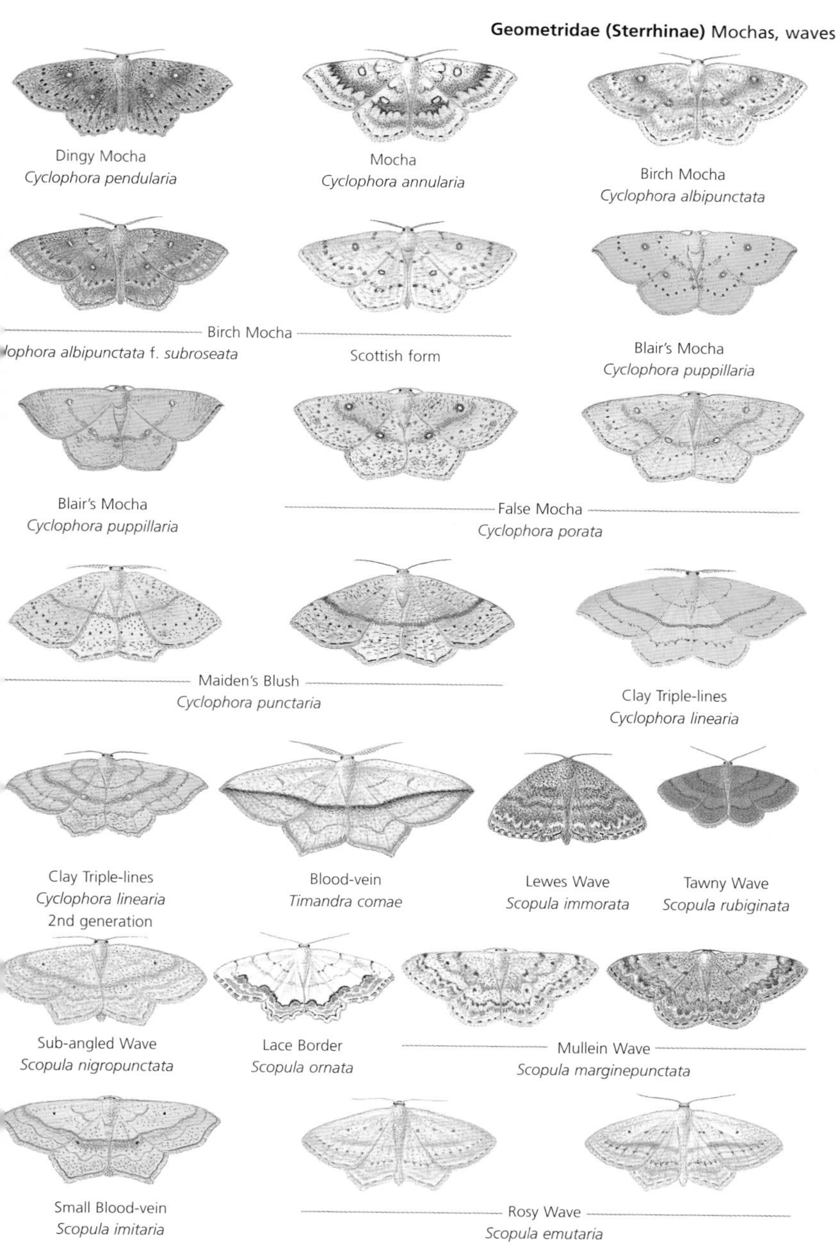

Dingy Mocha *Cyclophora pendularia*

Mocha *Cyclophora annularia*

Birch Mocha *Cyclophora albipunctata*

Birch Mocha *Cyclophora albipunctata* f. *subroseata*

Scottish form

Blair's Mocha *Cyclophora puppillaria*

Blair's Mocha *Cyclophora puppillaria*

False Mocha *Cyclophora porata*

Maiden's Blush *Cyclophora punctaria*

Clay Triple-lines *Cyclophora linearia*

Clay Triple-lines *Cyclophora linearia* 2nd generation

Blood-vein *Timandra comae*

Lewes Wave *Scopula immorata*

Tawny Wave *Scopula rubiginata*

Sub-angled Wave *Scopula nigropunctata*

Lace Border *Scopula ornata*

Mullein Wave *Scopula marginepunctata*

Small Blood-vein *Scopula imitaria*

Rosy Wave *Scopula emutaria*

Lesser Cream Wave *Scopula immutata*

Cream Wave

Scopula floslactata

f. *scotica*

Smoky Wave *Scopula ternata* Local N,W,(Ir) **FW** 12-15mm. Wings dull greyish white with grey-brown dusting, no central black dots and often blurred cross-lines. **FS** June-July. **Hab** A Up.

Bright Wave *Idaea ochrata* ssp. *cantiata* RDB SE **FW** 10-12mm. Sandy brown; forewing rather pointed; small blackish-brown dots in fringes. Three cross-lines usually evident, the innermost usually weak, the second stronger. See Ochraceous Wave, Tawny Wave. **FS** June-August. Flies in late afternoon and from dusk. **Hab** C.

Ochraceous Wave *Idaea serpentata* Rare immigrant; resident Jersey. Forewing narrower and less pointed than Bright Wave, and brighter orange-brown. Cross-bands stronger; usually 4 on forewing, 3 on hindwing, and black marks on outer margin stronger. **FS** In northern mainland Europe, July.

Purple-bordered Gold *Idaea muricata* Nb. S,C,(Ir) **FW** 8-10mm. Vivid pink and yellow markings; single dark outer cross-line. Yellow extensive or reduced to small central spots and fringes. See Tawny Wave. **FS** Late June-July. **Hab** Wt.

Least Carpet *Idaea rusticata* ssp. *atrosignaria* Local S **FW** 9-11mm. Whitish, with broad blackish central band and basal blotch on forewing. **FS** May-August; (September-October). **Hab** G H Sc.

Dotted Border Wave *Idaea sylvestraria* Nb. S,C **FW** 10-11mm. Wings brownish white or brown with thin blackish dusting, wavy brownish cross-lines, small central black dot and blackish dots along outer margin. See Silky Wave. Satin Wave whiter. Both have at most faint central and marginal dots. See also Dwarf Cream Wave. **FS** June-August. **Hab** A Sc.

Small Fan-footed Wave *Idaea biselata* Common T **FW** 10-11mm. Wings whitish buff with prominent black central dots. Forewing leading edge arched toward tip; outermost area usually darkened, often grey. Dwarf Cream Wave smaller, with forewing central dot usually after second cross-line; outer area not darker. **FS** June-August. **Hab** Wd.

Silky Wave *Idaea dilutaria* RDB W **FW** 8-10mm. Wings cream with light brown, slightly wavy, indistinct cross-lines and usually no central dark dots. Outer margin without conspicuous markings. Satin Wave is larger and whiter. See Dotted Border Wave, Dwarf Cream Wave, Isle of Wight Wave. **FS** Late June-late July. **Hab** CGr.

Dwarf Cream Wave *Idaea fuscovenosa* Local S,C **FW** 9-11mm. Wings cream; light brown cross-lines and blackish central dot. Forewing leading edge brown at base. Very fine blackish dashes along outer margins. Dotted Border Wave brownish, slightly larger, with outer margin dots conspicuous. See also Silky Wave, Small Fan-footed Wave, Isle of Wight Wave. **FS** June-July. **Hab** H BWd Wt Sc G.

Isle of Wight Wave *Idaea humiliata* Former resident; presumed extinct **FW** 9-10mm. Similar to Silky Wave and Dwarf Cream Wave but with reddish-brown streak along leading edge of narrower and yellower forewing. Sometimes very fine, brown line along outer margin. **FS** July. Flies sunset and at sunrise. **Hab** Cl.

Small Dusty Wave *Idaea seriata* Common S,C, **FW** 9-11mm. Wings light to dark grey, dusted dark grey, central dot and very fine dark dashes or dots along outer margin. Often mistaken for the small pugs, which have cross-lines angled near leading ec and fainter hindwing markings. **FS** In south, June-Ju August-September. In north, July-August. **Hab** G H.

Single-dotted Wave *Idaea dimidiata* Comm S,C,NW,Ir **FW** 9-11mm. Forewing rounded, straw white. Outermost cross-band thickened in hind corner, more or less forming a blotch. **FS** June-August. **Hab** BWd Wt H G.

Satin Wave *Idaea subsericeata* Common S,(C, **FW** 10-12mm. Wings greyish white; rather silky. Central and marginal dots absent or very faint. S Dotted Border Wave, Silky Wave. **FS** June-July; (ir south, August-September). **Hab** Wd Sc Gr H A.

Weaver's Wave *Idaea contiguaria* ssp. *britanniae* Na. WC **FW** 9-11mm. Elongate forewing; fir blackish cross-lines; blackish patches on leading edge. See Mullein Wave. **FS** Late June-July. **Hab** U

Treble Brown Spot *Idaea trigeminata* Local S **FW** 10-11mm. Forewing outer cross-band dark brown, pinched, nearly forming 3 blotches. Distir central dots. In Small Fan-footed Wave, outer ba less pinched or faint and hindwing similar. See al Single-dotted Wave. **FS** Late May-July; (in south-east, late July-late September). **Hab** Wd H G.

Small Scallop *Idaea emarginata* Local S,C **FW** 11-13mm. Sandy-brown wings, outer edges scalloped, fine curved cross-lines and central dots **FS** Mid June-late August. **Hab** Wd Wt H G.

Riband Wave *Idaea aversata* Common T **FW** 14-16mm. Forewing coarse sandy brown, strongly tapering; leading edge strongly arched to tip. Third cross-line usually with distinct kink near leading edge. See Plain Wave, Portland Ribbon Wave. **FS** Mid June-mid August; (in south September-October). **Hab** Ub.

Portland Ribbon Wave *Idaea degeneraria* R Immigrant S **FW** 13-15mm. Dark brown shading basal half of forewing. Dark band on some Riban Waves is in outer half. **FS** Mid June-mid July. **Hab**

Plain Wave *Idaea straminata* Local T **FW** 13-15mm. Very similar to un-banded Riband Wave, but slightly smaller, with smooth and rather silky muddy-brown wings and fainter cross-lines. Thir cross-line on forewing not kinked at leading edg **FS** Late June-early August. **Hab** Wd Sc H.

Vestal *Rhodometra sacraria* Immigrant T **FW** 12-14mm. Upright resting posture, with fore wings held at steep angle. Forewing lemon-yellov with vivid pink cross-band, or straw-yellow, leade brown or deep crimson with brown or black cros band. See Straw Belle (p.74). **FS** April-November, peaking August-September.

Smoky Wave
Scopula ternata

Bright Wave
Idaea ochrata cantiata

Ochraceous Wave
Idaea serpentata

Purple-bordered Gold
Idaea muricata
f. *auroraria*

Least Carpet
Idaea rusticata atrosignaria

Dotted Border Wave
Idaea sylvestraria
f. *circellata*

Small Fan-footed Wave
Idaea biselata
f. *fimbriolata*

Silky Wave
Idaea dilutaria

Dwarf Cream Wave
Idaea fuscovenosa

Isle of Wight Wave
Idaea humiliata

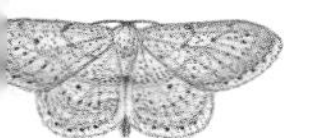

Small Dusty Wave
Idaea seriata

Single-dotted Wave
Idaea dimidiata

Satin Wave
Idaea subsericeata

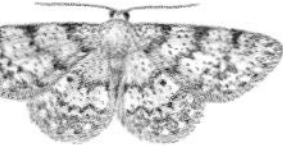

Weaver's Wave
Idaea contiguaria britanniae

Treble Brown Spot
Idaea trigeminata

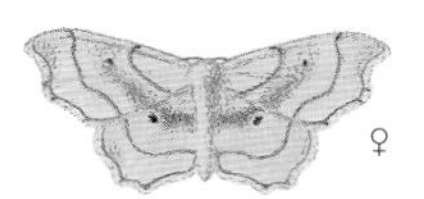

Small Scallop
Idaea emarginata

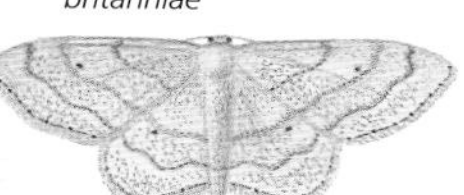

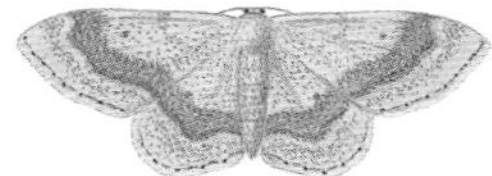

Riband Wave
f. *remutata*
Idaea aversata

Portland Ribbon Wave
Idaea degeneraria

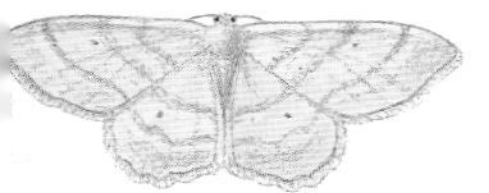

Plain Wave
Idaea straminata

Vestal
Rhodometra sacraria

Larentiinae Carpets, pugs and allies

Oblique Striped *Phibalapteryx virgata* Nb.;?immigrant S,WC **FW** 10-12mm. Forewing greyish; rather pointed, quite sharply in smaller female. Dark cross-bands of even thickness, edged greyish white. Short, dark, narrow diagonal dash at tip, sometimes absent. Oblique Carpet has longer, thicker streak at tip and is browner, with unevenly thickened cross-bands. **FS** May-June; August. **Hab** CGr Sd.

Oblique Carpet *Orthonama vittata* Local T **FW** 11-14mm. Forewing straw coloured, with dark streak from tip to fine, dark outer cross-lines. Outermost area pale, and darker central cross-band paler in leading half. See Many-lined, Oblique Striped. **FS** In south, late May-June; August-September. In north, July. **Hab** Wt BWd.

Gem *Orthonama obstipata* Immigrant T **FW** 12-14mm. In male, forewing orange-brown with narrow, irregular dark central cross-band and ill-defined dark streak at wing tip. In female, deep rosewood-brown with small, black, white-ringed central dot and sometimes very fine, wavy whitish cross-lines. **FS** April-November.

Balsam Carpet *Xanthorhoe biriviata* Uncommon S,SE **FW** 12-14mm. Pronounced, quite pointed projection on outer edge of dull black and dark grey central forewing cross-band. Spring moths pale, brownish whitish (see Sharp-angled Carpet – flies from late June). Summer moths darker. Common Carpet is greyer; hindwing more strongly banded. Central band of Dark-barred Twin-spot Carpet lacks strong projection. See also Large Twin-spot Carpet. **FS** Late April-June; July-early September. Flies in late afternoon and evening, and from dusk. **Hab** Wt Wd.

Flame Carpet *Xanthorhoe designata* Common T **FW** 11-14mm. Forewing grey with rather narrow rosewood and black striped central cross-band with double outer projection in leading half. See Red Carpet. **FS** In south, May-June; late July-August. In Scotland, June-July; (July-August). **Hab** Ub.

Red Carpet *Xanthorhoe decoloraria decoloraria* Common N,W,Ir; ssp. *hethlandica* Shetland **FW** 12-15mm. Ssp. *decoloraria:* Forewing light grey to tawny brown, quite pointed and broad; short, dark diagonal mark at tip. Central band reddish, often edged blackish brown, or as ground-colour. Ssp. *hethlandica*: Forewing dull tawny brown, with dull red band. Flame Carpet has two distinct projections on outer edge of central forewing band. Red Twin-spot Carpet usually has twin blackish spots near outer edge. Both have more rounded forewing, without diagonal mark at tip. **FS** Late June-mid August. **Hab** Up. Ssp. *hethlandica* Ub.

Red Twin-spot Carpet *Xanthorhoe spadicearia* Common T **FW** 12-13mm. Central forewing band reddish or purplish brown. Uncommon reddish-banded form of Dark-barred Twin-spot Carpet very similar, but with more understated markings (including underside); central band less distinctly edged white; pale, narrow band immediately beyond weaker and contrasting less sharply with ground-colour (especially outer area). If in doubt, examine genitalia for confirmation. **FS** In souther half of England, April-June; July-August. Elsewher May-July. **Hab** Ub. **Note** Presence or absence of notch on inner edge of central forewing band, ne leading edge, previously given in *Field Guide* as tc distinguish Red Twin-spot and Dark-barred Twin-spot Carpet, has recently been shown to be inval

Dark-barred Twin-spot Carpet *Xanthorho ferrugata* Common T **FW** 12-13mm. Central forewing cross-band usually blackish grey (f. *unidentaria*). Dark, atypical or worn Red Twin-spot Carpet retains reddish or purplish tint in ban Uncommon reddish-brown banded form very sim to Red Twin-spot Carpet. See under that species. **FS** In southern half of England, May-June; late Ju August. Elsewhere, May-July. **Hab** Ub.

Large Twin-spot Carpet *Xanthorhoe quadrifa siata* Local S,C **FW** 14-16mm. Central cross-band broad, light brown or greyish-brown forewing grey black (f. *thedenii*); usually a slightly elongated, dark central dot. Twin spots near outer edge often faint. Summer brood Balsam Carpet smaller; central cros band broader, darker, less irregular; central dot wea **FS** June-early August. **Hab** BWd Sc Wt.

Silver-ground Carpet *Xanthorhoe montanat montanata* Common T; ssp. *shetlandica* Shetland **FW** 14-17mm. White or brownish-white wings, an irregular light or dark brown cross-band on forewing (may be divided); hindwing rather plain. Ssp. *shetlandica* smaller, browner; central band le darkened. **FS** Mid May-late July. **Hab** Ub.

Garden Carpet *Xanthorhoe fluctuata* Commo T **FW** 13-16mm. Central cross-band on grey or greyish-white forewing blackish in leading half only (occasionally entirely dark). F. *thules* (mainly northern Scotland and London) dark grey or blackish. Galium Carpet has forewing leading edg slightly concave. See Striped Twin-spot Carpet, Twin-spot Carpet. **FS** In south, two or three overl ping generations, April-October. In north, one or two, May-September. **Hab** Ub.

Spanish Carpet *Scotopteryx peribolata* Immigra resident Channel Islands S **FW** 13-15mm. Forewin grey, with numerous strongly etched cross-lines. Outer edge of central band strongly kinked, straigh in plainer Lead Belle and July Belle. **FS** Late August September. **Hab** Sc.

Chalk Carpet *Scotopteryx bipunctaria* ssp. *cretata* Nb. S,C **FW** 15-18mm. Forewing with tw small black central dots; cold grey, with wavy cros lines. **FS** July-August. **Hab** CGr Q.

Shaded Broad-bar *Scotopteryx chenopodiata* Common T **FW** 16-19mm. Forewing smooth, lig tawny or dull brown, with distinct darker central cross-band, composed of several narrower bands, central one paler and often greyish. **FS** Late June August. Easily disturbed by day. **Hab** Gr.

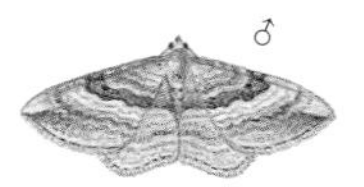

Oblique Striped
Phibalapteryx virgata

Oblique Carpet
Orthonama vittata

Gem
Orthonama obstipata

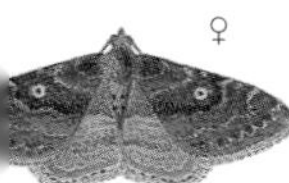

Gem
thonama obstipata

Balsam Carpet
Xanthorhoe biriviata
spring generation — summer generation

Flame Carpet
Xanthorhoe designata

Red Carpet
thorhoe decoloraria decoloraria — *Xanthorhoe decoloraria hethlandica*

Red Twin-spot Carpet
Xanthorhoe spadicearia

Dark-barred Twin-spot Carpet
Xanthorhoe ferrugata

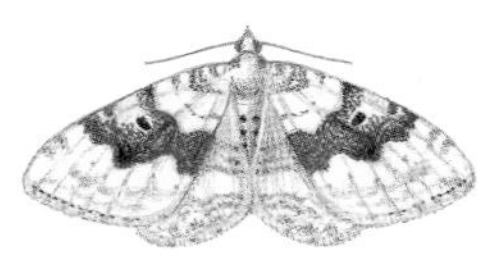

Dark-barred Twin-spot Carpet
Xanthorhoe ferrugata

Large Twin-spot Carpet
Xanthorhoe quadrifasiata

Silver-ground Carpet
Xanthorhoe montanata montanata

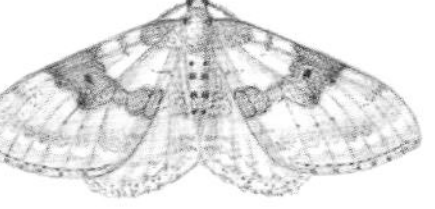

Silver-ground Carpet
Xanthorhoe montanata montanata

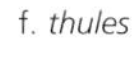

Garden Carpet
Xanthorhoe fluctuata
f. *thules*

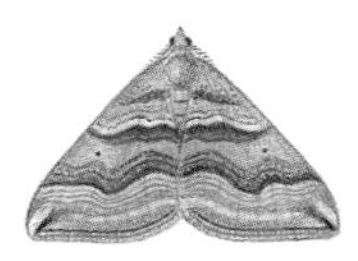

Spanish Carpet
Scotopteryx peribolata

Chalk Carpet
Scotopteryx bipunctaria cretata

Shaded Broad-bar
Scotopteryx chenopodiata

Lead Belle *Scotopteryx mucronata* ssp. *umbrifera* Local SW; ssp. *scotica* Local WC,N,Ir **FW** 15-19mm. Very similar to July Belle. Small black central forewing spot usually tear-shaped, roughly midway between second and third cross-lines, or closer to third. Zigzag outermost cross-line well defined. The features are variable, and although July Belle flight times are later, they may overlap with Lead Belle; if in doubt, examine genitalia. Ssp. *scotica* is darker but quite variable, including f. *luridaria*, blackish grey with pale-edged cross-lines. See also Spanish Carpet. **FS** Mid May-mid June. **Hab** A Sc.

July Belle *Scotopteryx luridata* ssp. *plumbaria* Common T **FW** 15-19mm. Very Similar to Lead Belle. Black central forewing spot usually smaller, round and nearer to second cross-line than third. Zigzag outermost cross-line usually faint. See also Spanish Carpet. **FS** June-early August. **Hab** CGr Sc Sh.

Ruddy Carpet *Catarhoe rubidata* Nb. S **FW** 13-15mm. Forewing dull pink or pinkish brown; grey central cross-band thickly edged black, except in trailing half of its outer edge, which forms a very fine, deeply-scalloped black line. **FS** June-July. **Hab** CGr H Sc Cl.

Royal Mantle *Catarhoe cuculata* Local S,(N,Ir) **FW** 12-14mm. Broad whitish central cross-band, its outer edge finely scalloped in trailing half; strong black and brown cross-bands. **FS** Late June-July. **Hab** CGr Cl.

Small Argent & Sable *Epirrhoe tristata* Common N,W,Ir **FW** 11-13mm. Not unlike a small, dark Common Carpet, but with evenly darkened markings, brightly chequered fringes and dark dots in white bands. **FS** Late May-early July; (August in south-west England and Ireland). Flies by day in sunshine and at dusk. **Hab** Up.

Common Carpet *Epirrhoe alternata alternata* Common T; ssp. *obscurata* Outer Hebrides **FW** 13-14mm. Blackish central forewing cross-band rather irregular, with one, rather blunt, outer projection. Basal area of hindwing well marked; white bands running across outer half of wings have grey line, sometimes rather faint. Ssp. *obscurata* is much paler and brownish. See Wood Carpet, Galium Carpet, Sharp-angled Carpet. **FS** As far north as Northumberland, May-June; July-early September (in far south, three overlapping generations May-October). In far north, June-July. Easily disturbed by day. **Hab** Ub.

Wood Carpet *Epirrhoe rivata* Local S,(C) **FW** 14-16mm. Very similar to Common Carpet, but slightly larger. White outer cross-band broader, with thin grey line very faint or largely absent on forewing and absent on hindwing. See also Sharp-angled Carpet (p.38). **FS** Mid June-early August. **Hab** BWd H Sc C.

Galium Carpet *Epirrhoe galiata* Local S,C,(N),I **FW** 13-15mm. Forewing leading edge slightly concave in middle; dark central cross-band broad with very irregular outer edge. Dark, brownish-gr forms with black forewing bands occur in wester Ireland. See Garden Carpet. **FS** In southern Britai and Ireland, late May-mid July; August. In north, June-early August. **Hab** C CGr Up.

Many-lined *Costaconvexa polygrammata* Extin recent rare immigrant S **FW** 11-12mm. In male, two conspicuous dark cross-bands on dull straw-coloured forewing, inner one stopping near cent spot, outer in leading half only. In female these a weak and light brown. Oblique Carpet has dark diagonal band extending from forewing tip. See also Oblique Striped and Traveller. **FS** Recorded in April, June, August and possibly September. Flies late afternoon and from dusk. **Hab** Wt.

Traveller *Costaconvexa centrostrigaria* Probable import (recorded once) **FW** 11-12mm. Similar to Many-lined, but cross-lines more wavy. Central black forewing spot larger and further from inne cross-lines.

Yellow Shell *Camptogramma bilineata bilinea* Common T; ssp. *atlantica* Shetland, Outer Hebrid ssp. *hibernica* Ir; ssp. *isolata* Blasket Islands, Ir **FW** 13-16mm. Ssp. *bilineata*: Yellow or orange-yellow (often brownish in north), with many fine wavy grey-brown cross-lines. Ssp. *atlantica*: Smaller, yellowish brown, often with strong band and cross-lines, hindwing sometimes yellowish. Ssp. *hibernica*: Forewing brown. Ssp. *isolata*: Dull blackish brown. **FS** June-August. **Hab** Ub.

Yellow-ringed Carpet *Entephria flavicinctata flavicinctata* Nb. NW,Ir; ssp. *ruficinctata* Local NW **FW** 17-18mm. Very similar to Grey Mountain Carpet, but with dusting of bright golden-orange scales through central bands of forewing (but sometimes very sparse so care needed), lacking ir Grey Mountain Carpet. Ssp. *ruficinctata* is darker. **FS** On west coast of mainland Scotland and Inne Hebrides, May; August. Elsewhere in northern Britain, July-early August. **Hab** Up.

Grey Mountain Carpet *Entephria caesiata* Common WC,N,Ir **FW** 16-19mm. Forewing grey to blackish with finely scalloped cross-lines. Centr band usually conspicuous, edged white. See Yellow-ringed Carpet. Striped Twin-spot Carpet is much smaller and less boldly marked. **FS** Late Jur early August. In northern Scotland, late July-early October. **Hab** Up.

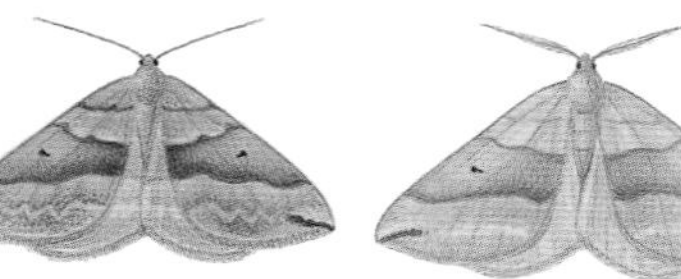

Lead Belle

Scotopteryx mucronata umbrifera

Scotopteryx mucronata scotica

July Belle
Scotopteryx luridata plumbaria

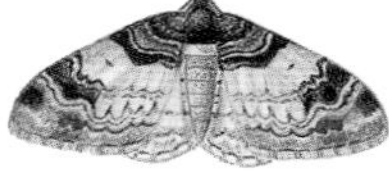

Ruddy Carpet
Catarhoe rubidata

Royal Mantle
Catarhoe cuculata

Small Argent & Sable
Epirrhoe tristata

Common Carpet

Epirrhoe alternata alternata

Epirrhoe alternata obscurata

Wood Carpet
Epirrhoe rivata

Galium Carpet
Epirrhoe galiata

dark form, Co. Clare

Many-lined
Costaconvexa polygrammata

Traveller
Costaconvexa centrostrigaria

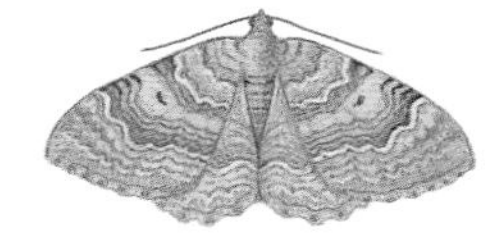

Yellow Shell

Camptogramma bilineata bilineata

Camptogramma bilineata atlantica

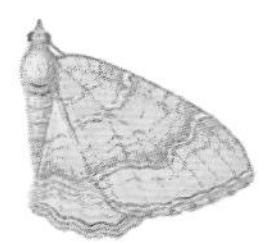

Yellow Shell

C. b. hibernica

C. b. isolata

Yellow-ringed Carpet

tephria flavicinctata flavicinctata

Entephria flavicinctata ruficinctata

Grey Mountain Carpet
Entephria caesiata

Mallow *Larentia clavaria* Common S,C,(N,Ir) **FW** 19-22mm. Deep reddish-brown, white-dusted forewing with pointed tip; cross-bands finely edged white, inner edge of central one irregular, outermost zigzagging. **FS** September-early November. **Hab** Gr Wt H G.

Shoulder Stripe *Anticlea badiata* Common S,C,(N),Ir **FW** 14-18mm. Quite broad, rich brown or charcoal-brown forewing, with distinct paler, straw-yellow, brownish-yellow or brown central cross-band. Cross-lines variably edged black, inner ones more so. **FS** March-May. **Hab** Wd H Sc G.

Streamer *Anticlea derivata* Common T **FW** 14-16mm. Forewing grey-brown (often violet-tinted when fresh), quite rounded with broad, paler, whitish, grey or brown central band, thickly edged black on basal side, its outer edge deeply elbowed, almost reaching margin, thickened in leading half. See Barberry Carpet (p.38). **FS** Late March/April-May. **Hab** Wd H Sc G.

Beautiful Carpet *Mesoleuca albicillata* Common S,C,(N),Ir **FW** 15-18mm. Very broad, rounded forewing with very broad, plain white central cross-band. Black, brown and purplish-blue basal and outer markings. **FS** Late May-early August. **Hab** Wd Sc H.

Dark Spinach *Pelurga comitata* Common S,C,(N),Ir **FW** 16-18mm. Forewing broad and quite rounded, yellow-brown. Central cross-band darker, pale centred (with small dark central dot), wavy, with strong outer projection. Northern Spinach has double outer projection on central band and plain fringes. See also Spinach. Both of these lack central dark dot. **FS** July-August. **Hab** R A C.

Water Carpet *Lampropteryx suffumata* Common T **FW** 14-17mm. Forewing rather shiny, tapering, brownish white, light brown or dark brown (f. *piceata*), with curved leading edge. Dark central cross-band has strong, double outer projection. Small Phoenix forewing has tooth-like marks near outer margin, is not shiny and cross-band lacks outer projection. See also Devon Carpet, Broken-barred Carpet. **FS** April-May. **Hab** Wd Sc H Wt Up.

Devon Carpet *Lampropteryx otregiata* Nb. S,SW **FW** 12-14mm. Not unlike a small Water Carpet, but forewing less tapered, and central cross-band irregular but less indented. Small Phoenix lacks outer projection on central cross-band. **FS** Mid May-June; early August-mid September. **Hab** Wd.

Purple Bar *Cosmorhoe ocellata* Common T **FW** 13-15mm. When freshly emerged, wings are smooth and silky; creamy white with broad, dark central cross-band composed of purplish grey, black and brown. **FS** In south, May-July; (August-September). In north, June-July. **Hab** Ub.

Striped Twin-spot Carpet *Nebula salicata* ssp. *latentaria* Common N,W,(SW),Ir **FW** 12-15mm Rather weakly marked, light to dark grey. Many faint cross-lines and slightly darker central cross-band, always with small blackish, rather elongate central spot. Garden Carpet f. *thules* usually has leading half of central cross-band darker. See also Twin-spot Carpet (p.40), Grey Mountain Carpet. **FS** May-July; (August-September at low altitude). **Hab** Up Wd Sd.

Phoenix *Eulithis prunata* Common T **FW** 17-19mm. Large, with broad forewing and v wavy outer edge to broad brown central band, a tooth-like marks near outer margin. Male rests w tip of abdomen curled upwards. **FS** July-August. **Hab** G Wd.

Chevron *Eulithis testata* Common T **FW** 13-19mm. Chevron-like central cross-band o bright brownish-orange, light or dark reddish-bro forewing, whitish frosting and short, diagonal whitish line at wing tip. Northern Spinach lacks whitish frosting, has dark line at forewing tip and central cross-band is not chevron-like. **FS** July-mi September. **Hab** Sc Wt Sd Up Wd.

Northern Spinach *Eulithis populata* Commor SW,W,C,N,Ir **FW** 13-18mm. Forewing straw yello to orange-brown or dark brown. Central cross-ba has distinct double tooth-like outer projection an often a chain of oval blotches. Short, dark diagor line at wing tip. Features often faint in dark exam ples, most frequent in north, especially Orkney ar Shetland. See Chevron, Spinach, Dark Spinach. **FS** July-August. **Hab** Up A Wd.

Spinach *Eulithis mellinata* Common S,C,(N,Ir) **FW** 16-18mm. Shares unique resting posture wit Barred Straw: wings held out horizontally, well cl of surface, with trailing edge of hindwing and tip of abdomen curled upwards. Central cross-band on forewing has large outer projection; fringes chequered. Northern Spinach rests with wings fla against surface and closer to the body. See also Barred Straw. **FS** Mid June-late August. **Hab** G W

Barred Straw *Eulithis pyraliata* Common T **FW** 15-18mm. Resting posture as Spinach, but central forewing cross-band narrower with parall V-shaped edges. Fringes plain brown. **FS** Late Ma late August. **Hab** H Wd Sc G.

Small Phoenix *Ecliptopera silaceata* Common T **FW** 13-17mm. Dark central forewing cross-band unbroken or with band broken by two broad wh lines (f. *insulata*), and dark tooth-like marks beyo central band. Male rests with tip of abdomen cur upwards. See Water Carpet, Broken-barred Carpe Phoenix, Netted Carpet, Devon Carpet. **FS** In sou end April-June; late July-August. Elsewhere, May-June; (late July-August). **Hab** Ub.

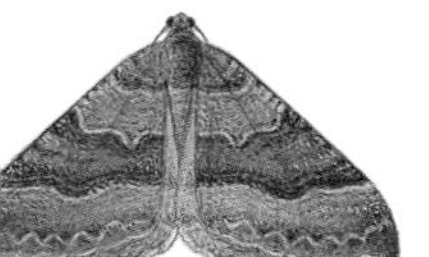

Mallow
Larentia clavaria

Shoulder Stripe
Anticlea badiata

Streamer
Anticlea derivata

Beautiful Carpet
Mesoleuca albicillata

Dark Spinach
Pelurga comitata

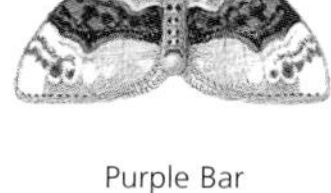

Water Carpet
Lampropteryx suffumata f. *piceata*

Devon Carpet
Lampropteryx otregiata

Purple Bar
Cosmorhoe ocellata

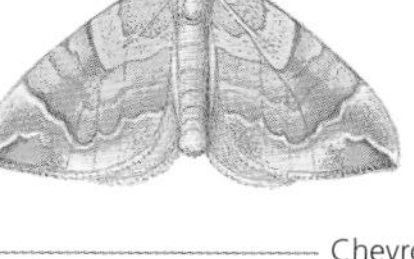
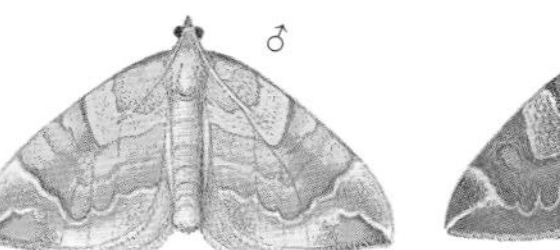

♂ ♀

riped Twin-spot Carpet
ebula salicata latentaria

Phoenix
Eulithis prunata

Chevron
Eulithis testata

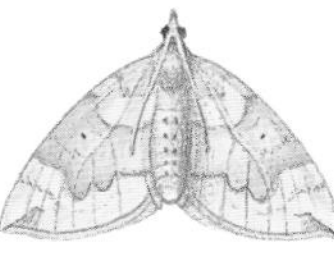
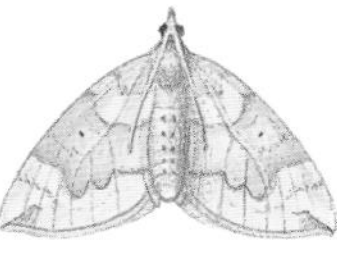

Northern Spinach
Eulithis populata

dark form, Scotland

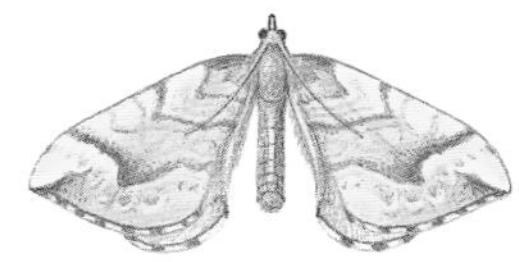

Spinach
Eulithis mellinata

Barred Straw
Eulithis pyraliata

Small Phoenix
Ecliptopera silaceata f. *insulata*

Red-green Carpet *Chloroclysta siterata* Common T **FW** 14-17mm. Quite variable; usually with reddish-brown marbling on forewing and black bar centrally on or near trailing edge. Band outside central cross-band white or paler near leading edge. Hindwing grey. Autumn Green Carpet has forewing broader without black bar on trailing edge, rarely with reddish marbling and hindwing whitish. See also Beech-green Carpet. **FS** September-November; March-May after hibernation. **Hab** Wd Up H G.

Autumn Green Carpet *Chloroclysta miata* Local T **FW** 15-17mm. Similar to Red-green Carpet (see under that species). Rarely, reddish-brown cross-bands either side of central cross-band. See also Beech-green Carpet. **FS** September-November, and March-May after hibernation. **Hab** Up Wd Sc H.

Dark Marbled Carpet *Chloroclysta citrata citrata* Common T; ssp. *pythonissata* Shetland and Orkney **FW** 14-19mm. Very similar to the equally variable Common Marbled Carpet, and Arran Carpet, but central projection on outer edge of central forewing cross-band longer and more pointed. On hindwing, central cross-line usually has sharp central point and is acutely angled (obtusely angled and more rounded in Common Marbled Carpet). See also on underside. Ssp. *pythonissata* is darker and less variable, often with narrow white cross-lines. **FS** In south, July-August. In north, late July-October. **Hab** Wd Up A Sc H G.

Arran Carpet *Chloroclysta concinnata* Na. NW **FW** 14-19mm. Very similar to darker forms of Common Marbled Carpet and may be a race of that species. Outer edge of central cross-band more irregular and sometimes more pointed; white on band more irregular and often rather blotchy. See also Dark Marbled Carpet. **FS** July-August. **Hab** Up.

Common Marbled Carpet *Chloroclysta truncata* Common T **FW** 14-19mm. Very variable. Form with large light brown central cloud on forewing unmistakable. Other forms very similar to Dark Marbled Carpet (see under that species). See also Arran Carpet. **FS** May-June; late August-early October. Early July-August in parts of north and Ireland. **Hab** Ub.

Barred Yellow *Cidaria fulvata* Common T **FW** 12-14mm. Rather plain bright orange-yellow forewing with darker central cross-band, dark diagonal streak at tip and chequered fringes. **FS** June-early August. **Hab** Wd Sc H G.

Blue-bordered Carpet *Plemyria rubiginata rubiginata* Common S,C,Ir; ssp. *plumbata* Local **FW** 12-15mm. Ssp. *rubiginata*: Rounded white forewing with blue-grey outer border. Brown ce cross-band disappearing in trailing half. Ssp. *plumbata*: Central cross-band complete or almost so. F. *semifumosa* has forewing dark grey frequent in ssp. *plumbata*, rare in ssp. *rubiginata* **FS** Late June-early August. **Hab** Wd H Wt G.

Pine Carpet *Thera firmata* Common T **FW** 13-16mm. Forewing sandy, greyish brown o dark reddish brown. Inner edge of central cross-band deeply indented. See Grey Pine Carpet. **FS** July-November. **Hab** CWd.

Grey Pine Carpet *Thera obeliscata* Commor **FW** 13-17mm. Forewing light sandy brown, ligh dark greyish brown or blackish. Central cross-ba not deeply indented; reddish brown, dark brown grey-brown, edges fairly smooth or slightly flute See Spruce Carpet, Pine Carpet. **FS** May-July; September-November. **Hab** CWd G.

Spruce Carpet *Thera britannica* Common T **FW** 13-17mm. Similar to Grey Pine Carpet, especially dark examples. Forewing light grey to blac grey, often heavily marked and dusted with whi especially either side of central cross-band, whic is usually more fluted and sometimes tinged wit brown. See also Juniper Carpet, Cypress Carpet. **FS** May-July; September-November. **Hab** CWd C

Red-green Carpet
Chloroclysta siterata

Autumn Green Carpet
Chloroclysta miata

Dark Marbled Carpet
Chloroclysta citrata citrata

C. c. pythonissata

Arran Carpet
Chloroclysta concinnata

Common Marbled Carpet
Chloroclysta truncata

views of undersides

Dark Marbled Carpet
Chloroclysta citrata citrata

Arran Carpet
Chloroclysta concinnata

Common Marbled Carpet
Chloroclysta truncata

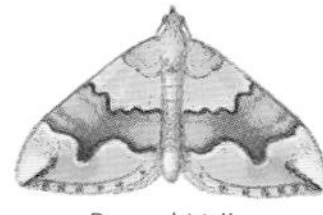

Barred Yellow
Cidaria fulvata

Blue-bordered Carpet
Plemyria rubiginata rubiginata

Plemyria rubiginata plumbata f. *semifumosa*

Pine Carpet
Thera firmata

Grey Pine Carpet
Thera obeliscata

Spruce Carpet
Thera britannica

Chestnut-coloured Carpet *Thera cognata* Nb. C,N,Ir **FW** 11-14mm. Rounded chestnut forewing with broad central cross-band lacking any major indentation. Moths from the Hebrides, Orkney and Shetland are larger and darker. In western Ireland large and pale, sometimes with violet tints. Juniper Carpet and Cypress Carpet have black streaks near tip of forewing. **FS** July-August. **Hab** Up C.

Juniper Carpet *Thera juniperata juniperata* Common S,C; ssp. *scotica* Local N; ssp. *orcadensis* possibly extinct, resident Orkney; ssp. (unnamed) Ir **FW** 11-14mm. Ssp. *juniperata*: Finely-marked, light brownish-grey forewing. Central cross-band variable, often composed of rounded, pebble-like blotches, narrowed or disappearing in trailing half, often with sharp inner indentation. 1-3 diagonal black dashes near wing tip. Ssp. *scotica*: Smaller and darker. Ssp. *orcadensis*: Also small; forewing paler, more strongly banded than ssp. *scotica*. In south-west Ireland also very pale, but less strongly marked and larger than ssp. *orcadensis*. Spruce Carpet is larger, more clouded, with single short, diagonal dash at forewing tip. See also Cypress Carpet. **FS** Ssp. *juniperata* late September-early November, ssp. *scotica* September-October. **Hab** Ssp. *juniperata* CGr G. Ssp. *scotica* and *orcdensis* Up C.

Cypress Carpet *Thera cupressata* Uncommon, on alien host (conifers) SE **FW** 12-15mm. Rather streaky in appearance. Several dark brown streaks or dashes near forewing tip, another in brown central band and a dark bar centrally on or close to trailing edge. Central cross-band on forewing often indistinct and can be absent in trailing half. Spruce Carpet lacks dark streaks. **FS** Late June-July; October-November. **Hab** G.

Netted Carpet *Eustroma reticulatum* RDB WC **FW** 13-14mm. Forewing with distinctive, complex network of white stripes. Central cross-band and patterns on Broken-barred Carpet have jagged edges. See also Small Phoenix, with central cross-band crossed by only two white lines. **FS** July-August. **Hab** Wd.

Broken-barred Carpet *Electrophaes corylata* Common T **FW** 14-16mm. Very irregular (even jagged) dark cross-band on forewing, usually broken or pinched in trailing half. Extensive whitish frosting and edging. F. *albocrenata*, found infrequently in Scotland, lacks dark central band. Water Carpet has rather shiny forewing and outer edge of dark central band is less irregular. See also Small Phoenix, Netted Carpet. **FS** May-July. **Hab** Wd H Sc G.

Beech-green Carpet *Colostygia olivata* Local N,WC,(S,Ir) **FW** 13-15mm. Forewing rounded, dul green (fading to yellowish or brownish); many fine wavy black cross-lines, and pronounced continuou narrow whitish cross-band outside darker central band. Hindwing grey-brown. Autumn Green Carpe has less ample forewing and whitish hindwing. See also Green Carpet. **FS** July-August. **Hab** Wd Up.

Mottled Grey *Colostygia multistrigaria* Commo T **FW** 13-17mm. Forewing whitish, somewhat tapered, especially in male; narrower in smaller female. Delicate markings, rather shiny texture (when fresh) and chequered veins on forewing. F. *nubilata* is dark brownish grey (Midlands, northern England and Scotland). **FS** March-April. **Hab** H Up CGr Wd.

Green Carpet *Colostygia pectinataria* Common T **FW** 12-15mm. Forewing green when freshly emerged. This quickly fades to whitish, but patter of black blotches and central and basal cross-ban on forewing is always recognisable. See Beech-green Carpet, which lacks the blotches. **FS** In sou May-mid July; August-early September. In north, June-August. **Hab** Ub.

July Highflyer *Hydriomena furcata* Common T **FW** 14-18mm. Forewings of all three 'highflyer are distinctly shouldered at base. July Highflyer fli later in year than May and Ruddy, and lacks point black streaks near forewing tip, but has diagonal dash at tip. Hindwing dull grey, with at most fain dark central cross-line. Extremely variable. In dens southern woodland, usually green or blackish brown. In open habitat, especially in north and west, paler and more variegated greyish or reddis forms predominate. Populations on moorland, especially if feeding on Bilberry, produce smaller moths. See May and Ruddy Highflyer. **FS** In south July-August. In northern Scotland, late July-early October. **Hab** Ub.

May Highflyer *Hydriomena impluviata* Comm T **FW** 13-16mm. Two to three short, parallel blackish streaks near tip of greyish (never reddish) forewing. Usually no diagonal dash at tip. F. *obsoletaria* blackish grey, with only faint markings, frequent in London. More variable in north. See a Ruddy Highflyer. **FS** May-early July. **Hab** BWd Wt.

Ruddy Highflyer *Hydriomena ruberata* Local N,W,(S,E),Ir **FW** 14-17mm. Forewing reddish, reddish brown or greyish, with distinct black das at tip and earlier flight season than July Highflye Some May Highflyers are very similar but forewir shorter and dark dash at tip usually absent. **FS** May-June. **Hab** Up A Wt Wd.

Chestnut-coloured Carpet
Thera cognata
Orkney specimen

Juniper Carpet
Thera juniperata juniperata *T. j. scotica*

Cypress Carpet
Thera cupressata

Netted Carpet
Eustroma reticulatum

Broken-barred Carpet
Electrophaes corylata
f. *albocrenata*

Argyll specimen

Beech-green Carpet
Colostygia olivata

Mottled Grey
Colostygia multistrigaria
f. *nubilata*

Green Carpet
Colostygia pectinataria

faded specimen

July Highflyer
Hydriomena furcata

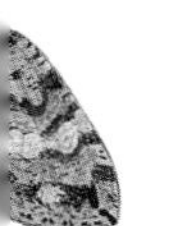

July Highflyer
Hydriomena furcata

May Highflyer
Hydriomena impluviata

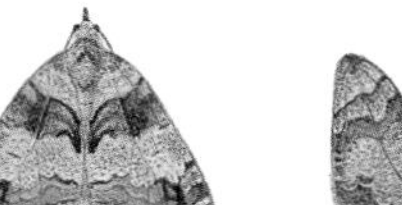

Ruddy Highflyer
Hydriomena ruberata

Slender-striped Rufous *Coenocalpe lapidata* Na. N,Ir **FW** 13-16mm. Forewing sandy brown in male, paler, whitish brown in smaller female, with numerous darker wavy cross-lines. Swept back pointed tip, more prominent in female.
FS September-early October. Flies in afternoon in sunshine. Rests on vertical plant stems after dark.
Hab Up.

Small Waved Umber *Horisme vitalbata* Common S,C **FW** 14-17mm. Broad, blackish band across forewing from leading half of outer edge to middle of trailing edge, merging with band on hindwing when at rest. See Waved Umber (p.64). **FS** May-June; August. **Hab** Wd Sc H.

Fern *Horisme tersata* Common S,(C) **FW** 14-18mm. In shape, like un-banded version of Small Waved Umber, but browner. Rather plain, with slightly rough texture. Fine black line across front end of abdomen coincides with second cross-line on forewings when moth is at rest, making a single black streak. **FS** Mid June-mid August. **Hab** Wd H Sc G.

Pretty Chalk Carpet *Melanthia procellata* Common S,(C) **FW** 16-18mm. Wings chalky white. Forewing broad, with dark brown central cross-band stopping abruptly before middle and central white blotch in dark brown outer border. **FS** Early June-late August. **Hab** Wd Sc H.

Barberry Carpet *Pareulype berberata* RDB (Protected) S **FW** 13-15mm. Dark edging to twin projections of irregular outer central forewing cross-band, in leading half, often forming crescent mark. Bold, dark brown central cross-band. Streamer has outer cross-line sweeping out almost to outer edge. **FS** Early May-June; late July-August. **Hab** H.

White-banded Carpet *Spargania luctuata* Na. SE **FW** 14-15mm. White outer cross-band on dark forewing; broader white band on hindwing. Double-lobed outer tooth on central cross-band. Cloaked Carpet has greenish scales, like algae, near forewing base. Sharp-angled Carpet has single sharp tooth on outer edge of central cross-band. Both have paler outer areas. **FS** Mid May-mid June; mid July-late August. Sometimes flies in sunshine in afternoon and early evening. **Hab** Wd.

Argent & Sable *Rheumaptera hastata hastata* Nb. S,C,Ir; f. *nigrescens* Nb. N
Ssp. *hastata*: **FW** 16-19mm. Generally larger; distinctive black and white wing pattern, markings intensely black. Includes f. *laxata*, with wider white central forewing cross-band and sometimes smaller. F. *nigrescens*: **FW** 13-15mm. Smaller, markings more intricate; often brownish black or greyish black. Small Argent & Sable (p.30) is superficially like f. *nigrescens* but smaller, with straighter leading edge to forewing and regular, uninterrupted bands. **FS** May-June. Active only by day.
Hab Ssp. *hastata* Wd. F. *nigrescens* Up.

Scarce Tissue *Rheumaptera cervinalis* Local S,C **FW** 19-22mm. Similar to Tissue, but with forewing slightly narrower and more pointed, rather rough textured and not marked with pink. Central cross-lines closer together, often merged, usually blackish brown. Hindwing irregularly saw-toothed rather than scalloped. On underside, small dark central spots bold and intense; two small dark spots near base of forewing on leading edge. See also Irish Annulet (p.72). **FS** April-June. **Hab** H G.

Scallop Shell *Rheumaptera undulata* Local S,C,(N),Ir **FW** 16-19mm. Numerous tightly-packed, scalloped, dark brown wavy cross-lines on broad, whitish-buff wings. **FS** June-July. **Hab** Wd Wt.

Tissue *Triphosa dubitata* Local S,C,(N),Ir **FW** 19-22mm. Wings ample. Forewing grey-brown, rather shiny, sometimes delicately marbled pink. Forewing outer edge scalloped, hindwing heavily so. On underside, dark central spots small; that on forewing narrow. Forewing base plain or with dark, roughly elliptical mark on leading edge. See Scarce Tissue, Irish Annulet (p.72). **FS** August-October. After hibernation, April-May. **Hab** BWd Sc H.

Brown Scallop *Philereme vetulata* Local S,(not SW),C,(Ir) **FW** 13-16mm. Muddy, light grey-brown; numerous very faint cross-lines and very small round dark central dot on forewing. Fringes chequered grey and buff; hindwing scalloped. See Dark Umber. **FS** Late June-July. **Hab** BWd Sc H.

Dark Umber *Philereme transversata* ssp. *britannica* Local S,(SW),C,(Ir) **FW** 17-20mm. Rich brown to very dark brown, with broad and rather tapering forewing. Cross-lines and bands strongly angled at leading edge, especially outer edge of central band. Outer margins scalloped, hindwing strongly. See Brown Scallop, which is smaller and paler. **FS** July-August. **Hab** BWd Sc H.

Cloaked Carpet *Euphyia biangulata* Nb. W,S,SE,Ir **FW** 14-17mm. Dark central cross-band on rather ample, tapered forewing, with double-toothed outer edge. Greenish scales on base, like algae. See Sharp-angled Carpet and White-banded Carpet, both smaller with less tapered forewing and not greenish. **FS** Late June-mid August.
Hab BWd H.

Sharp-angled Carpet *Euphyia unangulata* Local S,(C,N),Ir **FW** 13-15mm. Outer edge of central cross-band forms single sharp point, and contrasts strongly with whitish band beyond it. Hindwing whitish basally, with faint grey lines. Common Carpet and Wood Carpet have more irregular central cross-band, with blunt outer projection, and hindwing more strongly marked basally. See also White-banded Carpet, Cloaked Carpet, Balsam Carpet (p.28). **FS** Late June-early August.
Hab BWd H.

Slender-striped Rufous
Coenocalpe lapidata

Small Waved Umber
Horisme vitalbata

Fern
Horisme tersata

Pretty Chalk Carpet
Melanthia procellata

Barberry Carpet
Pareulype berberata

White-banded Carpet
Spargania luctuata

Argent & Sable
Rheumaptera hastata hastata
Rheumaptera hastata f. *nigrescens*

Scarce Tissue
Rheumaptera cervinalis

Scallop Shell
Rheumaptera undulata

Tissue
Triphosa dubitata

Brown Scallop
Philereme vetulata

Dark Umber
Philereme transversata britannica

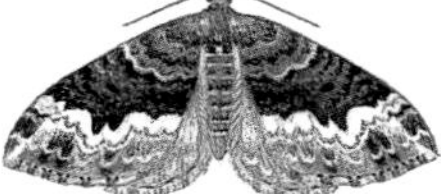

Cloaked Carpet
Euphyia biangulata

Sharp-angled Carpet
Euphyia unangulata

November Moth *Epirrita dilutata* Common T **FW** 15-20mm. Very similar to Pale November and Autumnal Moth. Wing markings not fully reliable and reference to morphological features often needed. On forewing, central spot usually within outer central cross-band, but markings may be absent or different. In Pale November and Autumnal Moth central spot usually separate from cross-band; in Autumnal Moth more so and band more sharply angled. Central dark V- or X-mark often more prominent in Autumnal Moth; usually more strongly banded. **FS** Early October-November, but from mid-September in north. **Hab** Ub.

Pale November Moth *Epirrita christyi* Common S,C,(N,Ir) **FW** 15-20mm. See November Moth. **FS** Late September-November, peaking mid-late October. **Hab** BWd.

Autumnal Moth *Epirrita autumnata* Common T **FW** 16-20mm. See November Moth. **FS** October-November (usually 2-3 weeks later than November Moth in same area). **Hab** Wd A Up.

Small Autumnal Moth *Epirrita filigrammaria* Common N,C,W,Ir **FW** 14-18mm. Similar to Autumnal Moth; usually smaller, with earlier flight season. **FS** August-September. **Hab** Up.

Winter Moth *Operophtera brumata* Common T **FW** 13-16mm. Drab light to dark brown; darker central forewing cross-band, often indistinct. Hindwing brown. Wing-stumps of female black-banded. See Northern Winter Moth, *Epirrita* species, March Moth (female) (p.22), Early Moth (p.72). **FS** October-January. **Hab** Ub.

Northern Winter Moth *Operophtera fagata* Common T **FW** 14-18mm. Similar to Winter Moth, but light brown, rather silky and often larger; hindwing whitish. In female, wings three times longer. See also *Epirrita* species. **FS** October-December, peaking November. **Hab** BWd A Sc G O.

Barred Carpet *Perizoma taeniata* Na. C,N,Ir **FW** 11-12mm. Forewing brown, sometimes heavily marked dark grey; grey basal blotch and gently curved grey, finely scalloped central cross-band. Dark outer band in leading half, then sometimes a white patch. Thorax dark. Barred Rivulet smaller, central cross-band narrower; forewing tip more pointed. Foxglove Pug and Toadflax Pug have pale thorax, well-marked hindwing and different resting posture. See also Yellow-barred Brindle (p.50). **FS** June-September. Sometimes flies in late afternoon. **Hab** BWd.

Rivulet *Perizoma affinitata* Common T **FW** 12-15mm. Forewing dark grey-brown; narrow white cross-band beyond middle, with single (rarely a second, much smaller) rounded central inner indentation. At most a faint pale inner cross-band. Hindwing usually with distinct whitish central cross-band. See Small Rivulet. **FS** In south, late May-mid July; August-September. In north, late May-July. **Hab** BWd H Sc.

Small Rivulet *Perizoma alchemillata* Common T **FW** 9-11mm. Similar to but smaller than Rivulet, with two or more roughly equal inner indentations on white cross-band; often a second, usually fainter white inner cross-band. Hindwing usually only faintly banded. **FS** Early June-August. **Hab** BWd H Sc Wt G.

Barred Rivulet *Perizoma bifaciata* Local S,C,(N,Ir **FW** 9-11mm. Dull greyish-brown forewing with fine chalky white edging on rather narrow, dark grey central cross-band. Heath Rivulet is smaller and greyer, with coarse whitish markings. See also Barred Carpet. **FS** July-August. **Hab** Gr.

Heath Rivulet *Perizoma minorata* ssp. *ericetata* Nb. N,C,(Ir) **FW** 8-10mm. Grey, coarse-textured forewing markings; strong, well-defined, irregular whitish cross-lines and bands. See Barred Rivulet. **FS** July-August. Flies in sunshine and at night. **Hab** Up CGr C.

Pretty Pinion *Perizoma blandiata blandiata* Local N,W,Ir; ssp. *perfasciata* Hebrides/Rum **FW** 9-11mm. Ssp. *blandiata:* Forewing white, with grey markings and black central spot. Central dark grey cross-band usually faint centrally; sometimes pinched or broken. Ssp. *perfasciata:* Stronger markings; central band les faint in middle. **FS** Late May-early August. Flies in late afternoon and after dark. **Hab** Up.

Grass Rivulet *Perizoma albulata albulata* Local T ssp. *subfasciaria* Shetland **FW** 10-12mm. Ssp. *albulata*: Soft grey-brown cross-bands on chalky white forewing. Whitest forms on chalk in south; generally darker in north. Ssp. *subfasciaria*: Smaller, darker, often entirely grey-brown, with fai paler markings. **FS** May-early July. Flies by day, esp cially late, and after dark. **Hab** Gr C.

Sandy Carpet *Perizoma flavofasciata* Common T **FW** 11-14mm. Irregular, sandy brown cross-ban and lines on white forewing. Central cross-band with double outer projection. **FS** June-July. Flies mainly at dusk. **Hab** Wd H CGr Sd.

Twin-spot Carpet *Perizoma didymata didymat* Common T; ssp. *hethlandica* Shetland **FW** 11-15mm. Ssp. *didymata*: Has two blackish spots, often joined at base, in leading half of forewing outer area. Coarse texture. Ground-colo in male grey; whitish in generally smaller female. Ssp. *hethlandica:* Often duller and browner. On Orkney, male dark grey, blackish or reddish brown female pale. Striped Twin-spot Carpet and Garden Carpet f. *thules* have less pointed forewing, withc the twin spots. **FS** June-August. Male mainly activ by day and at dusk. Female more sedentary; rests on vegetation at night. **Hab** Ub.

Marsh Carpet *Perizoma sagittata* Na. EC **FW** 13-17mm. Dark grey or blackish, white-edgec central cross-band with strong outer projection, o sandy brown forewing. **FS** June-August. **Hab** Wt.

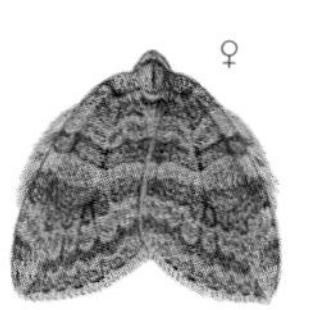

♂ ♂ ♂ ♀

November Moth
Epirrita dilutata

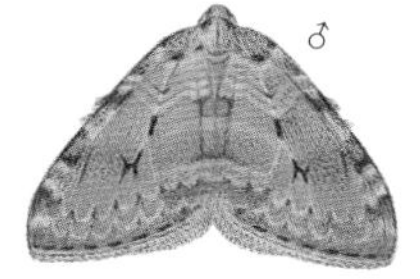

♂ ♂

Pale November Moth
Epirrita christyi

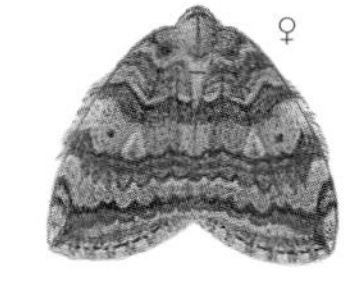

♂ ♀

Autumnal Moth
Epirrita autumnata

♂ ♀

Small Autumnal Moth
Epirrita filigrammaria

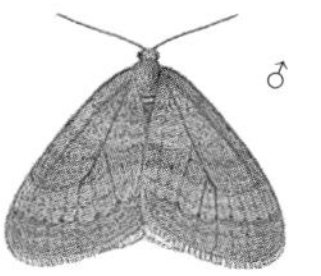
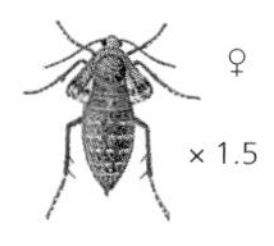

♂ ♀ × 1.5

Winter Moth
Operophtera brumata

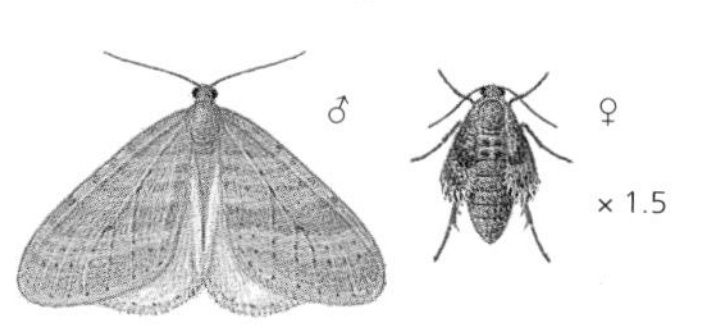

♂ ♀ × 1.5

Northern Winter Moth
Operophtera fagata

Barred Carpet
Perizoma taeniata

Rivulet
Perizoma affinitata

Small Rivulet
Perizoma alchemillata

Barred Rivulet
rizoma bifaciata

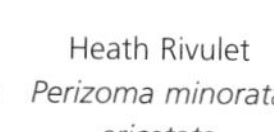

Heath Rivulet
Perizoma minorata ericetata

Pretty Pinion
Perizoma blandiata blandiata

Grass Rivulet
Perizoma albulata albulata
Perizoma albulata subfasciaria

Sandy Carpet
rizoma flavofasciata

Twin-spot Carpet
Perizoma didymata didymata
Wigtownshire specimen Ross-shire specimen Berkshire specimen

Marsh Carpet
Perizoma sagittata

Pugs

General A large group, most having a distinctive resting posture: wings stretched out with leading edges lined up, or nearly so. Many are difficult to identify, and examination of genitalia or other morphological features is often required, especially on worn moths or melanic forms.

Slender Pug *Eupithecia tenuiata* Common T **FW** 8-10mm. Rounded grey-brown forewing with distinct, round, black central spot. Often dark blocks along leading edge. F. *johnsoni* darker grey-brown (north-east England and Midlands). See Maple Pug, Small Dusty Wave (p.26). **FS** June-July. **Hab** Wd Sc Wt G.

Maple Pug *Eupithecia inturbata* Local S,C **FW** 8-10mm. Similar to Slender Pug, but forewing more brownish, often yellowish brown; generally rougher, more blotchy, slightly narrower and less rounded. Central spot usually smaller. Darker or blackish forms in some areas. See also Small Dusty Wave (p.26). **FS** July-August. **Hab** BWd Sc H.

Haworth's Pug *Eupithecia haworthiata* Local S,C,(Ir) **FW** 8-9mm. Reddish band at base of abdomen. Forewing grey-brown, rounded, rather weakly marked. Central spot faint or absent. See Lead-coloured Pug. **FS** June-July. **Hab** Wd Sc H G.

Lead-coloured Pug *Eupithecia plumbeolata* Nb. S,C,NW,(Ir) **FW** 9-10mm. Very similar to Haworth's Pug but reddish abdomen band absent, forewing less rounded, usually a washed-out, yellowish grey ground-colour; cross-lines faint, slightly wavy. Central spot small or absent. See Valerian Pug, with more pointed forewing, and Marsh Pug. **FS** Late May-late June. **Hab** Wd Gr Sd.

Cloaked Pug *Eupithecia abietaria* Uncommon; suspected immigrant T **FW** 11-15mm. Forewing broad with large, bold, black central spot. Central cross-bands edged black. Tawny cross-bands near base and outer edge, and on abdomen near base, sometimes more extensively darkened. Dwarf Pug is smaller, lacking tawny bands. **FS** June-July. **Hab** CWd.

Toadflax Pug *Eupithecia linariata* Common S,C,(N) **FW** 9-10mm. Similar to Foxglove Pug, but slightly smaller, markings neater, emerges later. Central cross-band darker, its outer edge curved near leading edge; base only dark near leading edge. See also Barred Carpet. **FS** July-August. **Hab** CGr G.

Foxglove Pug *Eupithecia pulchellata pulchellata* Common T; ssp. *hebudium* Hebrides/Wales **FW** 10-12mm. Broad grey central cross-band, with outer edge kinked near leading edge. Western ssp. *hebudium* greyish white, with brown bands dull. See Toadflax Pug, Barred Carpet. **FS** May-June; (August). In north, May-July. **Hab** Ub.

Marbled Pug *Eupithecia irriguata* Nb. S **FW** 9-11mm. Rather pointed, narrow, whitish forewing, with discrete dark blotches on leading and outer edges; large, black, usually quite elongated central spot. Dwarf Pug is more brownish with broader forewing and dark markings less bol **FS** Late April-May. **Hab** BWd.

Mottled Pug *Eupithecia exiguata exiguata* Common S,C,(N),Ir; ssp. *muricolor* Aberdeenshire **FW** 11-12mm. Forewing pale grey or warm grey, leading edge curved. Central spot conspicuous, rather elongated; small black wedges beyond it. Narrow, pale outer central cross-band, kinked nea leading edge, with two straw-coloured smears extending towards outer edge. Ssp. *muricolor* mousey-grey (Aberdeenshire). Brindled Pug is simil in shape; forewing predominantly brownish. **FS** May-June. **Hab** Wd Sc H G.

Pinion-spotted Pug *Eupithecia insigniata* Nb. S,C,not SW **FW** 10-12mm. Forewing mauvish gre with dark brown blocks along leading edge and prominent, elongated, dark central spot. See Nett Pug. **FS** Late April-May. Seldom seen, except at light. **Hab** H.

Valerian Pug *Eupithecia valerianata* Nb. T **FW** 8-10mm. Forewing rather pointed, grey-brow weakly marked. Zigzag whitish outer cross-line or spots, and distinct white spot at trailing corner (al on hindwing). Central spot elongated, often faint or absent. See Lead-coloured Pug. Common Pug has rougher texture, usually browner and larger, with round central spot. **FS** June-early July. **Hab** W BWd CGr.

Marsh Pug *Eupithecia pygmaeata* Nb. T **FW** 8-9mm. Wings rich dark brown; forewing leading edge very straight. Broken, white outermo cross-line and usually whitish trailing corner spot. Fringes usually chequered brown and white; centr spot faint or absent. When worn, see Lead-colour Pug, which has more rounded forewing and is usually larger, without the white outer markings. **FS** May-June. Active by day. Occasional at light. **Hab** Wt Gr Sd.

Netted Pug *Eupithecia venosata venosata* Local S,C,NE; ssp. *hebridensis* Hebrides; ssp. *fumosae* Shetland/Orkney; ssp. *ochracae* Orkney; ssp. *plumbea* Ir **FW** 10-14mm. Forewing broad, rounded, milky brown; prominent fine dark cross-lines and veins and narrow white cross-bands produce netted effect. Ssp. *fumosae* darker sandy brown, ssp. *ochracae* light sandy brown with dark markings weak, ssp. *plumbea* dark grey, ssp. *hebr densis* usually darker but sometimes sandy. Pinion-spotted Pug has smaller, narrower, pointed forewi with dark blocks on leading edge. **FS** May-June. **Hab** CGr H C.

All shown × 1.25

Slender Pug
Eupithecia tenuiata
f. *johnsoni*

Maple Pug
Eupithecia inturbata

Haworth's Pug
Eupithecia haworthiata

Lead-coloured Pug
Eupithecia plumbeolata

Cloaked Pug
Eupithecia abietaria

Toadflax Pug
Eupithecia linariata

Foxglove Pug
Eupithecia pulchellata pulchellata
Eupithecia pulchellata hebudium

Marbled Pug
Eupithecia irriguata

Mottled Pug
Eupithecia exiguata exiguata
Eupithecia exiguata muricolor

Pinion-spotted Pug
Eupithecia insigniata

Valerian Pug
Eupithecia valerianata

Marsh Pug
Eupithecia pygmaeata

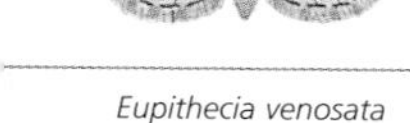

Netted Pug
Eupithecia venosata venosata
Eupithecia venosata fumosae
Eupithecia venosata plumbea
Eupithecia venosata ochracae

Fletcher's Pug (Pauper Pug) *Eupithecia egenaria* RDB SW,S,E **FW** 11-13mm. Forewing light grey, rather rounded and tapered. Central dark spot conspicuous, elongated. Two pairs of dark, central cross-lines, gently angled or curved in leading half. Grey Pug is more coarsely marked, usually darker and central cross-lines more angled. Larch Pug also has different, more acutely angled central cross-lines and a small white crest on back of thorax. **FS** May-June. **Hab** BWd.

Lime-speck Pug *Eupithecia centaureata* Common T **FW** 10-12mm. White with bluish-grey or black blotch on leading edge, sometimes faint. See Marbled Pug, Pretty Pinion. **FS** In south, late April-October. In north, May-August. Often seen at rest by day. **Hab** Ub.

Triple-spotted Pug *Eupithecia trisignaria* Local T **FW** 10-11mm. Forewing dark grey-brown, quite broad and rounded. Round dark central spot and two spots on leading edge; other markings faint, or plain. No white trailing corner spot (see Currant, Grey and Common Pugs). Blackish-brown f. *angelicata* is frequent; usually with obvious group of three spot markings, but sometimes with only central spot. **FS** Late June-July. **Hab** Wt Wd.

Freyer's Pug *Eupithecia intricata arceuthata* Common S,C; **Edinburgh Pug** ssp. *millieraria* Common N; **Mere's Pug** ssp. *hibernica* Ir **FW** 12-13mm. Blackish-brown belt near base of abdomen. Forewing leading edge quite straight. Cross-lines angled near leading edge, especially near conspicuous central dot. Freyer's Pug is soft grey-brown, cross-lines quite strong. Edinburgh Pug is smaller, brown, markings weaker. Mere's Pug is also smaller, strongly marked, with a greyish-white tint. **FS** May-June. **Hab** Freyer's Pug: G CWd. Edinburgh Pug: Up C. Mere's Pug: CGr.

Satyr Pug *Eupithecia satyrata satyrata* Local S; ssp. *callunaria* Common N,Ir (moorland); ssp. *curzoni* Shetland **FW** 9-13mm. Forewing leading edge almost straight. Central dot small but conspicuous. Veins chequered black and white. Whitish spots near outer edge, largest in trailing corner. Ssp. *satyrata* pale, weakly marked, soft grey-brown. Ssp. *callunaria* smaller, darker, often more banded. Ssp. *curzoni* also smaller, heavily banded. Common Pug (veins not chequered, and more reddish brown in south) and Golden-rod Pug (larger central spot) have arched leading edge. Narrow-winged Pug (cf. ssp. *curzoni*) has more pointed forewing. **FS** May-June. **Hab** Up CGr Wt Wd A.

Wormwood Pug *Eupithecia absinthiata* Common T; **Ling Pug** *E. absinthiata* f. *goossensiata* Local T **FW** 11-13mm. Forewing quite broad, rather elongated, brown. Dark spots on leading edge, large dark central spot, whitish broken outermost cross-line and whitish trailing corner spot. Black band on abdomen. Ling Pug (previously considered a separate species) is usually smaller and greyer. Currant Pug smaller, with forewing more rounded and with more prominent white trailing corner spot. Bleached Pug paler, forewing more rounded, weak trailing corner spot. See also Campanula Pug, White-spotted Pug, Pimpinel Pug. **FS** June-July. **Hab** Wormwood Pug: Ub. Ling Pug: A Up.

Currant Pug *Eupithecia assimilata* Common T **FW** 9-12mm. Strong black central and leading edge spots on plain warm brown forewing (when fresh). Conspicuous large cream corner spot and other cream markings near outer edge. See Wormwood Pug, White-spotted Pug. **FS** May-June; August. In north, June-July. **Hab** G H Wd.

Bleached Pug *Eupithecia expallidata* Nb. SE,(W,N),Ir **FW** 12-13mm. Large, pale, plain pinkish grey-brown, with bleached look. Several black marks on leading edge; central spot elongated, with black dotted cross-lines either side. Whitish trailing corner spot weak or absent. See Wormwood Pug. **FS** Late June-August. **Hab** Wd.

Common Pug *Eupithecia vulgata vulgata* Common S,C; ssp. *scotica* Common N,Ir; ssp. *clarensis* SW Ireland **FW** 10-12mm. Ssp. *vulgata*: Forewing brown, leading edge curved, texture coarse. Central spot very small or absent; whitish outermost cross-line and trailing corner spot. Cross-lines vary in strength, angled near leading edge. Ssp. *scotica*: Greyer, cross-lines stronger. Ssp. *clarensis*: Whitish brown. See Triple-spotted Pug, Satyr Pug, Valerian Pug. **FS** May-June; August. In Scotland and Ireland, May-July. **Hab** Ub.

White-spotted Pug *Eupithecia tripunctaria* Local S,C,(N),Ir **FW** 10-12mm. Forewing brownish grey, central dark spot conspicuous. White spot at trailing corner of both wings, also in outer area of forewing, on back of thorax and side of abdomen. Larch Pug has white spot on thorax on more sharply-angled cross-lines; trailing corner spot less distinct, as in Grey Pug and Golden-rod Pug. Melanics may retain some white spots, or are entirely dark, when they cannot be distinguished with certainty from those of Grey and Golden-rod Pugs. **FS** May-June; August. **Hab** Wd H Wt G.

Campanula Pug *Eupithecia denotata denotata* Na. S,E; **Jasione Pug** ssp. *jasioneata* Na. SW,WC,Ir **FW** 11-13mm. **Campanula Pug:** Forewing broad and rounded, rather plain. Central spot conspicuous. Pale outermost cross-line most evident. No black band on abdomen. See Wormwood Pug, Pimpinel Pug. **Jasione Pug:** Smaller, forewing narrower, grey; stronger markings. See Golden-rod Pug (outer central cross-line less angled) and Larch Pug (white spot on thorax). **FS** July. **Hab** Campanula Pug: Wd H Sc. Jasione Pug: Gr H A C.

All shown × 1.25

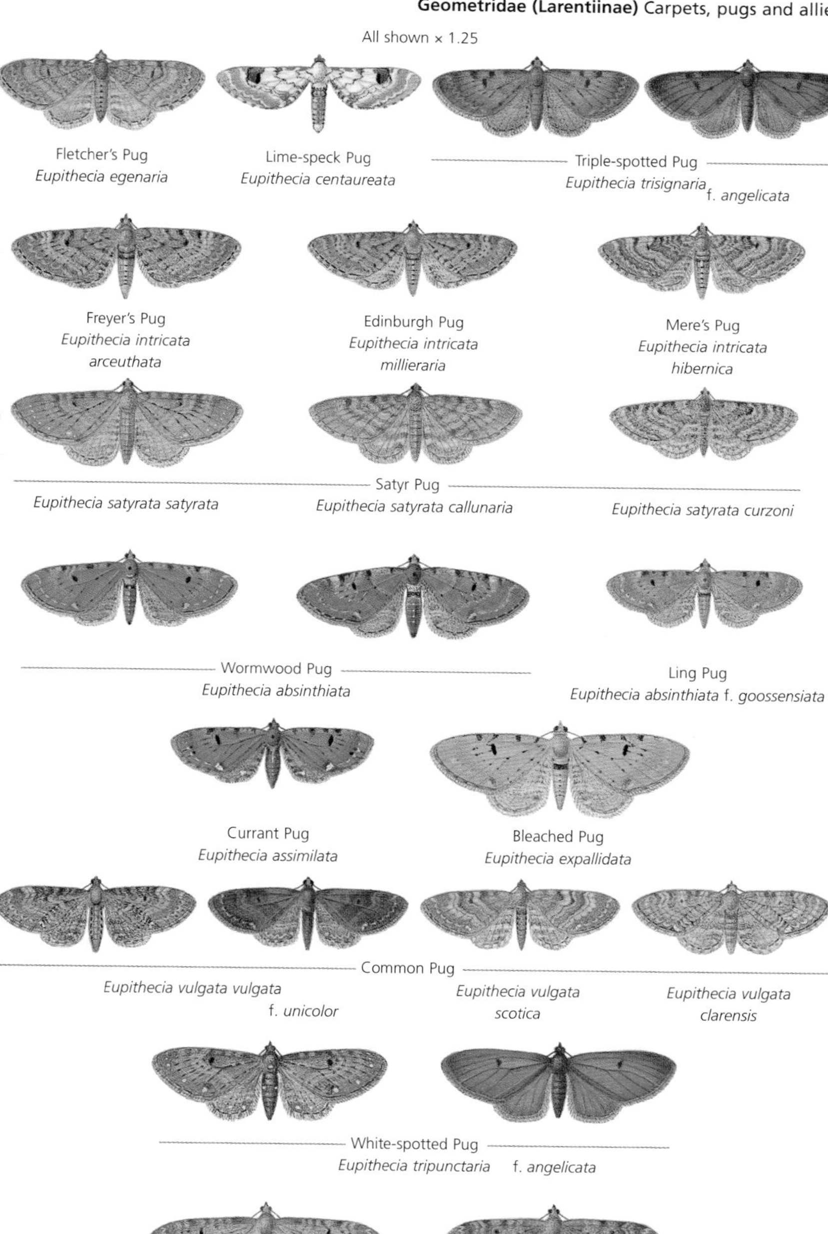

Grey Pug *Eupithecia subfuscata* Common T **FW** 10-12mm. Forewing grey to blackish; black central spot conspicuous. Cross-lines vary in strength; usually with wavy whitish outermost cross-line and trailing corner spot, often indistinct and forming part of the outermost cross-line. Golden-rod Pug usually with chequered veins on forewing (morphological examination needed for confirmation). Larch Pug has white thoracic spot and more oblique cross-lines. Melanics are not safely separable from several species on wing markings. See also Fletcher's Pug, White-spotted Pug, Triple-spotted Pug, Yarrow Pug, Green Pug. **FS** May-June; (August). **Hab** Ub.

Tawny Speckled Pug *Eupithecia icterata* Common T **FW** 11-13mm. F. *subfulvata*, with large orange-brown blotch, is distinctive. Forms with strong cross-lines and orange-brown reduced or absent predominate in the north and are not unlike the smaller Grey Pug. **FS** July-August. **Hab** Ub.

Bordered Pug *Eupithecia succenturiata* Common S,C,(N,Ir) **FW** 12-13mm. Forewing, thorax and abdomen base white. Central spot large. F. *obscurata* forewing darker, base white. See Shaded Pug. **FS** July-August. **Hab** Ub.

Shaded Pug *Eupithecia subumbrata* Local SE,(T) **FW** 10-12mm. Forewing rather narrow and pointed, leading edge almost straight. Markings with variable chalky-white component. Central spot often small or absent; cross-lines evident. Thorax grey-brown. Grey Pug has arched leading edge. See also Bordered Pug, Yarrow Pug. **FS** June-early July. **Hab** Gr C.

Yarrow Pug *Eupithecia millefoliata* Nb. SE **FW** 12-13mm. Forewing greyish, sometimes brown-tinged; leading edge straight, cross-lines and bands angled near leading edge. Central spot evident, slightly blurred, often with slight outer white 'halo'. Fletcher's, Plain and Grey Pug (usually smaller) have curved leading edge. Freyer's Pug is browner. Shaded Pug has narrower, usually whiter, forewing. Pimpinel Pug has dark spots on leading edge. **FS** June-July. **Hab** Gr C Sc.

Plain Pug *Eupithecia simpliciata* Local S,C,(Ir) **FW** 11-13mm. Forewing quite full, light sandy brown (or grey-tinged). Conspicuous curved narrow whitish outer central cross-band. See Yarrow Pug. **FS** Mid June-early August. **Hab** R C.

Goosefoot Pug *Eupithecia sinuosaria* Suspected rare immigrant S **FW** 10-12mm. Irregular, narrow, darker, partly black-edged central cross-band on brownish forewing, its inner edge strongly angled in leading half. Central spot elongated. Usually dark blotches or dashes near tip. **FS** In mainland Europe, June-August. **Hab** R.

Thyme Pug *Eupithecia distinctaria constrictata* Nb. T,not SE **FW** 8-10mm. Bold, black, linear central spot and dark leading edge spots on grey forewing; usually two very fine, black central cross-lines. Hindwing usually well marked. Ochreous Pug has narrower, more pointed forewing, and both wings generally plainer. See also Channel Islands Pug. **FS** June-July. **Hab** CGr Cl Sd.

Ochreous Pug *Eupithecia indigata* Common T **FW** 8-10mm. Narrow, pointed, pale sandy or greyish forewing. Rather plain, but for conspicuous elongated black central spot, and dark spots (often weak) on leading edge. See Thyme Pug. **FS** April-May. **Hab** CWd G.

Pimpinel Pug *Eupithecia pimpinellata* Local S,C,(Ir) **FW** 11-12mm. Easily confused with Wormwood Pug, but with soft, light grey tinge to forewing, especially along leading edge, which has smaller dark markings. See also Campanula Pug, Yarrow Pug. **FS** June-July. **Hab** CGr Wd.

Narrow-winged Pug *Eupithecia nanata* Common T **FW** 9-12mm. Forewing very narrow, elongated, with light and dark, tightly-packed, grey-brown, strongly-angled cross-lines. Shetland f. *curzoni* of Satyr Pug has shorter, more rounded forewing. See also Scarce Pug. **FS** Late April-June; (in south, late July-August). **Hab** A M, occasionally G.

Scarce Pug *Eupithecia extensaria occidua* RDB E **FW** 11-13mm. Forewing leading edge very straight, silvery white with distinctive light brown oblique cross-bands. See Narrow-winged Pug. **FS** June-July. **Hab** Sm.

Angle-barred Pug *Eupithecia innotata* Common T; **Ash Pug** *Eupithecia innotata* f. *fraxinata* Common T; **Tamarisk Pug** *Eupithecia innotata* f. *tamarisciata* Uncommon on alien foodplants S **FW** 10-12mm. Forewing narrow, elongated; rather plain, brown or grey-brown. Central spot small, black, elongated; cross-lines sharply angled, absent in melanic f. *unicolor.* **FS** Late May-mid June; August. **Hab** Angle-barred Pug: Sd Wd. Ash Pug: BWd H G. Tamarisk Pug: C G.

Golden-rod Pug *Eupithecia virgaureata* Local W,(E),Ir **FW** 10-11mm. Forewing greyish brown, sometimes veins chequered and white spot on thorax. Central spot quite large. Melanic f. *nigra*, almost uniformly dark grey. See Grey Pug, Jasione Pug, Satyr Pug, Larch Pug, White-spotted Pug. **FS** May-June; August. In parts of Scotland, May-June only. **Hab** Wd H Sc Gr.

All shown × 1.25

Brindled Pug *Eupithecia abbreviata* Common T **FW** 10-12mm. Forewing mottled, usually brown; quite broad, leading edge curved, central dark spot small, elongated, narrow. Inner edge of outer central cross-band with very fine black wedges. Blackish forms are widespread and frequent; distinguished from other melanic pugs by forewing shape. See Oak-tree Pug, Mottled Pug. **FS** March-May. **Hab** BWd H G.

Oak-tree Pug *Eupithecia dodoneata* Common S,C,(Ir) **FW** 8-11mm. Very similarly marked to Brindled Pug; usually smaller with round central forewing dot, often with whitish patch beyond. Dwarf Pug has larger black central spot and stronger cross-lines; wedges and white patch beyond central spot absent. See also Juniper Pug. **FS** April-early June. **Hab** Wd H Sc.

Juniper Pug *Eupithecia pusillata pusillata* Common T; ssp. *anglicata* Former resident; extinct **FW** 9-11mm. Forewing brown or whitish, darker brown, grey or blackish. Small pale patch beyond small black central spot; fine black wedges on inner edge of outer central cross-band. Melanics usually retain a hint of pale patch and cross-lines. Oak-tree Pug is slightly smaller with earlier flight season. **FS** July-September. Occasionally flies in hot sunshine. **Hab** Up CGr G.

Cypress Pug *Eupithecia phoeniceata* Uncommon S,(Ir) **FW** 10-11mm. Forewing elongated and rounded, pale brown. Oblique cross-lines with black edging and distinctive black streaks. Central spot small. Black belt on abdomen near thorax. **FS** Mainly August-September, occasionally from May or in October. **Hab** G.

Channel Islands Pug *Eupithecia ultimaria* Uncommon S **FW** 7-10mm. Conspicuous dark elongated central spot and numerous weak cross-lines. Smaller than Thyme Pug, with less bold cross-lines and more rounded forewing. **FS** Late June-late August. **Hab** C G.

Larch Pug *Eupithecia lariciata* Common T **FW** 10-12mm. Forewing cross-lines quite strong, rather oblique and sharply angled; white spot or crest on back of thorax. See Grey Pug and Fletcher's Pug. Melanic f. *nigra* (frequent in London and elsewhere) is inseparable on wing markings from melanic Grey Pug, Golden-rod Pug and White-spotted Pug. See also Jasione Pug. **FS** May-July. **Hab** CWd G.

Dwarf Pug *Eupithecia tantillaria* Common T **FW** 9-11mm. Forewing rounded, whitish brown with darker mottling and cross-lines. Central spot large and conspicuous. See Oak-tree Pug, Marbled Pug, Cloaked Pug. **FS** May-June. **Hab** CWd. G.

V-Pug *Chloroclystis v-ata* Common T **FW** 8-11mm. Forewing rounded, green when fresh, fading to yellowish. Bold black V-mark near leading edge. Hindwing grey. Rests with wings drawn further back than other pugs. **FS** May-June; mid July-late August. In north, late June-July. **Hab** Ub.

Sloe Pug *Pasiphila chloerata* Common S,C **FW** 9-10mm. Similar to Green Pug, but only faintly green when fresh, fading to brownish grey; salmon pink band (fading to pinkish brown) near base of abdomen. Narrow pale outer central forewing cross-band not or only slightly wavy in leading half, not edged black. See also Bilberry Pug. **FS** May-early July. **Hab** H Sc Wd.

Green Pug *Pasiphila rectangulata* Common T **FW** 8-11mm. Forewing green, blackish green or black, usually retaining at least a hint of green. Narrow pale outer central cross-band strongly edged black in leading half. Abdomen with black band near base. See Sloe Pug, Bilberry Pug, V-Pug, Grey Pug. **FS** June-early August. **Hab** Ub.

Bilberry Pug *Pasiphila debiliata* Nb. S,W,(N,Ir) **FW** 9-11mm. Wings delicate pale lime green when fresh, fading to pale brown, and rather plain. Pale narrow outer central cross-band with small black dots on inner edge. Dark band on abdomen near base. See Green Pug, Sloe Pug (pink band on abdomen, and darker). **FS** June-July. **Hab** A Up Wd

Double-striped Pug *Gymnoscelis rufifasciata* Common T **FW** 8-10mm. Forewing brownish, sometimes reddish; leading edge straight. Black inner edging, blotches or wedges on leading half of narrow, rather wavy outer central cross-band, persisting when worn. Markings vary in strength. **FS** Late March-May; July-August; (in south-east England, occasionally September-October). In parts of north, June-July. Sometimes flies in hot sunshine. **Hab** Ub.

Dentated Pug *Anticollix sparsata* Na. S,C **FW** 11-13mm. Forewing broad, rounded, fawnish brown with delicate markings. Hindwing scalloped, larger indentation in leading half. Brown Scallop (p.38) is larger, with hindwings evenly scalloped. **FS** June-July. **Hab** Wt Wd.

Streak *Chesias legatella* Common T **FW** 17-19mm. Long, pale streak in leading half of broad, rounded, elongated dark brownish or grey forewing, roughly elliptical central mark, and tent resting posture. Broom-tip has similar forewing shape but lacks pale streak and flies earlier in the year. **FS** September-early November. **Hab** Sc Wd H

Broom-tip *Chesias rufata rufata* Nb. SE,W; ssp. *scotica* Nb. N **FW** 14-16mm. Ssp. *rufata*: Large black comma, forming leading half of narrow central cross-band on grey forewing, and pale reddish-brown bands. Ssp. *scotica*: Forewing bluish grey with stronger markings. See Streak. **FS** April-July. **Hab** Sc Wd.

All pugs shown × 1.25

f. *hirschkei*

Brindled Pug
Eupithecia abbreviata

Oak-tree Pug
Eupithecia dodoneata

Scottish specimen

melanic form

Juniper Pug
Eupithecia pusillata pusillata

Cypress Pug
Eupithecia phoeniceata

Channel Islands Pug
Eupithecia ultimaria

Larch Pug
Eupithecia lariciata

f. *nigra*

Dwarf Pug
Eupithecia tantillaria

V-Pug
Chloroclystis v-ata

Sloe Pug
Pasiphila chloerata

Green Pug
Pasiphila rectangulata

f. *anthrax*

Bilberry Pug
Pasiphila debiliata

Double-striped Pug
Gymnoscelis rufifasciata

Dentated Pug
Anticollix sparsata

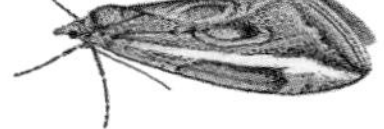

Streak
Chesias legatella

Broom-tip
Chesias rufata rufata

Manchester Treble-bar *Carsia sororiata* ssp. *anglica* Nb. N,C,(Ir) **FW** 11-15mm. On forewing, leading half of outer dark cross-band jagged, with reddish flush beyond. Undersides pinkish brown, fringes chequered. Treble-bar and Lesser Treble-bar are larger, with less extensive, brownish flush. **FS** July-September. **Hab** Up AWt.

Treble-bar *Aplocera plagiata plagiata* Common T; ssp. *scotica* Common N **FW** 19-22mm. Ssp. *plagiata*: Narrow basal forewing cross-band roundly angled, slightly obtusely or at 90°. Abdomen tip pointed in male; claspers long. Ssp. *scotica*: Forewing bluish grey. See Lesser Treble-bar and Purple Treble-bar. **FS** In south, May-June; late July-September. In northern England and Scotland, July-August. Easily disturbed by day. **Hab** CGr Up C Wd G.

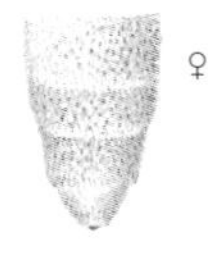

Treble-bar   Lesser Treble-bar

Lesser Treble-bar *Aplocera efformata* Common S,C **FW** 16-19mm. Very similar to Treble-bar. Narrow basal cross-band with pointed angle, usually slightly acute. Abdomen tip blunt, male claspers short. Slightly smaller, forewing cross-bands usually less intense. **FS** May-June; late July-September. Easily disturbed by day. **Hab** CGr Up C Wd G.

Purple Treble-bar *Aplocera praeformata* Suspected rare immigrant **FW** 20-25mm. Larger than Treble-bar; short brown bar before first dark central cross-band; angle of basal cross-band acute and pointed.

Chimney Sweeper *Odezia atrata* Common N,C,(S),Ir **FW** 12-15mm. Plain sooty black, fading to brownish black. Forewing fringes white around wing tip. **FS** June-August. Active only by day. **Hab** Gr.

Grey Carpet *Lithostege griseata* RDB E **FW** 14-16mm. Almost plain pale grey, rather pointed forewing; very fine blackish line on outer edge, white fringes and sometimes faint, narrow outer cross-band. **FS** Late May-early July. **Hab** Gr R.

Blomer's Rivulet *Discoloxia blomeri* Nb. S,C,W **FW** 10-13mm. Large, rusty-brown black-edged blotch near tip of grey forewing. **FS** Late May-early July. **Hab** Wd H.

Welsh Wave *Venusia cambrica* Local W,N,Ir **FW** 13-15mm. Two blackish spikes centrally on outside of fine blackish outer central cross-line. F. *bradyi*, frequent in northern England, dark grey. Waved Carpet is smaller; lacks black cross-lines or spikes. **FS** June-August. **Hab** Up A Wd.

Dingy Shell *Euchoeca nebulata* Local S,C,(N) **FW** 9-12mm. Always rests with wings closed. Sandy brown undersides with several faint, darker cross-lines. Small central projection on hindwing. Fringes chequered cream and brown. Upperside of forewing is sandy, banded and dusted darker. Oute area is muddy brown. **FS** Late May-early August. **Hab** Wd Wt.

Small White Wave *Asthena albulata* Common S,C,(N,Ir) **FW** 9-11mm. Wings pure white, with brown, very wavy cross-lines. **FS** May-early July; (in southern England, August-mid September). **Hab** BW

Small Yellow Wave *Hydrelia flammeolaria* Common S,C,(N,Ir) **FW** 9-11mm. Wings straw-yellow; very irregular sandy brown cross-lines and forewing with black central spot; outer cross-lines often linked centrally by brown bar. **FS** Late May-July. **Hab** BWd H.

Waved Carpet *Hydrelia sylvata* Nb. W,SE,SW **FW** 11-13mm. Both wings with diffuse brown cross-bands and lines, peppering of brown scales, and greyish-white ground-colour. See Welsh Wave **FS** June-early August. **Hab** BWd Sc C.

Drab Looper *Minoa murinata* Nb. W,S,(SW) **FW** 9-11mm. Entirely plain, light to dark muddy-brown wings. **FS** May-June; (August). Male active by day. Occasional at light. **Hab** Wd.

Seraphim *Lobophora halterata* Local T **FW** 12-15mm. Dark grey cross-band near base of broad, rounded forewing. Variable; plain forms sometimes creamy buff. Early Tooth-striped is usually larger, with dark basal cross-bands weak or narrow. **FS** May-June. **Hab** BWd.

Barred Tooth-striped *Trichopteryx polycommata* Na. S,C,N **FW** 14-17mm. Brown and blackis central cross-band, elbowed and divided in two in leading half of rounded, tapered light to dark grey brown forewing. **FS** Mid March-mid or late April. **Hab** Sc Wd H.

Early Tooth-striped *Trichopteryx carpinata* Common T **FW** 13-18mm. Broad, rounded pale grey, darker, brownish- or greenish-grey forewing; sometimes with delicate pink flush along leading edge. Central cross-bands usually faint and pale; in f. *fasciata* (frequent in Wales and Scotland) bold and dark, and sometimes broadly merged. See Seraphim. **FS** April-May. **Hab** Wd Sc Wt.

Small Seraphim *Pterapherapteryx sexalata* Loc T **FW** 9-12mm. Broad forewing with broad grey central cross-band, paler in trailing half; small but conspicuous black central spot near inner edge. **FS** May-June; July-early August. North of Midlands June-July. **Hab** BWd Sc Wt.

Yellow-barred Brindle *Acasis viretata* Local S,C,NW,Ir **FW** 10-14mm. Forewing green when fresh, rapidly fading to yellowish. Usually a distinct broad, blackish-green central cross-band, sometim reduced to fine, wavy cross-lines. See Barred Carp (p.40), with dark forewing base and thorax. **FS** In south, May-June; late July-early September. In north, May-June only. **Hab** BWd H G.

Manchester Treble-bar
Carsia sororiata anglica

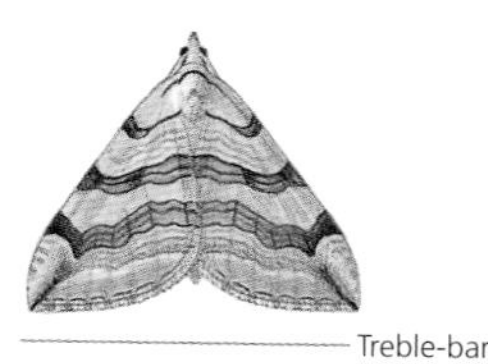

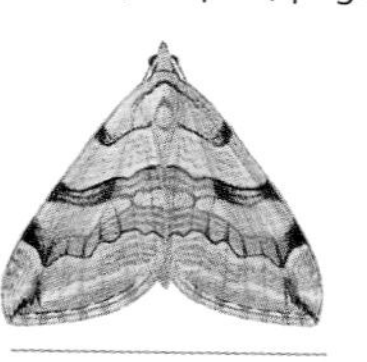

Treble-bar
Aplocera plagiata plagiata
Aplocera plagiata scotica

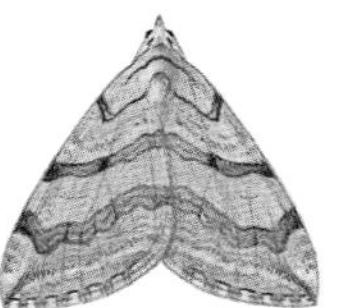

Lesser Treble-bar
Aplocera efformata
f. *fimbriata*

Purple Treble-bar
Aplocera praeformata

Chimney Sweeper
Odezia atrata

Grey Carpet
Lithostege griseata

Blomer's Rivulet
Discoloxia blomeri

Welsh Wave
Venusia cambrica
f. *bradyi*

Dingy Shell
Euchoeca nebulata

Small White Wave
Asthena albulata

Small Yellow Wave
ydrelia flammeolaria

Waved Carpet
Hydrelia sylvata

Drab Looper
Minoa murinata

Seraphim
Lobophora halterata

Barred Tooth-striped
Trichopteryx polycommata

Early Tooth-striped
Trichopteryx carpinata

Early Tooth-striped
Trichopteryx carpinata
f. *fasciata*

Small Seraphim
Pterapherapteryx sexalata

Yellow-barred Brindle
Acasis viretata

Ennominae
Thorns, beauties, umbers and allies

Magpie *Abraxas grossulariata* Common T **FW** 18-25mm. Usual forms unmistakable. Extent of black and yellow markings variable, but overall pattern remains. Extreme almost black to almost all-white forms are rare in wild. **FS** Late June-August. In the Hebrides, large numbers fly up by day from roosting in heathers. Plays 'dead' if captured and handled. **Hab** Ub.

Clouded Magpie *Abraxas sylvata* Local S,C,(N,Ir) **FW** 18-22mm. Rests with wings flat and partly spread, exposing blurred black and yellow blotches on hindwing in addition to those on forewing at base and trailing corner. Grey markings along leading edge of forewing limited, and tip white. **FS** Late May-July. Sometimes seen by day resting on low foliage. **Hab** BWd Sc.

Clouded Border *Lomaspilis marginata* Common T **FW** 11-14mm. Irregular and variable brownish-black borders on both wings, sometimes extended into centre of wings. Rests with wings fully spread. **FS** June-July (from mid-May in south); (August). **Hab** Ub.

Scorched Carpet *Ligdia adustata* Local S,(C),Ir **FW** 12-14mm. Wings creamy white. Blackish basal patch and broad black outer cross-band, both with blue-grey scales when freshly emerged. **FS** In south, late April-June; late July-early September. In northern England and parts of Wales, June-early July. **Hab** BWd Sc H G.

Dorset Cream Wave *Stegania trimaculata* Rare immigrant S **FW** 10-13mm. Two fine, dark cross-lines on creamy forewing, both angled and thickened near leading edge. Further dark spot near to wing tip, and sometimes blotches along outer edge of outer line. Hindwing with single, curved outer cross-line.

Ringed Border *Stegania cararia* Rare immigrant **FW** 10-12mm. Wings straw yellow, extensively speckled and marked brown. Fore- and hindwing with undulating outer cross-line, touching or almost touching outer edge, and area beyond line often less heavily speckled. [Not illustrated.]

Peacock Moth *Macaria notata* Local S,WC,NW,Ir **FW** 14-16mm. Black central paw-print mark, dark-edged concavity in outer edge of whitish, grey-brown speckled forewing, and strongly pointed hindwing. Only Sharp-angled Peacock is similar (see under that species). **FS** In southern England, late May-early July; (late July-August). Elsewhere, late May-June. **Hab** BWd.

Sharp-angled Peacock *Macaria alternata* Local S,(C,Ir) **FW** 13-15mm. Very similar to Peacock Moth, but forewing with distinct grey cross-band (or less often more extensively grey) running through paw-print mark, continuing on hindwing. Paw-print mark often smaller, less well-formed; brown blotch on leading edge often narrower and more tapered (roughly rectangular on Peacock). Concavity in outer edge very dark, blackish (lighter, brownish in Peacock). On hindwing, fine dark line around edge usually well broken or consisting of dots (usually continuous in Peacock). If worn or atypical, examination of genitalia may be necessary for confirmation. **FS** Late May-mid July; (August). **Hab** Wd Sc.

Dusky Peacock *Macaria signaria* Immigrant; recent established very locally in S **FW** 13-14mm. Rather indistinctly marked, with thickly-speckled dirty white wings, roughly square dark grey blotch beyond centre of forewing, three diffuse dark spots on leading edge and slightly pointed hindwing. Worn Tawny-barred Angle has orange-brown outer cross-band on forewing. **FS** Recorded in Britain late May-end July. **Hab** CWd in mainland Europe.

Tawny-barred Angle *Macaria liturata* Common T **FW** 14-17mm. Orange-brown outer cross-band on both wings, slight concavity in leading half of outer edge of forewing, hindwing slightly pointed. F. *nigrofulvata* is dark brownish grey. See Dusky Peacock. **FS** In parts of southern Britain, mid May-mid June; August-September. Elsewhere, one protracted generation. In Scotland, late April-mid September, peaking early July. **Hab** CWd H G.

Netted Mountain Moth *Macaria carbonaria* RDB N **FW** 10-11mm. Both wings with wavy, roughly parallel blackish-brown cross-bands. Varies from forms with substantial whitish frosting to almost completely black. See Black Mountain Moth (p.74). In small upland forms of Common Heath (p.70) (especially female), central forewing bands converge or unite in trailing half and male (usually larger) has more strongly feathered antennae. **FS** April-early June, varying with altitude and season. Active only by day. In windy weather walks or makes short hopping flights just above vegetation. **Hab** Up.

V-Moth *Macaria wauaria* Local S,C,N,(Ir) **FW** 14-17mm. Forewing pale grey with bold black V in centre, and black marks on leading edge. Intensity of ground-colour and markings varies, sometimes with a violet tinge. **FS** July-August. **Hab** G.

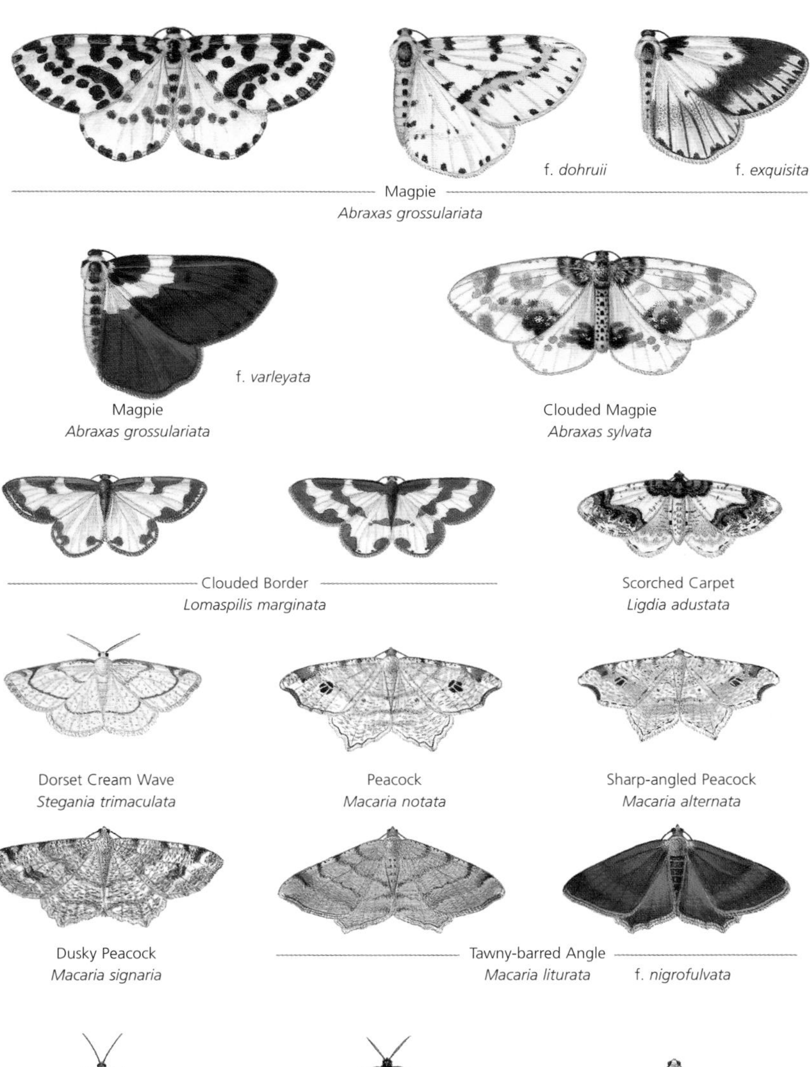

f. *dohruii* f. *exquisita*

Magpie
Abraxas grossulariata

f. *varleyata*

Magpie
Abraxas grossulariata

Clouded Magpie
Abraxas sylvata

Clouded Border
Lomaspilis marginata

Scorched Carpet
Ligdia adustata

Dorset Cream Wave
Stegania trimaculata

Peacock
Macaria notata

Sharp-angled Peacock
Macaria alternata

Dusky Peacock
Macaria signaria

Tawny-barred Angle
Macaria liturata f. *nigrofulvata*

Netted Mountain Moth
Macaria carbonaria

V-Moth
Macaria wauaria

Latticed Heath *Chiasmia clathrata clathrata* Common S,C,N; ssp. *hugginsi* Ir **FW** 11-15mm. Often lands and perches with wings partly raised. Ssp. *clathrata*: Crisp network effect created by dark cross-lines and veins; two outer forewing bands may form a distorted swastika if merged. Ssp. *hugginsi*: Has pure white ground-colour. In Common Heath (p.70) markings less crisp, veins not dark; male with strongly feathered antennae and wings held flat. **FS** May-June; July-September. In north-west Britain, May-July. Active by day and from dusk. **Hab** F Gr A Up.

Rannoch Looper *Itame brunneata* Na. N, Immigrant S,C,N **FW** 11-13mm. Wings orange-brown; forewing tip rather rounded, with four darker red-brown cross-lines; male often with central dot. Female more strongly marked, forewing slightly narrower, more pointed. **FS** Late June-July. Male active by day. Both sexes are active after dark. **Hab** Wd Up.

Frosted Yellow *Isturgia limbaria* Former resident S,N; presumed extinct **FW** 13-15mm. Wings orange-yellow, speckled brown with chocolate-brown borders, less pronounced in female. At rest wings held closed. Hindwing underside greenish brown with strong speckling and white streaks. Male has feathered antennae. **FS** In south, May-early June; late July-August. In Scotland, June. Flies only in sunshine. Readily disturbed from foodplant (Broom). **Hab** Sc.

Little Thorn *Cepphis advenaria* Nb. W,S(not SW),(Ir) **FW** 14-17mm. Rests with wings held partly open up over back, somewhat like Purple Thorn. Distinctive golden patterning, double-pointed hindwing and greyish clouding. **FS** Late May-June. Female occasionally flies in late afternoon. **Hab** Wd Sc.

Brown Silver-line *Petrophora chlorosata* Common T **FW** 15-18mm. Holds forewings back, covering hindwings when at rest. Two central silvery cross-lines on forewing, edged brown, and dark central spot. **FS** May-June, from mid-April in south. Easily disturbed by day. **Hab** Wd A Sc Up.

Barred Umber *Plagodis pulveraria* Local T **FW** 17-19mm. Forewing softly speckled pinkish brown (sometimes purple tinged, or more greyish). Outer edge of broad darker central cross-band jagged, sometimes less distinct, blurred. Underside freckled red and gold. **FS** May-June. **Hab** BWd Sc.

Scorched Wing *Plagodis dolabraria* Local T **FW** 16-19mm. Trailing corners of both fore- and hindwing darkened as if scorched. Forewing with slight cut-aways at trailing corner and crumpled appearance. The many fine, brown cross-lines almost make the wings appear to be in motion. In male, tip of abdomen curled up at rest. **FS** Mid May-late June. Seldom seen by day. Female rarely seen. **Hab** BWd Sc G.

Horse Chestnut *Pachycnemia hippocastanaria* Nb. S,EC **FW** 14-16mm. Forewing narrow and rounded, unlike most other geometrids; grey-brown (sometimes purplish-tinged), overlapping at rest. Two cross-lines usually conspicuous, the inner sharply angled, the outer curved. **FS** April-May; August. **Hab** A.

Brimstone Moth *Opisthograptis luteolata* Common T **FW** 14-21mm. Bright yellow, with chestnut-brown marks on forewing tip and leading edge; dark-ringed elongated fairly central spot. Moths of later generations usually smaller. **FS** Usually two or three generations, April-October. Possibly a pattern of three generations over two years. In northern Scotland, June-July. **Hab** Ub.

Bordered Beauty *Epione repandaria* Common T **FW** 13-16mm. Broad pinkish or fawnish-brown border of orange forewing narrows to a point at tip. Male Dark Bordered Beauty similar, but dark border not narrowed towards tip, and slightly smaller. **FS** July-September. **Hab** Wt Wd H.

Dark Bordered Beauty *Epione vespertaria* RDB NE **FW** 12-14mm. For male, see Bordered Beauty. Female virtually un-freckled, wings lemon yellow, with central indentation in reddish-brown border. **FS** Late June-late August. Male active by day and both sexes are easily disturbed. Active at night and flies at dawn. **Hab** Sc.

Speckled Yellow *Pseudopanthera macularia* Common T,(Ir) **FW** 13-15mm. Bold brownish blotches on yellow wings. **FS** Mid May-late June. Active only by day. **Hab** Wd Sc.

Lilac Beauty *Apeira syringaria* Local S,C,Ir **FW** 19-22mm. Unusual resting posture, with forewings slightly raised and leading edge broadly creased. Lilac markings, with bold brown line running obliquely across forewing. Male smaller, more orange. Female greyer. Second-generation moths are smaller. **FS** Late June-July; (recently, late August-mid September in England north to Cheshire). **Hab** BWd Sc G.

♂
♀
Latticed Heath
Chiasmia clathrata clathrata
f. *alboguttata*
Rannoch Looper
Itame brunneata
♂
♀
Frosted Yellow
Isturgia limbaria
Little Thorn
Cepphis advenaria
Brown Silver-line
Petrophora chlorosata
♂
♀
Barred Umber
Plagodis pulveraria
Scorched Wing
Plagodis dolabraria
Horse Chestnut
Pachycnemia hippocastanaria
Brimstone Moth
Opisthograptis luteolata
Bordered Beauty
Epione repandaria
♂
♀
Dark Bordered Beauty
Epione vespertaria
Speckled Yellow
Pseudopanthera macularia
♂
♀
Lilac Beauty
Apeira syringaria

Large Thorn *Ennomos autumnaria* Nb. SE,(Ir) **FW** 21-28mm. Large, with extensive dark speckling (rarely absent) and rather indistinct cross-lines. Female much larger than other female thorns (all with un-feathered antennae); male (feathered antennae) can be similar in size to females of other species. Rests with wings half raised. **FS** September-early October. Seldom seen by day. **Hab** BWd Sc G.

August Thorn *Ennomos quercinaria* Local S,C,(N),Ir **FW** 18-22mm. Slimmer than related thorns, with broader forewing, especially in male (except much larger Large Thorn), held at lower angle when at rest. On forewing, outer cross-line usually kinked near leading edge, turning towards then usually away from base; inner one usually with longer, more pronounced angle at leading edge than in similar species. Forewing speckled or plain, sometimes with extensive brown outer shading. Male quite orange, female paler, straw-coloured. See Canary-shouldered Thorn, September Thorn, Dusky Thorn. **FS** July-September. Seldom seen by day. **Hab** BWd H Sc G.

Canary-shouldered Thorn *Ennomos alniaria* Common T **FW** 16-20mm. Thorax usually bright canary-yellow, wings orange-yellow with varying degree of dark speckling. Outer cross-line on forewing sweeps in a gentle arc to leading edge (usually kinked in August Thorn, straighter in Dusky and September Thorns), meeting it between three-quarters to four-fifths to the wing tip (about two-thirds on September Thorn). A form with buff thorax has been reported from Kent, mainly late in the flight period. **FS** Late July-mid October. Seldom seen by day. **Hab** BWd Sc H G.

Dusky Thorn *Ennomos fuscantaria* Common S, **FW** 17-21mm. On forewing, dark mauvish-grey or grey-brown shading beyond outer cross-line; cross-lines slightly variable, closest to Canary-shouldered Thorn but less curved. Often softly speckled. A rare form has uniform dark shading over both wings. See also September Thorn, August Thorn, Large Thorn. **FS** Late July-early October. Seldom seen by day. **Hab** BWd H G.

September Thorn *Ennomos erosaria* Common S,C,(N,Ir) **FW** 17-21mm. Plain or very slightly speckled, orange-brown or fawn wings and central forewing crescent almost always absent. Cross-line slightly variable, generally straighter than in related species, sometimes slightly kinked, or thickened, at leading edge. Moths emerging early in the flight period are paler. See Dusky Thorn, Canary-shouldered Thorn, August Thorn. **FS** July-early October. Seldom seen by day. **Hab** BWd G.

Clouded August Thorn *Ennomos quercaria* Doubtfully British. Similar to September Thorn in size, resting posture and appearance, but paler, more whitish, with two cross-lines on forewing converging less closely at trailing edge.

Early Thorn *Selenia dentaria* Common T **FW** 14-23mm. Distinguished from all other British thorns by resting position, with wings held closed like a butterfly. Summer-generation moths are smaller and paler, usually with larger tawny orange patches on undersides. A rare form, f. *harrisoni*, is rather uniform dark brown with pale cross-lines. Less extreme brownish and greyish forms are more frequent. **FS** Mid February-May; July-September. In north, May-June. Seldom seen by day. **Hab** BWd H Sc G.

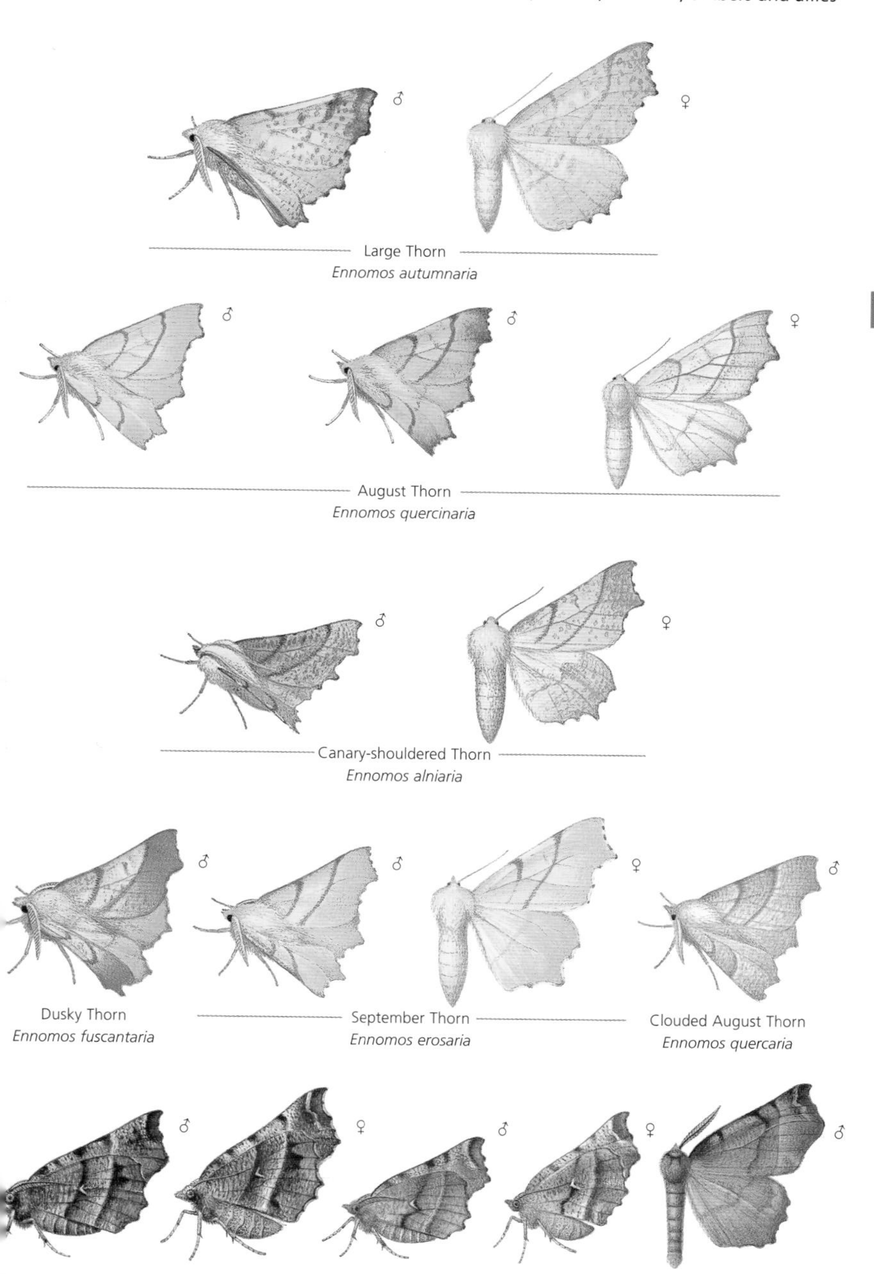

Large Thorn
Ennomos autumnaria

August Thorn
Ennomos quercinaria

Canary-shouldered Thorn
Ennomos alniaria

Dusky Thorn
Ennomos fuscantaria

September Thorn
Ennomos erosaria

Clouded August Thorn
Ennomos quercaria

Early Thorn
Selenia dentaria

1st generation

2nd generation

f. *harrisoni*

Lunar Thorn *Selenia lunularia* Local T
FW 16-22mm. Resting posture is like that of similar Purple Thorn. On upperside of forewing, outer cross-line almost straight; hindwing distinctly scalloped, with large central indentation and no dark spot in outer area. Very variable in colour: pale straw to reddish or purplish brown, especially in Scotland. Often extensively speckled, sometimes very darkly, but not infrequently plain. Second-generation moths are smaller, often more richly coloured and strongly marked, sometimes pinkish. **FS** May-June; (in southern England, July-August, annually in Channel Islands). Seldom seen by day. **Hab** BWd Sc.

Purple Thorn *Selenia tetralunaria* Common S,C,(N) **FW** 17-23mm. Rests with wings open and half-raised, with forewings slightly curled. Dark spot on hindwing upperside, in outer area. Outer forewing cross-line distinctly bowed. See Lunar Thorn, with hindwing usually more deeply scalloped. Second-generation moths are much smaller and paler, often tawny rather than purple. **FS** In south, April-May; July-August; (late September-October). In north, May-June. Seldom seen by day. **Hab** BWd Sc G.

Scalloped Hazel *Odontopera bidentata*
Common T **FW** 20-24mm. Rests with wings flat, appearing very triangular, with forewing outer edge strongly and irregularly scalloped. Small dark central ring on both wings. Forewing varies from whitish brown, often tawny, to deep chocolate brown, darker between two cross-lines, producing a central band, or more uniform. Dark forms are widespread but more frequent in north-west England and western Scotland. In Orkney, smaller and rather greyish brown. See Scalloped Oak. **FS** May-June. Seldom seen by day. **Hab** Wd Sc H G.

Scalloped Oak *Crocallis elinguaria* Common T **FW** 18-22mm. Rests with wings flat. Forewing usually straw-yellow, outer edge rounded, only slightly scalloped. Central band darker, with solid black central spot. Some forms are uniformly orange-brown, deep brown, even blackish, but cross-lines and central spot tend to remain visible. Darker forms are more frequent in north-west England, Scotland and Ireland. See Dusky Scalloped Oak. **FS** Late June-August. Seldom seen by day. **Hab** Wd Sc H G.

Dusky Scalloped Oak *Crocallis dardoinaria* Guernsey; rare immigrant SW **FW** 18-24mm. Compared to Scalloped Oak forewing less yellowis usually straw-coloured, or dull reddish brown rathe than orange-brown, with central mark composed of four small black spots. Either plain or (especially in female) with heavy, coarse freckling. **FS** June; September, based on occurrence in Guernsey. **Hab** Not known on Guernsey.

Swallow-tailed Moth *Ourapteryx sambucaria* Common T **FW** 22-30mm. Unlike any other Britis moth. Pale lemon yellow when fresh, becoming whiter with age. Hindwing with substantial tail, with two dark brown spots at base. Two darker cross-lines and a central dash on forewing, one cross-line on hindwing. **FS** Late June-mid August; (October). Sometimes disturbed by day. **Hab** Wd Sc H G.

Feathered Thorn *Colotois pennaria* Common
FW 19-23mm. Rests with wings flat, and flies late in the year than other thorns. Male has broadly feathered antennae, more so than vaguely similar species. Forewing outer edge slightly scalloped; ti slightly hooked. Often a dark-edged whitish spot near tip; two cross-lines usually conspicuous but c be blurred or incomplete. In male, forewing usual orange-brown, sometimes fawn-brown or brick-re In female narrower, often paler or grey-brown. Se Scalloped Oak f. *unicolor*. **FS** Mid September-early December. Occasionally found at rest by day. **Hab** BWd H G.

Swallow-tailed Moth
Ourapteryx sambucaria

Orange Moth *Angerona prunaria* Local S,(C,Ir) **FW** 20-30mm. Forewing very broad, rounded. Male orange, with variable brown flecking and, normally, brown central dash or crescent on both wings; antennae feathered. Female similar, pale yellow with antennae un-feathered. Less frequent f. *corylaria* has extensive uniform dark brown areas, with ground-colour restricted to central bands, or panels of various sizes. Fringes chequered, except in extreme panelled forms. **FS** Late June-July. Male flies from early dusk, female late in the night. **Hab** BWd Sc H.

Small Brindled Beauty *Apocheima hispidaria* Local S,(C) **FW** 15-17mm. In male, forewing rather narrow, tapered. Variable; pale with distinct cross-lines, the outer slightly jagged, or plainer dark brown. Usually, outermost area paler. Stocky, with massively furry thorax. Wingless female generally dark or blackish brown, rather furry, squat and stocky across thorax. Female Pale Brindled Beauty is noticeably thinner, less furry and generally paler. Brindled Beauty is much larger; forewing broader. **FS** Mid February-March. Female rests low down on tree trunks, after dawn. **Hab** BWd.

Pale Brindled Beauty *Phigalia pilosaria* Common T **FW** 19-24mm. Slighter in build than Brindled Beauty, generally paler, without the heavy black cross-lines. Abdomen pinkish when fresh. In male, dark brindle markings (i.e. cross-lines) on greyish or greenish-grey forewing vary in extent and intensity. Dark, sometimes blackish forms predominate in some areas (e.g. London and north-west Britain). Wingless female brownish, rather smooth. See female Small Brindled Beauty, female March Moth (p.22). **FS** Late December-March. Female rests low down on tree trunks, just after dawn, sometimes later. **Hab** BWd Sc H G.

Brindled Beauty *Lycia hirtaria* Common S,C,(N,Ir) **FW** 19-23mm. Forewing pattern variab but usually some heavy blackish cross-lines and/or banding, especially conspicuous at leading edge. Many have a golden-yellow component, others are predominantly grey. Female is rather thinly scaled; forewing leading edge more arched. Almo uniformly blackish form is rare (southern England Scottish examples are larger and more brightly marked. See Pale Brindled Beauty. **FS** Early March late May. Sometimes found on tree trunks and fences by day. Male flies late at night and comes light. Female does so very rarely. **Hab** BWd Sc H

Belted Beauty *Lycia zonaria britannica* RDB WC,Ir; ssp. *atlantica* Na. NW **FW** 13-16mm. Male with silvery grey and brown stripes on forewing, their thickness somewhat variable. Female wingle In both sexes, abdomen with orange rings. Ssp. *atlantica,* of questionable validity, described from the Isle of Baleshare on the basis that male slightl smaller than mainland specimens, not the case on other Hebridean islands, where some individuals a actually larger than those from the mainland. See Rannoch Brindled Beauty. **FS** March-April. Male is sometimes active by day in afternoon, but usually flies late at night, and can be found at rest. Fema basks in sunshine on posts and vegetation, and is active at night. **Hab** C.

Rannoch Brindled Beauty *Lycia lapponaria scotica* Na. N **FW** 14-16mm. Both sexes have a r of orange spots on thorax and abdomen, forming broken dorsal stripe. In male, wings grey and sem transparent, with narrow, dark cross-bands, variab in extent, and central crescent mark. A brown for is often found at Dalwhinnie quarry, Morayshire. Wingless female is black, furry. See Belted Beauty, but note difference in range and habitat. **FS** Late March-early May, depending on altitude and season. By day rests on plant stems, rocks and fer posts. Male presumably flies at night, but it is not known if it comes to light. **Hab** Up.

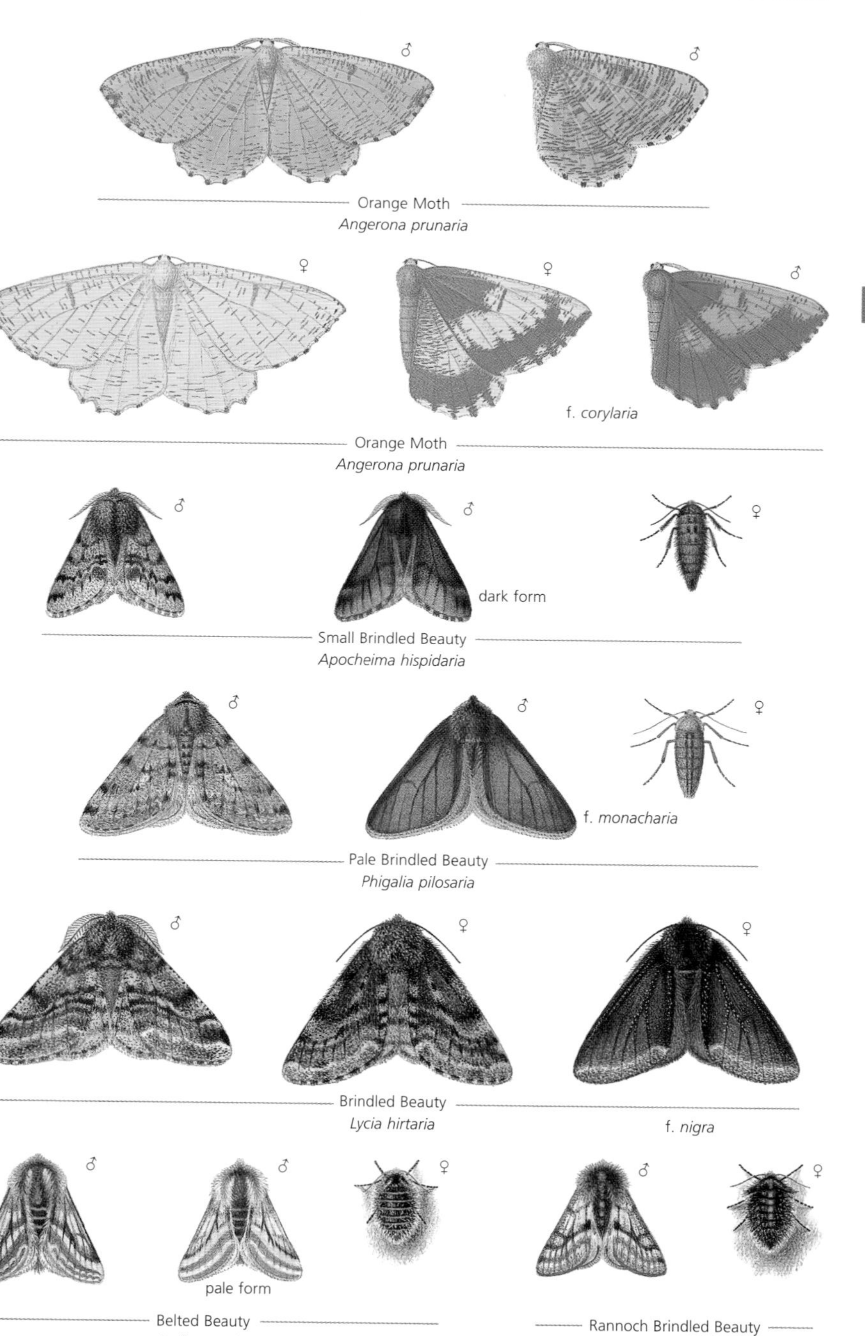
♂
♂
Orange Moth
Angerona prunaria
♀
♀
♂
f. corylaria
Orange Moth
Angerona prunaria
♂
♂
♀
dark form
Small Brindled Beauty
Apocheima hispidaria
♂
♂
♀
f. monacharia
Pale Brindled Beauty
Phigalia pilosaria
♂
♀
♀
Brindled Beauty
Lycia hirtaria
f. nigra
♂
♂
♀
pale form
Belted Beauty
Lycia zonaria
♂
♀
Rannoch Brindled Beauty
Lycia lapponaria scotica

Oak Beauty *Biston strataria* Common S,C,(N,Ir) **FW** 17-27mm. Male has two black-edged broad brown bands, variable in width, on white to greenish-grey forewing. Female is often whiter, and larger. Male has feathered antennae. Peppered Moth never has light brown banding. **FS** Late February-April. Sometimes found by day at base of tree trunks. **Hab** BWd Sc G.

Peppered Moth *Biston betularia* Common T **FW** 22-28mm. The white, black-peppered form predominates in most rural areas. Black and intermediate forms, including f. *carbonaria* and f. *insularia* which have dominated in the past in areas with high levels of atmospheric pollution, are now in general decline, but still frequent in some places. See Oak Beauty (earlier flight season). **FS** Early May-late August (one generation). Seldom seen by day. **Hab** Wd Sc H G.

Spring Usher *Agriopis leucophaearia* Common S,C,(N,Ir) **FW** 14-17mm. Forewing in male very triangular, with rounded tip. Variable, but with wavy outer cross-line and curved inner one, sometimes forming edges of pale central band. May also be dark brown and almost or entirely uniform. See March Moth (p.22). Female dark grey or blackish, wing-stumps very small. Other species are larger or with larger wing stumps (see Winter Moth (p.40) and March Moth). **FS** January or early February-mid March. Male sometimes rests by day on tree trunks. Female rests low down on tree trunks in early morning. **Hab** BWd G.

Scarce Umber *Agriopis aurantiaria* Common T **FW** 17-21mm. Male has warm, golden orange-yellow forewing with brown markings. Cross-lines distinct, variable edging, blotches and freckling, and often central spot. See highly variable Mottled Umber, with forewing more elongated, never golden, often with bold, round central spot. See also Dotted Border (different flight season). Flightless female is dark brown; wing stumps evident, brown, usually black-banded. Female Mottled Umber is usually paler, with wing stumps minute. **FS** October-December. Female can be found low down on tree trunks in early morning. **Hab** BWd Sc G.

Dotted Border *Agriopis marginaria* Common T **FW** 16-20mm. Forewing in male pale brown, variably clouded with darker brown, dark brown or blackish brown (f. *fuscata*). Black dots along edges of both wings, less obvious or absent in da forms. Outer cross-line bowed outwards in leadin half. On Orkney, moths are small and rather dark greyish brown. Mottled Umber male has forewing more elongated; outer edge plain but fringes ofte spotted or chequered. Flightless female Dotted Border has substantial, brown, variably banded wing stumps. Flightless female of micro-moth *Diurnea fagella* is similar in size, also in early sprir and also has relatively large wings but these are very pointed. See also Scarce Umber. **FS** February April. Female can be found low down on tree trunks in early morning. **Hab** Ub.

Mottled Umber *Erannis defoliaria* Common T **FW** 18-25mm. Highly variable. Forewing rather elongated, from whitish to dark brown. Cross-bands, when present, brown or blackish and rath irregular. Often a bold, dark central spot. Outer edges plain, but fringes often chequered. Equally frequent orange-brown and dark brown forms m be speckled and otherwise unmarked. Flightless female with minute wing-stumps, yellowish whit with black dots, or black. See Scarce Umber, Dott Border. **FS** October-January. Male flies from dusk. Female can be found on tree trunks after dark. **Hab** Ub.

Oak Beauty
Biston strataria
♂
♂
f. *insularia*
♀
f. *carbonaria*
Peppered Moth
Biston betularia
♂
♀
× 1.25
Spring Usher
Agriopis leucophaearia
♂
♀
× 1.25
Scarce Umber
Agriopis aurantiaria
♂
f. *fuscata*
♀
♀
♀
× 1.25
× 1.25
× 1.25
Dotted Border
Agriopis marginaria
♂
♀
× 1.25
Mottled Umber
Erannis defoliaria

Waved Umber *Menophra abruptaria* Common S,(C) **FW** 18-21mm. Rests with wings flat, so that dark brown markings on fore- and hindwing are parallel. Hindwing quite deeply scalloped. Ground-colour whitish brown, especially in female, to deep tawny brown. F. *fuscata* (frequent in London and occurs throughout southern England) is dark brown with markings faint. Small Waved Umber (p.38) is smaller, with black band continuous across both wings and hindwing not scalloped. **FS** Mid April-June; (August). **Hab** BWd Sc H G.

Willow Beauty *Peribatodes rhomboidaria* Common T **FW** 17-24mm. On forewing, outer central cross-line fine, strongly-kinked near leading edge, otherwise more or less straight, angled to almost meet inner line, forming a dot on each vein. Hindwing smooth or slightly scalloped. On underside, outer central cross-line (when present) angled centrally. Male antennae feathered, with feathering tapered and ending 2mm from tip. Grey-brown, grey (f. *perfumaria*) to blackish grey. Blackish f. *rebeli* is widespread, and sometimes numerous in industrial areas. Second-generation moths are often smaller. See Feathered Beauty, Lydd Beauty, Mottled Beauty, Great Oak Beauty, Satin Beauty. **FS** In south, early June-August; (late August-early October). Elsewhere, mid June-August. **Hab** Wd Sc H G.

Feathered Beauty *Peribatodes secundaria* Uncommon on alien foodplant (Norway Spruce) SE **FW** 17-20mm. Similar to Willow Beauty and Lydd Beauty. On forewing, outer central cross-line strongly curved in trailing half; usually less kinked near leading edge. In male, antennae more broadly feathered, with feathering ending abruptly 1mm from tip. Outer line on hindwing underside not angled centrally. Usually more heavily dark-speckled than Willow Beauty, including underside. Blackish form occurs occasionally. **FS** July-early August. **Hab** CWd.

Lydd Beauty *Peribatodes ilicaria* Rare immigrant SE **FW** 16-20mm. Similar to Feathered Beauty and Willow Beauty, but outer central cross-line on hindwing (upperside) strongly-curved (fairly straight in Willow and Feathered Beauty). Also more heavily and coarsely speckled, especially female, and in male antennae less strongly feathered. **FS** In France July-September. **Hab** In mainland Europe, Wd G.

Bordered Grey *Selidosema brunnearia scandinaviaria* Na. S,WC,NW,NE,Ir; ssp. *tyronensis* (Ir), possibly extinct **FW** 16-22mm. Brownish grey, purplish tinged when fresh, with broad, darker brown borders on both wings. Forewing cross-lines indicated on leading edge in very dark brown, otherwise diffuse, the central strongest. Male has feathered antennae. Female smaller and browner. Dull brown f. *atlantica* has no grey tinge, and reduced markings (found on limestone in Co. Clare). Ssp. *tyronensis* (described from a bog near Lough Neagh, Co. Tyrone) is smaller with shading on forewing narrower and paler. **FS** July-August. Easily disturbed by day. **Hab** A AWt CGr Sd.

Ringed Carpet *Cleora cinctaria cinctaria* Na. S; ssp. *bowesi* Na. NW,WC,Ir **FW** 16-20mm. Forewing rather triangular; leading edge almost straight. A small, dark, elongated central 'ring', sometimes obscured (also on hindwing), and (usually) strong dark basal cross-band. Ssp. *cinctaria* is rather brownish, especially male. Ssp. *bowesi* has silvery white ground-colour and better-defined, blacker markings. See Square Spot (p.70), Engrailed and Small Engrailed (p.68), lacking central ring, with forewing more rounded. **FS** Late April-May. **Hab** A Up.

♂
♂
Waved Umber
Menophra abruptaria
f. *fuscata*
♂
♂
♂
f. *perfumaria*
f. *rebeli*
Willow Beauty
Peribatodes rhomboidaria
♂
♂
♀
f. *nigrata*
Feathered Beauty
Peribatodes secundaria
♂
♀
Lydd Beauty
Peribatodes ilicaria
♂
♀
Bordered Grey
Selidosema brunnearia scandinaviaria
♂
♀
♀
Ringed Carpet
Cleora cinctaria cinctaria
Cleora cinctaria bowesi

Satin Beauty *Deileptenia ribeata* Common S,C,(N),Ir **FW** 18-26mm. Forewing broad and rather rounded; outer margins smooth or faintly scalloped (as on hindwing). Male with broadly-feathered antennae. Dark, obscurely marked f. *sericearia* predominates in many places. Uniform blackish-brown f. *nigra* is more local (e.g. Boxhill, Surrey). Cross-lines, when evident, closest to Willow Beauty (which has less rounded forewing). See also Mottled Beauty. **FS** Late June-August. **Hab** Wd.

Mottled Beauty *Alcis repandata repandata* Common T; ssp. *sodorensium* Outer Hebrides **FW** 19-26mm. Dark outer central cross-line of fore-wing solid, smooth and wavy, with distinctive large crescent-like curve in leading half. Outer edge of hindwing scalloped. Highly variable in colour, from whitish brown (mainly in north-west Britain, f. *muraria*) to pale brown, through various shades of grey or brown to almost uniformly black (mainly in industrial areas). F. *conversaria* has a dark central band. Ssp. *sodorensium* is small and dark grey. In Willow Beauty, outer central forewing cross-line is straight in trailing half; hindwing slightly scalloped or smooth, and in male antennae are more strongly feathered. See also Satin Beauty. **FS** Early June-mid August. Easily disturbed by day from tree trunks, etc. **Hab** Ub.

Dotted Carpet *Alcis jubata* Local W,N,(Ir) **FW** 13-16mm. Wings whitish, with bold black central spot on forewing and fine black cross-lines, strongest at leading edge and varying in intensity. See Grey Birch (p.70). **FS** Late June-mid September peaking late July. **Hab** Wd Sc.

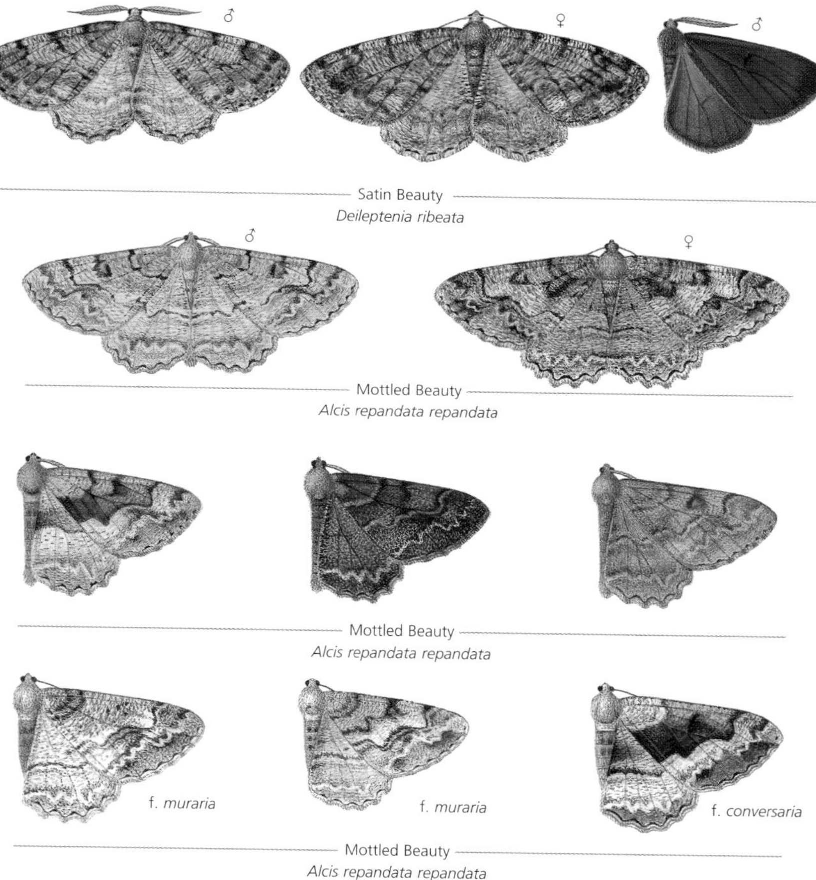

Satin Beauty
Deileptenia ribeata

Mottled Beauty
Alcis repandata repandata

Mottled Beauty
Alcis repandata repandata

Mottled Beauty
Alcis repandata repandata

Dotted Carpet
Alcis jubata

Great Oak Beauty *Hypomecis roboraria*
Nb. S,(C) **FW** 21-32mm. Large. Wings grey, with solid central dark spot on hindwing. Central dark forewing cross-lines converging and thickened near trailing edge, more or less forming a blotch. Dark grey f. *infuscata* is frequent in some areas. In Pale Oak Beauty central cross-lines on forewing not forming blotch at trailing edge and (usually) with central ring on hindwing; usually less strongly marked, and male has less thickly-feathered antennae. Willow Beauty is similarly marked but smaller, and more brownish. **FS** Mid June-mid July. Occasionally comes to sugar. **Hab** BWd.

Pale Oak Beauty *Hypomecis punctinalis*
Common S,(C) **FW** 22-26mm. Wings grey, rather weakly marked. Usually, hindwing with small dark pale-centred central ring. Dark f. *humperti* is quite frequent. See Great Oak Beauty, Willow Beauty. **FS** Late May-mid July; (possibly September-October in south). **Hab** Wd Sc.

Brussels Lace *Cleorodes lichenaria*
Local W,WC,(S,N),Ir **FW** 14-18mm. Whitish or olive green, with a varying degree of darker speckling, sometimes very heavy and appearing blackish. Outer cross-line on fore- and hindwing fine, jagged and irregular. See Grey Birch and Brindled White-spot (with outer cross-line not jagged). **FS** June-mid August; (September-October). **Hab** Wd Sc Cl.

Speckled Beauty *Fagivorina arenaria*
Former resident S; extinct **FW** 15-17mm. Forewing white with coarse, irregular brown and black speckling and blotches, and rather fine black cross-lines. Hindwing pale with no cross-lines, fine dark line around edge, faint speckling and black spots along trailing edge. **FS** July-early August. **Hab** BWd.

Engrailed *Ectropis bistortata* Common T
FW 15-22mm. Wings brownish white, brown or grey-brown, with darker brown or greyish markings. Outer central cross-line shallowly scalloped, with dashes on veins, central ones close together with a W beyond and sometimes shading, often forming a diffuse blotch. Not infrequently wings almost uniformly dark brown. Sometimes a dark outer central band, especially in Scotland. Second- and third-generation moths are much smaller, also compared to Small Engrailed. See also Brindled White-spot, Ringed Carpet, Square Spot.
FS In south, March-mid May; mid June-August; (September-October). In north, April-June.
Hab BWd Sc H G.

Small Engrailed *Ectropis crepuscularia* Local S,C,(N) **FW** 16-19mm. Very similar to Engrailed and difficult to distinguish. Wings from predominantly white with dark markings, through coarsely freckled dark grey, to black. Forewing generally slightly less rounded. Engrailed usually browner. The status of Small Engrailed is somewhat unclear. In mainland Europe, only one species is recognised but in southern Britain there are populations slight different in appearance to Engrailed with slightly later flight season, and producing only one generation per year, even in captivity. See also Square Spot, Ringed Carpet, Brindled White-spot. **FS** Mostly early May-mid June, but has been recorded late April-late June. **Hab** BWd Sc H G.

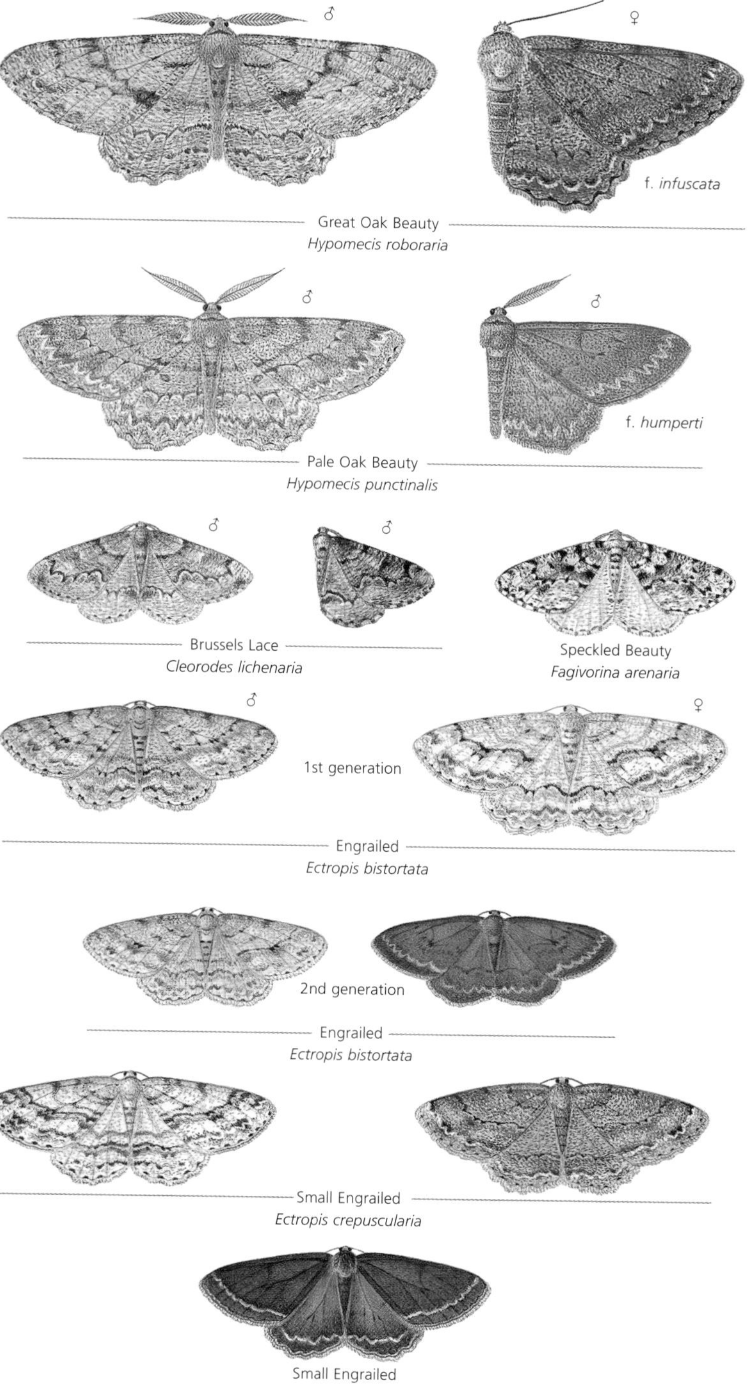

♂
♀
f. *infuscata*
Great Oak Beauty
Hypomecis roboraria
♂
♂
f. *humperti*
Pale Oak Beauty
Hypomecis punctinalis
♂
♂
Brussels Lace
Cleorodes lichenaria
Speckled Beauty
Fagivorina arenaria
♂
1st generation
♀
Engrailed
Ectropis bistortata
2nd generation
Engrailed
Ectropis bistortata
Small Engrailed
Ectropis crepuscularia
Small Engrailed
Ectropis crepuscularia

Square Spot *Paradarisa consonaria* Local S,W **FW** 18-20mm. Forewing rather rounded, outer central cross-line quite smooth, without projecting dashes. Usually a dark linear central spot. Broad central band noticeably paler. In most frequent forms, a roughly square dark blotch centrally before pale wavy outermost cross-line. In rarer black form, markings may be obscured, but base is whitish. See Engrailed, Small Engrailed, Ringed Carpet. **FS** Late April-mid June. **Hab** Wd Sc G.

Brindled White-spot *Parectropis similaria* Local S,(C) **FW** 17-20mm. Dense dark flecking on straw-yellow wings suggests a slightly greenish tint. Forewing rather rounded, somewhat elongated. There is a conspicuous pale patch in centre of pale, wavy outermost cross-line, and a dark linear central spot, with narrow dark curved cross-band just beyond. Brussels Lace is smaller, with forewing less rounded and without outer pale patch. **FS** Late May-June. **Hab** BWd.

Grey Birch *Aethalura punctulata* Common S,C,N,Ir **FW** 13-16mm. Wings light to dark grey. Forewing rounded; fine black cross-lines, some often only evident on leading edge. Central dot small, round. Brussels Lace has jagged outer cross-line, and is usually greenish. Dotted Carpet is whitish; forewing with larger and more conspicuous black central dot. Both have less rounded forewing than Grey Birch. **FS** May-June. Easily disturbed by day from tree trunks. **Hab** BWd Sc.

Common Heath *Ematurga atomaria atomaria* Common T **FW** 12-15mm. Very variable. Wings from white (especially female) to warm light brown yellowish brown or dark grey; usually freckled. Dar cross-bands usually discernible, central ones on forewing often approaching or merging in trailing half. Sometimes bands blurred or lacking. Male has feathered antennae. Small form on northern moorland (f. *minuta*). See Latticed Heath (p.54), Lewes Wave (p.24) (wings softly marbled grey-brown, antennae in male only slightly feathered). I northern Britain, see also Netted Mountain Moth (p.52). **FS** May-June; (August). Active only by day, and easily disturbed. **Hab** A Up Gr.

Bordered White *Bupalus piniaria* Common T **FW** 17-19mm. Rests with wings closed up, showir conspicuous whitish streak and dark broken cross-lines on hindwing underside. Male has feathered antennae. Pattern fairly constant, but pale patches yellow in south, paler, often white, in north. Fema orange-brown or tawny brown; darker in north, pale patches less contrasting. **FS** May-June, until early August in parts of northern Britain. Male active by day. Both sexes are active after dark. **Hab** CWd.

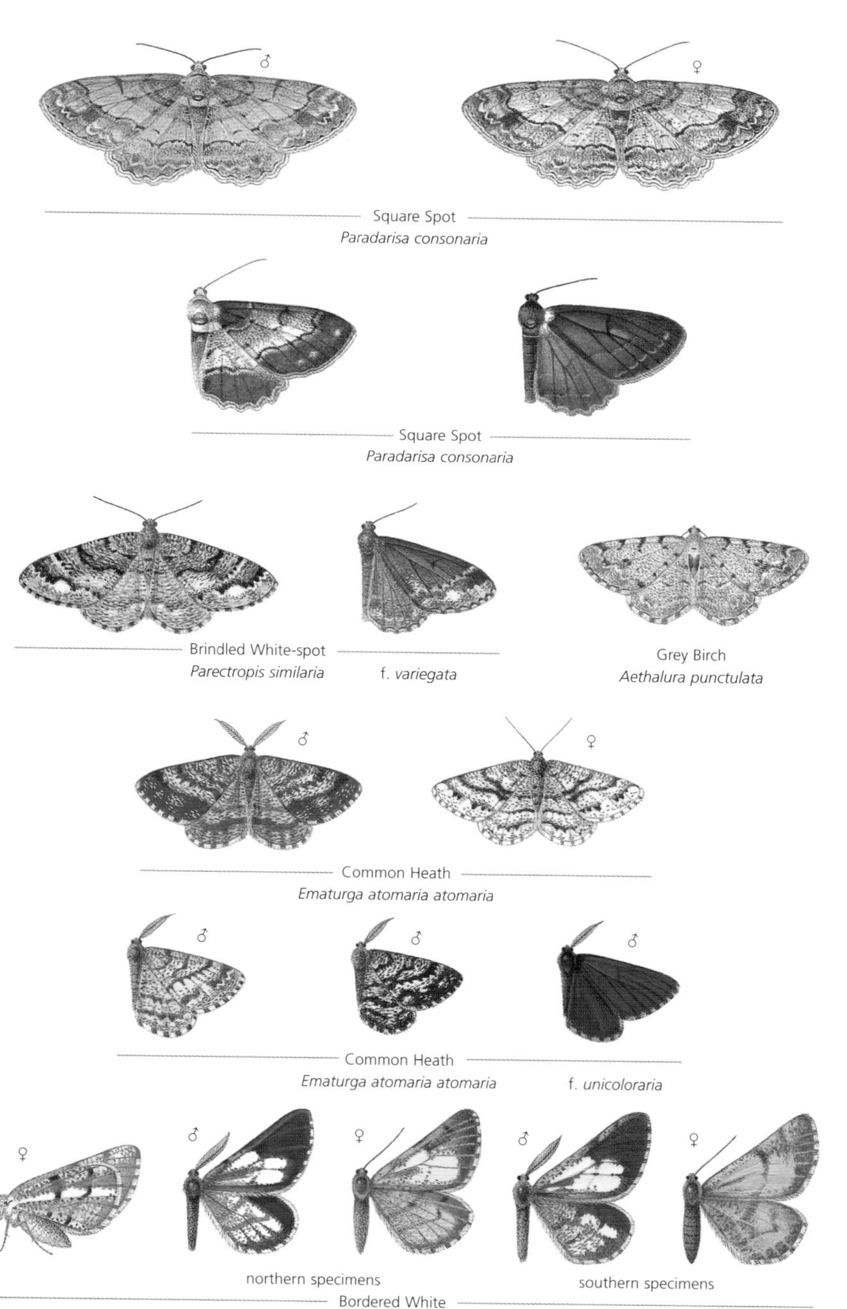

Square Spot
Paradarisa consonaria

Square Spot
Paradarisa consonaria

Brindled White-spot
Parectropis similaria
f. *variegata*

Grey Birch
Aethalura punctulata

Common Heath
Ematurga atomaria atomaria

Common Heath
Ematurga atomaria atomaria
f. *unicoloraria*

Bordered White
Bupalus piniaria

Common White Wave *Cabera pusaria* Common T **FW** 15-17mm. White, finely peppered with grey to a variable degree. Three distinct and rather straight silver-grey cross-lines on broad, rather rounded forewing, and two on hindwing. Larger than other white waves. See Common Wave, Grass Wave. **FS** In south, May-June; late July-August (generations may merge). In Scotland, May-September, peaking late June-July. Easily disturbed from foliage by day. **Hab** Wd Sc.

Common Wave *Cabera exanthemata* Common T **FW** 14-16mm. Similar in shape to Common White Wave, but with brownish-grey freckling (variable, usually heavier in female). Cross-lines brown and curved, notably the outer two, and often indistinct. **FS** In south, May-early July; July-early September. In Scotland, May-mid October, peaking mid June-early July. Easily disturbed from foodplant by day. **Hab** Wd Wt.

White-pinion Spotted *Lomographa bimaculata* Common S,C **FW** 13-14mm. White, with two blackish spots on leading edge of forewing, each extended into a cross-line of dark dots. **FS** May-early July. **Hab** Wd Sc H G.

Clouded Silver *Lomographa temerata* Common S,C,(N),Ir **FW** 13-15mm. White, with blackish clouding in outer area of forewing, extent and intensity variable, generally weaker in female. Dark central spot. **FS** May-early July. **Hab** Wd Sc H G.

Sloe Carpet *Aleucis distinctata* Nb. SE,S **FW** 13-14mm. Similar to Early Moth, but outer central forewing cross-band jagged and irregular, forewing tip pointed; dark central hindwing spot faint or absent, white spots on abdomen; male antennae not feathered. **FS** March-April. Can be found at rest on twigs after dark. **Hab** Sc.

Early Moth *Theria primaria* Common S,C,(N),Ir **FW** 14-17mm. In male, forewing brown (sometimes pinkish-tinged); two dark cross-lines and dark central spot. Forewing tip rounded. Hindwing pale, with dark central spot. Antennae slightly feathered. See Sloe Carpet. Female wing-stumps brown, square-ended, with dark brown cross-band. See female Dotted Border (p.62) (larger with longer wing stumps) and Winter Moth (p.40) (rounded wing stumps). **FS** January-March. After dark can be found at rest on twigs of foodplants (Hawthorn and Blackthorn). **Hab** BWd Sc H.

Light Emerald *Campaea margaritata* Common T **FW** 18-26mm. Greenish white when fresh, fading to whitish. Reddish forewing tip hooked. White, fairly straight dark-edged cross-lines, angled at leading edge. Hindwing with central projection. Second-generation moths are smaller and darker. See Barred Red f. *prasinaria*, Small Emerald (p.22). **FS** In south, late May-early August; (late July-September). In north, late May-early September; (September-late October). **Hab** BWd Sc H G.

Barred Red *Hylaea fasciaria* Common T **FW** 17-21mm. Wings pinkish red, reddish brown to dull grey. F. *prasinaria* is dull green (rare, Kent and Suffolk). Forewing usually with two curved, roughly parallel cross-lines (inner one can be faint or absent). Outer edge of both wings smoothly curved. Barred Umber (p.54) has jagged outer edge to forewing central band. See Light Emerald. **FS** Mid June-early August. **Hab** CWd G.

Irish Annulet *Odontognophos dumetata hibernica* Ir **FW** 18-20mm. Wings dark grey-brown, densely and finely freckled. Forewing broad, leading edge straight. Outer edge scalloped in both wings, more strongly on hindwing. Fine blackish cross-lines, inner central one sharply angled in leading half of forewing. Scotch Annulet is smaller. Forewing with central spot and smooth outer edge, cross-lines not angled. Tissue and Scarce Tissue (p.38) are brownish, with more rounded forewing; cross-lines different. **FS** August. **Hab** Sc.

Scotch Annulet *Gnophos obfuscatus* Nb. N,Ir **FW** 17-21mm. Wings densely speckled dark grey or blackish. Forewing rather elongated; leading edge almost straight, slightly concave centrally. Fine dark, curved, scalloped cross-lines and central spot (usually solid) often obscured. Annulet is smaller, forewing less elongated, leading edge slightly curved outwards and usually a central ring on both wings. **FS** July-August. **Hab** Up.

Annulet *Charissa obscurata* Local T **FW** 15-18mm. Forewing with two scalloped cross-lines and central ring (also on hindwing). Markings often obscured, especially in dark forms. Very variable in colour. On chalk and limestone very pale, sometimes almost white; on heaths, bogs and dark rocks, brown to black. See Scotch Annulet. **FS** July-August. Easily flushed by day. **Hab** CGr A Up Cl Sd

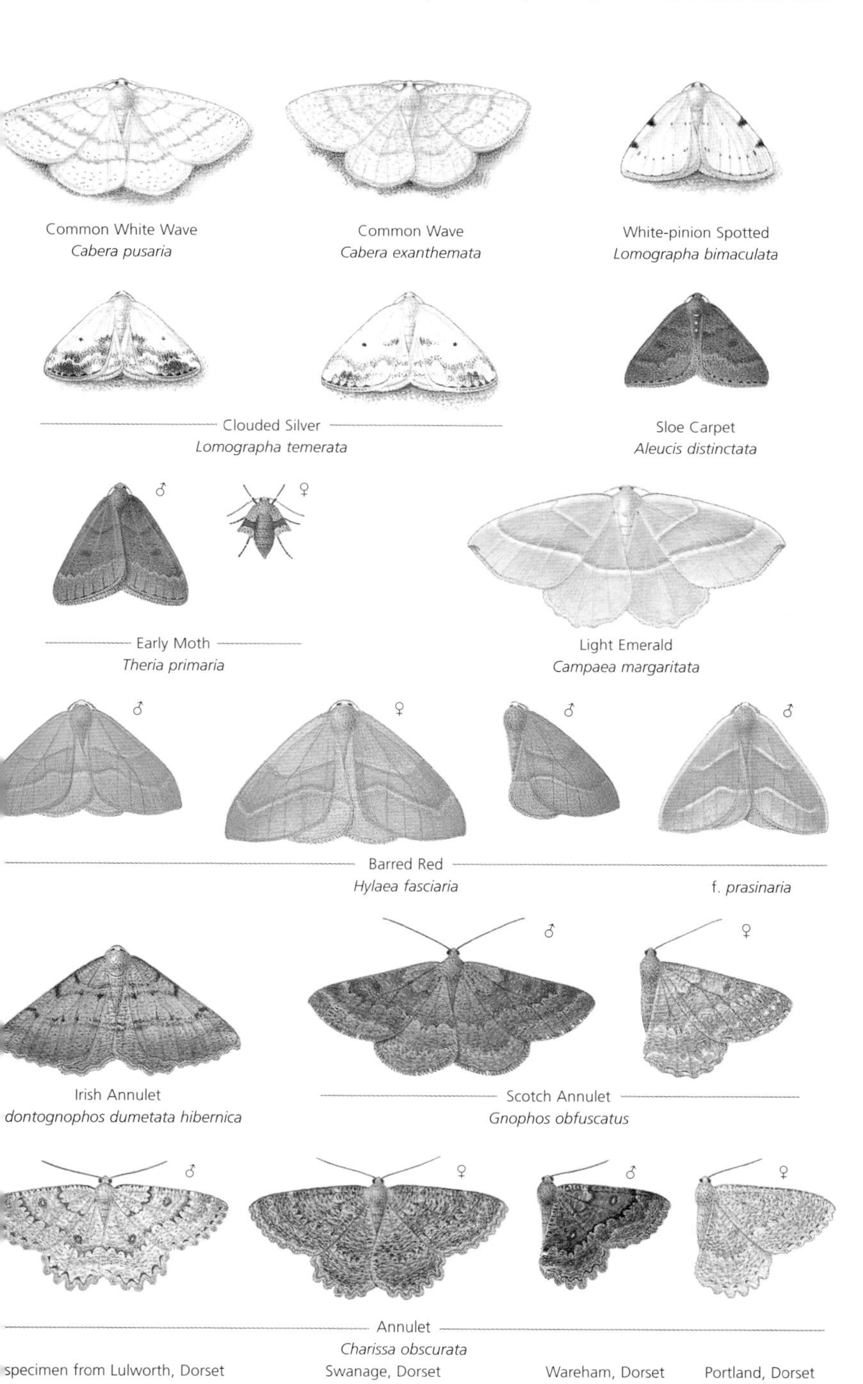
Common White Wave
Cabera pusaria
Common Wave
Cabera exanthemata
White-pinion Spotted
Lomographa bimaculata
Clouded Silver
Lomographa temerata
Sloe Carpet
Aleucis distinctata
♂
♀
Early Moth
Theria primaria
Light Emerald
Campaea margaritata
♂
♀
♂
♂
Barred Red
Hylaea fasciaria
f. *prasinaria*
Irish Annulet
dontognophos dumetata hibernica
♂
♀
Scotch Annulet
Gnophos obfuscatus
♂
♀
♂
♀
Annulet
Charissa obscurata
specimen from Lulworth, Dorset
Swanage, Dorset
Wareham, Dorset
Portland, Dorset

Black Mountain Moth *Glacies coracina* Na. N **FW** 10-13mm. Unusual in shape, with fore- and hindwings similar in size; dark brownish black (greyer in female). Two scalloped cross-lines on forewing and dark central spot. Netted Mountain Moth (p.52) is slimmer and slightly smaller, with smoother cross-lines and shorter hindwing. **FS** June-July, depending on altitude and season. Male flies in sunshine. Female crawls over rocks and lichens. **Hab** Up.

Black-veined Moth *Siona lineata* RDB (Protected) SE **FW** 19-22mm. Wings white (creamy tinged when fresh), veins darker, otherwise unmarked on upperside. Undersides with bold black veins and dark cross-band (unlike any other white or cream geometrid in the British Isles). Often alights with wings closed up, but flat when fully at rest. Male has long, slender, upturned abdomen. Micro-moth *Sitochroa palealis* (Pyralidae), with **FW** 14-16mm (also in CGr by day) is whitish when faded, with dark veins and banded underside, but has forewing narrower and always sits with wings flat. **FS** Late May-early July. Readily flushed by day, nectars in sunshine. Male flies from dusk. **Hab** CGr.

Straw Belle *Aspitates gilvaria gilvaria* RDB SE; ssp. *burrenensis* Ir **FW** 15-18mm. Forewing pale yellow, with single oblique red or reddish-brown stripe from tip almost to trailing edge. Underside hindwing with greyish cross-line and central spot, both visible from upperside. Male has feathered antennae. Female more heavily freckled. Ssp. *burrenensis* is darker, forewing markings more brownish; hindwing band heavier, almost reaches trailing edge. See Yellow Belle. Vestal (p.26) is smaller and slighter, holds wings at steep angle when at rest and has plain hindwing. **FS** From mid June in Kent but July-early September in Surrey. Easily disturbed by day. **Hab** CGr.

Yellow Belle *Semiaspilates ochrearia* Local S **FW** 12-16mm. Forewing yellowish, finely speckled. Two brownish, slightly wavy cross-lines, the outer starting from leading edge. Female paler, less yellow. Straw Belle has more pointed forewing, with single straight cross-line starting from tip. **FS** May-June; August-September. Active by day and easily disturbed. Rests on plant stems after dark. **Hab** Sd Sh Sm (very locally A Gr inland).

Grey Scalloped Bar *Dyscia fagaria* Local T **FW** 15-21mm. Wings white (especially in uplands), grey, dark grey or brownish (heathland and lowlands). Forewing rather elongated in male, leading edge slightly concave, shorter in generally darker female. Two dark cross-lines, the outer bowed in leading half, with a bold dark central spot. **FS** Late May-early August. Male basks on stones and bare ground, and is easily disturbed by day. Both sexes can be found at rest on heather after dark. **Hab** A Up AWt.

Grass Wave *Perconia strigillaria* Local T **FW** 15-20mm. Wings silvery grey, with narrow, rather diffuse brown cross-lines, sometimes united to form a broad central band, and fine speckling. Forewing somewhat pointed; leading edge quite straight. Male has feathered antennae. See Common White Wave (whiter, with fewer cross-lines), also Common Wave (cross-lines curved). Both have more rounded forewing. **FS** May-July. Readily disturbed and sometimes active by day. **Hab** A AWt Up.

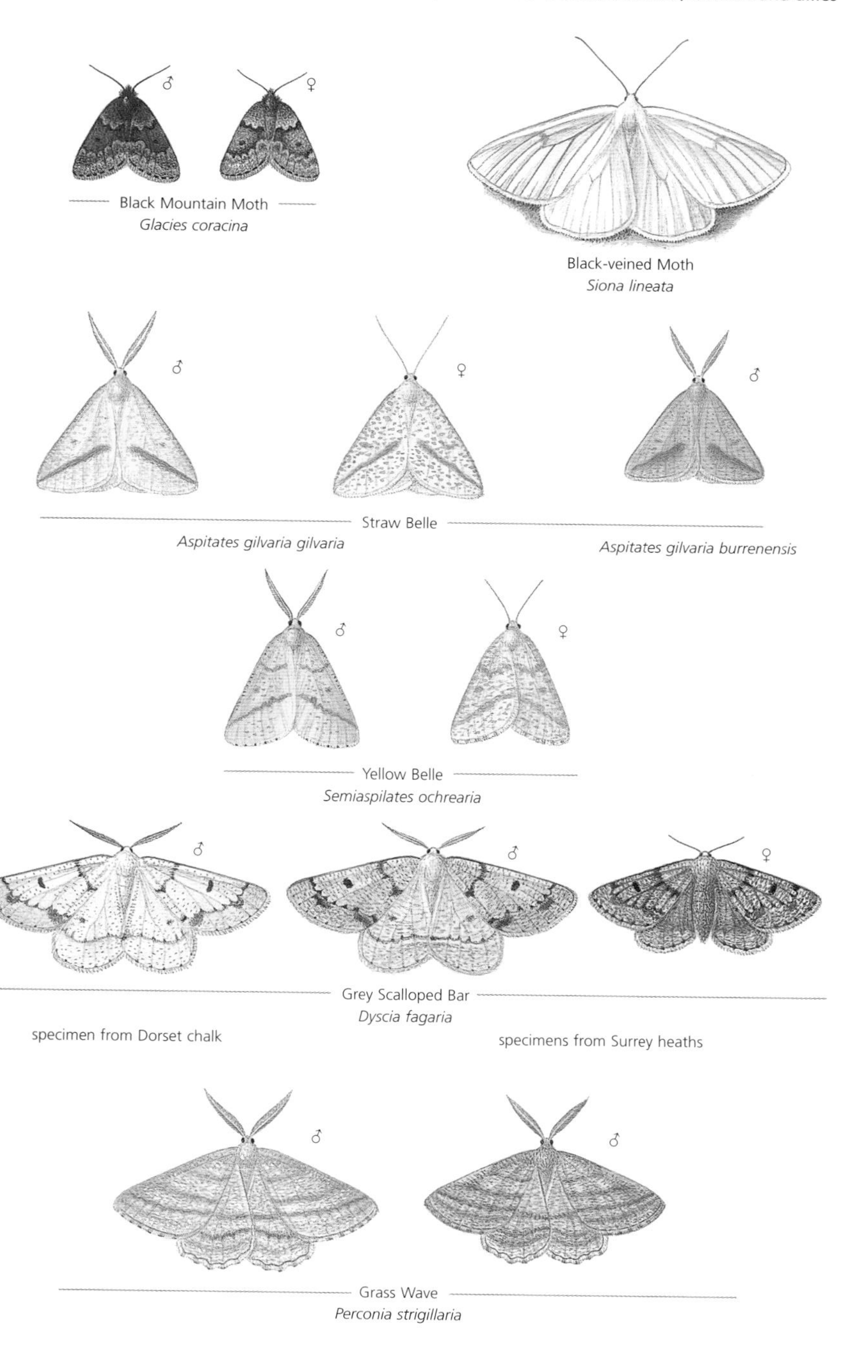

Black Mountain Moth
Glacies coracina

Black-veined Moth
Siona lineata

Straw Belle
Aspitates gilvaria gilvaria
Aspitates gilvaria burrenensis

Yellow Belle
Semiaspilates ochrearia

Grey Scalloped Bar
Dyscia fagaria
specimen from Dorset chalk
specimens from Surrey heaths

Grass Wave
Perconia strigillaria

Sphingidae Hawkmoths

Impressive medium to large moths, often strikingly coloured and including the largest species in Britain. With the exception of those active by day, all come to light, and are sometimes found by day at rest on fence posts, tree trunks and in vegetation, often when newly emerged. The Sphinginae hold their wings at a steep angle close to the body when at rest. The Smerinthinae do not feed and the wings are held with the forewing leading edge at roughly 45° to the body, like the Macroglossinae, which have rather narrow, elongated forewings, so that they are shaped rather like jet-fighters. They have long tongues and hover to take nectar from flowers by day, at dusk or at dawn. Two British species have evolved a resemblance to bees, with largely transparent wings and squat bodies.

Sphinginae

Convolvulus Hawkmoth *Agrius convolvuli*
Immigrant T **FW** 50-55mm. Wings grey, forewing variably marbled and extensively streaked. Male heavily marked with blackish streaks and bands, often with broad, dark central cross-band. Female larger and plainer, with shorter, thinner antennae. Abdomen banded pink and black. Pine Hawkmoth is smaller, lacks pink bands on abdomen, and forewing plainer. See also Privet Hawkmoth, which is brown. **FS** June-December, mainly August-November. Feeds at dusk, and sometimes at dawn, at tubular flowers such as tobacco plants, Petunia, lilies and Phlox. **Hab** Ub.

Death's Head Hawkmoth *Acherontia atropo*
Immigrant T **FW** 52-60mm. Forewing blackish brown, marbled with lighter brown and yellowish. Body very stout. Skull-like marking on thorax, and banded yellow abdomen and hindwing. When disturbed, makes an audible squeaking sound by expelling air through the proboscis. **FS** May-November, but mainly late August-October. Seldon seen except in light-traps. Does not feed at flowers and has a relatively short proboscis, adapted for stealing honey from nesting bees.

Privet Hawkmoth *Sphinx ligustri* Common S,(
FW 41-55mm. Dark chocolate-brown, pale-cloude forewing, pink and black banded hindwing and abdomen, and blackish thorax. See Convolvulus Hawkmoth. **FS** June-July. **Hab** Sc H BWd W G.

Pine Hawkmoth *Hyloicus pinastri* Local S,C
FW 35-41mm. White-dusted grey or brownish-gre forewing, with black streaks in centre, chequered outer margin and uniformly dark brown hindwing. Abdomen banded black and white. See Convolvul Hawkmoth. **FS** May-early August. Feeds from flowers after dark, particularly Honeysuckle. **Hab** CWd.

Convolvulus Hawkmoth
Agrius convolvuli

Pine Hawkmoth
Hyloicus pinastri

Death's Head Hawkmoth
Acherontia atropos

Privet Hawkmoth
Sphinx ligustri

Smerinthinae

Lime Hawkmoth *Mimas tiliae* Common S,C
FW 23-39mm. Forewing usually a rich green, velvety when fresh; dark olive-green central forewing blotches may be enlarged and fused to form a cross-band, or reduced to one small spot (f. *centripunctata*). Uncommon f. *brunnea* is largely reddish brown with central markings brick-red. See Willowherb Hawkmoth. **FS** May-early July. Often comes to light early in the night. **Hab** BWd G.

Eyed Hawkmoth *Smerinthus ocellata*
Common S,C,Ir **FW** 36-44mm. Forewing pinkish brown to deep chocolate, or even blackish. Large eye-spots on pinkish hindwing. When disturbed, it exposes these and rocks to and fro, which has been proved to deter insectivorous birds. Hindwings project beyond leading edge of forewing when at rest. Poplar Hawkmoth lacks eye-spots. **FS** Early May-mid July; (in south, early August-late September). **Hab** Ub.

Poplar Hawkmoth *Laothoe populi* Common T
FW 30-46mm. Usually grey, sometimes with strong pinkish or violet tinge. Chestnut-brown patch on hindwing. Less commonly buff (more frequently the female). At rest, hindwing projects well beyond leading edge of forewing. See Eyed Hawkmoth. **FS** May-July or early August; (in south, August-September). Male usually comes to light after midnight, female may come earlier. **Hab** Ub.

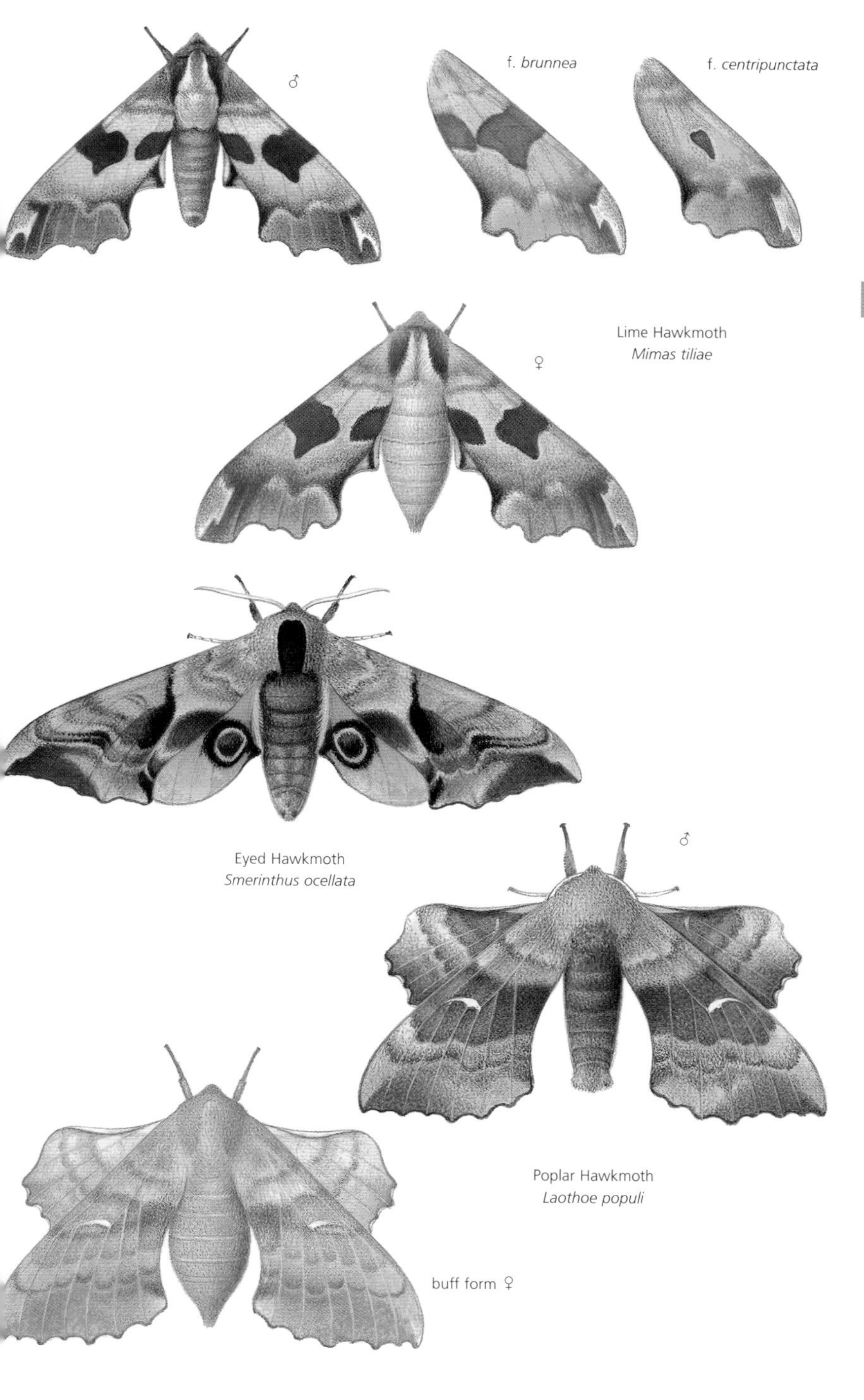

Lime Hawkmoth
Mimas tiliae

Eyed Hawkmoth
Smerinthus ocellata

Poplar Hawkmoth
Laothoe populi

Macroglossinae

Narrow-bordered Bee Hawkmoth *Hemaris tityus* Nb. SW,WC,NW,(E),Ir **FW** 18-21mm. Wings largely transparent. Similar to Broad-bordered Bee Hawkmoth, but dark brown outer bands on wings narrower, especially on hindwing and in trailing half of forewing. Transparent window (or cell) in leading half of base clear (in Broad-bordered divided in two by a longitudinal vein, and short dark central cross-vein thicker). When freshly emerged, both species have thin covering of grey scales, lost on first flight. They are more agile than bumblebees, do not alight to feed, and are much larger than bee-flies (*Bombylius* sp.). See also Hummingbird Hawkmoth, which can look similar in flight. **FS** Mid May-June or early July (exceptionally April). Active only by day, in sunshine, particularly in late morning and early afternoon. Feeds at flowers such as Bugle, Ground Ivy, louseworts, Viper's-bugloss, Common Bird's-foot-trefoil, Rhododendron and Red Valerian. **Hab** Gr A AWt.

Broad-bordered Bee Hawkmoth *Hemaris fuciformis* Nb. S,EC,(WC) **FW** 20-24mm. See Narrow-bordered Bee Hawkmoth. **FS** May-early July; (in southern England, August-September). Active only by day, in sunshine, particularly in late morning and early afternoon. Feeds at tubular flowers such as Bugle, Honeysuckle, Ragged-Robin, louseworts, Viper's-bugloss, Yellow-rattle, Rhododendron and Aubretia. **Hab** Wd A.

Hummingbird Hawkmoth *Macroglossum stellatarum* Immigrant T; suspected resident SW **FW** 20-24mm. Resembles a hummingbird in flight. Orange-brown hindwing and underside are evident in flight as it flits rapidly between plants, hovering to feed at tubular flowers of such species as Viper's-bugloss, Red Valerian, Phlox, Jasmine, Buddleias, Petunia and Lilac. See bee hawkmoths. **FS** April-December, most frequent August-September. Hibernators from January onwards. Active by day, mainly in sunshine, but sometimes in overcast weather, rain, at dusk or after dark. **Hab** Ub.

Willowherb Hawkmoth *Proserpinus proserpina* Rare immigrant/import S,E **FW** 18-21mm. Thickset, with jagged-edged, banded, green or brownish-green forewing and orange-yellow, broadly black-bordered hindwing. Antennae white-tipped. Abdomen narrows abruptly, with two prominet lobes at tip. See Lime Hawkmoth. **FS** Only two records, one in May, one in July.

Oleander Hawkmoth *Daphnis nerii* Immigrant T **FW** 48-51mm. Swirling cream and pinkish-brown markings on green forewing and thorax. Whitish band across base of abdomen. **FS** August-October. Feeds on the wing after dusk at tubular flowers such as Honeysuckle and tobacco plants.

Narrow-bordered Bee Hawkmoth
Hemaris tityus

Broad-bordered Bee Hawkmoth
Hemaris fuciformis

Hummingbird Hawkmoth
Macroglossum stellatarum

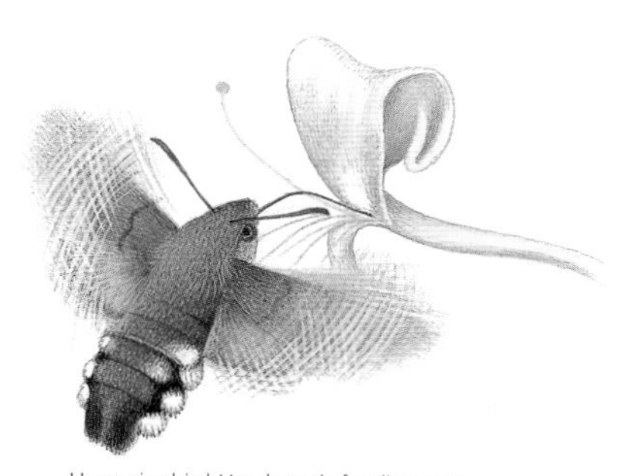

Hummingbird Hawkmoth feeding at a honeysuckle flower

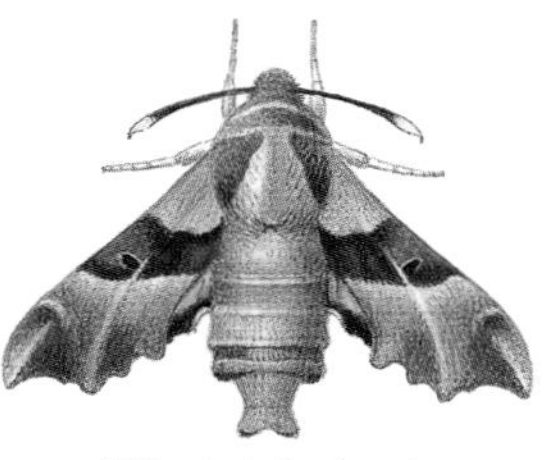

Willowherb Hawkmoth
Proserpinus proserpina

Oleander Hawkmoth
Daphnis nerii

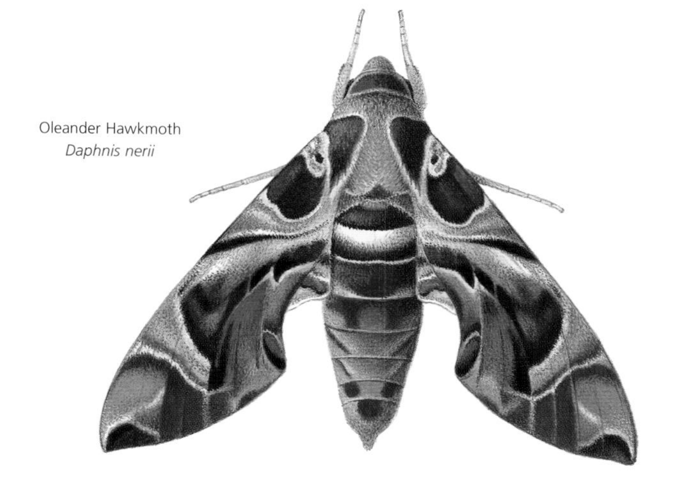

Spurge Hawkmoth *Hyles euphorbiae* Immigrant S,(T) **FW** 28-31mm. Forewing dull olive green with broad, pale, sometimes pink-tinged and/or speckled stripe, extending close to and sometimes reaching leading edge. Undersides of fore- and hindwings pinkish. See Bedstraw Hawkmoth and Striped Hawkmoth. **FS** Recorded in Britain in every month from May-October.

Bedstraw Hawkmoth *Hyles gallii* Immigrant T; transitory resident E **FW** 34-38mm. Similar to Spurge Hawkmoth, but forewing stripe narrower and extensions not approaching leading edge; undersides of wings not pink. See also Striped Hawkmoth. **FS** May-August. Flies from dusk and visits flowers. **Hab** Sd Gr.

Striped Hawkmoth *Hyles livornica* Immigrant S,SW,(T),Ir **FW** 33-42mm. Similar to Bedstraw and and Spurge Hawkmoths, but with white stripes highlighting veins on forewing, and on thorax. Main forewing stripe narrow. See also Silver-striped Hawkmoth. **FS** April-October, mainly May-early June and August. Flies mainly at dusk and just before dawn, feeding at flowers such as Red Valerian and Petunia, but when migrating active during the night. **Hab** C G Wd.

Elephant Hawkmoth *Deilephila elpenor* Common S,C,(N),Ir **FW** 28-33mm. Unmistakable; pink and olive-green forewing and pink and black hindwing, and clearly defined pink pattern on olive-green thorax and abdomen. Small Elephant Hawkmoth is pink and yellowish brown, and much smaller. **FS** May-early August. Flies from dusk, feeding at Honeysuckle and other tubular flowers. **Hab** Ub.

Small Elephant Hawkmoth *Deilephila porcellus* Local S,C,(N),Ir **FW** 21-25mm. The only small, pink and yellowish-brown hawkmoth found in the British Isles. Elephant Hawkmoth is much larger, with olive-green markings. **FS** May-July. Flies from dusk and visits flowers such as Viper's-bugloss, campions, Honeysuckle, Red Valerian and Rhododendron. **Hab** Gr.

Silver-striped Hawkmoth *Hippotion celerio* Immigrant S,(T) **FW** 33-35mm. Smooth-edged, tapered, cream and silver stripe running along grey brown forewing in a gentle curve from basal half o trailing edge to wing tip. Pale, pinkish-yellow band on hindwing is crossed by dark brown veins. See Striped, Bedstraw and Spurge Hawkmoths. **FS** May October, mainly from August. Flies from dusk and visits nectar flowers, including Ivy.

Spurge Hawkmoth
Hyles euphorbiae

Bedstraw Hawkmoth
Hyles gallii

Striped Hawkmoth
Hyles livornica

Elephant Hawkmoth
Deilephila elpenor

Small Elephant Hawkmoth
Deilephila porcellus

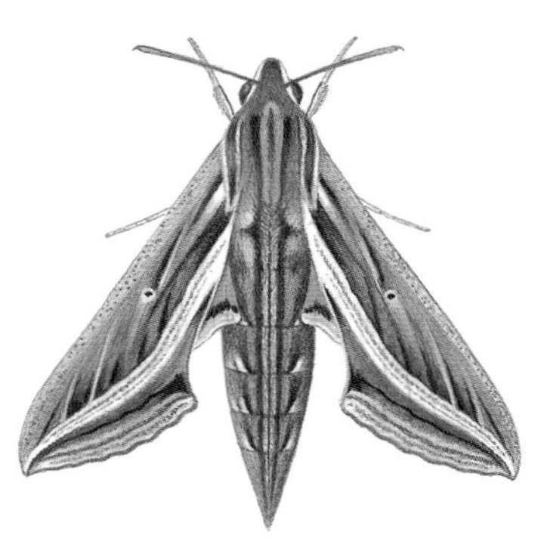

Silver-striped Hawkmoth
Hippotion celerio

Notodontidae

Notodontinae Prominents and allies

Furry, thickset moths. Wings, in most cases, held close to body when at rest, often steeply angled. Trailing edge of forewing and thorax often with prominent tufts. Antennae usually feathered in male. All fly at night and come to light, especially males, but they do not feed.

Puss Moth *Cerura vinula* Common T **FW** 29-38mm. Forewing white or greyish white, with black spots near base (and on thorax) and grey, steeply-contoured lines in outer half. See Leopard Moth (p.6), which lacks contoured lines. **FS** May-July. **Hab** Ub.

Alder Kitten *Furcula bicuspis* Local SW,SE,E,WC **FW** 16-19mm. Forewing markings intense blackish grey. Central band irregular, deeply pinched in leading half, and wider at trailing edge, often reaching trailing corner. See Poplar and Sallow Kitten. **FS** Mid May-early July. **Hab** BWd.

Sallow Kitten *Furcula furcula* Common T **FW** 14-18mm. Central forewing cross-band grey; inner edge fairly straight, dark outer edge rather irregular and usually fine in leading half. See Poplar Kitten and Alder Kitten. **FS** May-June; July-August. In Scotland and Ireland, June-early July. **Hab** Ub.

Poplar Kitten *Furcula bifida* Local S,C,(Ir) **FW** 16-22mm. Very similar to Sallow Kitten, but dark outer edge of central forewing cross-band smooth, obtusely angled or gently curved, quite thick in leading half. Generally larger (female of both species larger, with un-feathered antennae). See also Alder Kitten. **FS** May-July. **Hab** BWd G.

Iron Prominent *Notodonta dromedarius* Common T **FW** 18-24mm. In south, forewing dark grey-brown, with rusty-brown and yellowish markings and yellowish basal blotch. Darker in northern England and Scotland, with rusty and yellow markings duller and fainter. See Large Dark Prominent. **FS** May-June; late July-August in south, June-July in north. **Hab** BWd A Wt G.

Large Dark Prominent *Notodonta torva* Rare immigrant S,E **FW** 19-25mm. Forewing greenish grey, dusted yellowish. Two darker, wavy cross-lines, sometimes faint. An elongated pale, dark-centred central spot. Great Prominent is larger, with extensive dark markings. See also Iron Prominent. **FS** May; August (in central Europe).

Three-humped Prominent *Notodonta tritophus* Immigrant S **FW** 22-27mm. Forewing broad, rounded. Blackish-grey base, central cross-line and large outer blotch, extending from leading edge. Central band and outer edge light brown. Pale central mark (often with internal dark line) more elongate than in Iron Prominent. See also Pebble Prominent. **FS** In Britain, May-August. **Hab** In mainland Europe, Wd G.

Pebble Prominent *Notodonta ziczac* Commo T **FW** 17-24mm. Forewing light brown (occasionally reddish brown); large, black, curved central mark demarcating outer pebble-like blotch. See Three-humped Prominent. **FS** In south and centra Britain, May-June; late July-August. In north, June July. **Hab** Ub.

Lesser Swallow Prominent *Pheosia gnoma* Common T **FW** 20-26mm. Distinct, clean white wedge extending from trailing corner of forewing, reaching less than halfway to base. Dark blotch at trailing corner of hindwing without pale line. See Swallow Prominent. **FS** Late April-June; July-Augus In northern Scotland, late May-early August. **Hab** U

Swallow Prominent *Pheosia tremula* Comm T **FW** 22-28mm. Very like Lesser Swallow Promine but wedge in trailing corner of forewing greyish white, narrower and longer, extending at least halfway to base. On hindwing a fine whitish line through dark blotch at trailing corner. **FS** In south April-June; August. In north, June-August. **Hab** U

Coxcomb Prominent *Ptilodon capucina* Common T **FW** 17-22mm. Forewing pale to dark warm brown, distinct dark scale tuft on trailing edge and large quiff-like, cream-centred tuft on thorax. See Maple Prominent. **FS** Late April-June; August-early September. In far north, May-July. **Hab** BWd Sc H G.

Maple Prominent *Ptilodon cucullina* Local S,E **FW** 15-20mm. Forewing brown, distinctly paler yellowish brown in leading basal half and large whitish blotch on outer margin. See Coxcomb Prominent. **FS** May-July, sometimes later. **Hab** BW Sc H G.

Scarce Prominent *Odontosia carmelita* Local S,C,N,(Ir) **FW** 18-21mm. Forewing reddish brown or purplish brown, heavily dusted grey, especially trailing half. Distinct creamy-white comma mark c leading edge in outer half. Fringes chequered cre and dark brown. **FS** April-May. **Hab** BWd.

Pale Prominent *Pterostoma palpina* Common S,C,(N),Ir **FW** 18-25mm. In male, palps large and abdomen very long; large tail tufts protrude wher at rest. Forewing greyish straw, with dark veins ar fine dots. **FS** May-June; July-August. In northern Britain, May-June. Female very infrequent at light. **Hab** Ub.

White Prominent *Leucodonta bicoloria* Forme resident C,Ir; suspected immigrant S **FW** 16-19m White, with unique orange and black markings o rounded forewing. **FS** June. **Hab** BWd.

Plumed Prominent *Ptilophora plumigera* Na. **FW** 16-19mm. Wings rather narrow, thinly scaled In male, antennae broadly feathered, forewing straw yellow with reddish-brown blotches, to larg reddish brown. Female duller, even more thinly scaled and antennae not feathered. **FS** November December. Male comes to light early in night, female later. **Hab** BWd H.

Puss Moth
Cerura vinula

Alder Kitten
Furcula bicuspis

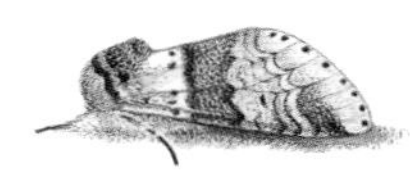

Sallow Kitten
Furcula furcula

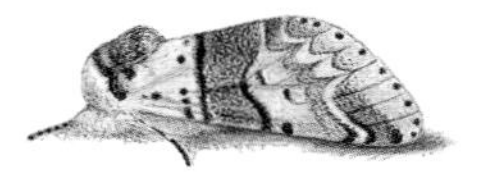

Poplar Kitten
Furcula bifida

Iron Prominent
Notodonta dromedarius northern form

Large Dark Prominent
Notodonta torva

Three-humped Prominent
Notodonta tritophus

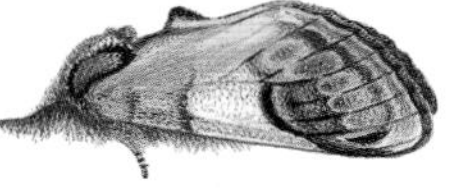

Pebble Prominent
Notodonta ziczac

Lesser Swallow Prominent
Pheosia gnoma

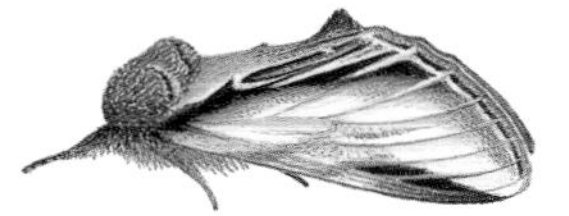

Swallow Prominent
Pheosia tremula

Coxcomb Prominent
Ptilodon capucina dark form

Maple Prominent
Ptilodon cucullina

Scarce Prominent
Odontosia carmelita

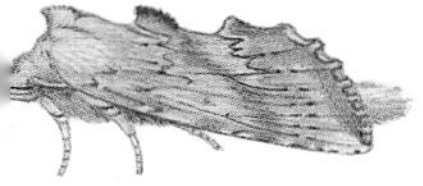

Pale Prominent
Pterostoma palpina

White Prominent
Leucodonta bicoloria

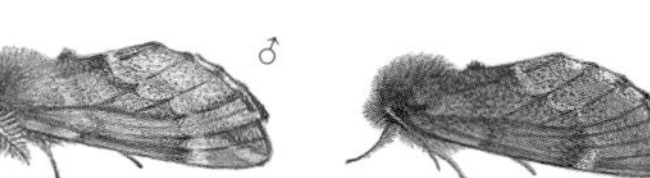

Plumed Prominent
Ptilophora plumigera

Marbled Brown *Drymonia dodonaea* Local S,C,NW,(Ir) **FW** 17-20mm. Forewing whitish or grey. A broad, dark, pinched cross-band before middle with paler band beyond. A rare form has blackish forewing. See Lunar Marbled Brown, which lacks dark, pinched band. **FS** Late May-early July. **Hab** BWd.

Lunar Marbled Brown *Drymonia ruficornis* Common S,C,(N),Ir **FW** 16-20mm. Forewing grey with prominent black central comma. Central band usually whitish, sometimes darkened. A blackish form is rare. See Marbled Brown. **FS** April-May. **Hab** BWd G.

Dusky Marbled Brown *Gluphisia crenata* ssp. *vertunea* Rare immigrant; possible former resident S **FW** 14-15mm. Not unlike a dark form of Marbled Brown or Lunar Marbled Brown; smaller with small but distinct pale central comma mark on forewing, and central cross-band brownish. **FS** April-July.

Pygaerinae

Small Chocolate-tip *Clostera pigra* Nb. T **FW** 11-14mm. Smaller than Chocolate-tip and Scarce Chocolate-tip, with poorly-defined chocolate-brown blotch near tip of forewing. **FS** In south, May; August; (October). In northern Britain and Ireland, June-July. **Hab** Sc A Up Wt Wd.

Scarce Chocolate-tip *Clostera anachoreta* RDB SE **FW** 14-19mm. Similar to Chocolate-tip, but with prominent black spot near trailing corner, and chocolate-brown blotch at tip of forewing extends both sides of outer white cross-line. See also Small Chocolate-tip. **FS** April-May; late July-August; (October). **Hab** Sh.

Chocolate-tip *Clostera curtula* Local S,(C,N) **FW** 13-18mm. Well-defined outer chocolate-brown blotch at tip of forewing stops abruptly at outer white cross-line. See Scarce Chocolate-tip, Small Chocolate-tip. **FS** April-May; August-September. In Scotland, June. **Hab** Wd Sc H G.

Phalerinae

Buff-tip *Phalera bucephala* Common T **FW** M 22-26mm F 26-34mm. Unmistakable. When at rest closely resembles a broken birch twig. **FS** May-July. Comes to light, usually late at night. **Hab** Wd Sc H G.

Heterocampinae

Lobster Moth *Stauropus fagi* Common S,WC,(Ir) **FW** 24-33mm. Rests with forewings at a shallow angle with hindwings protruding. Wings grey-brown with yellowish dusting and markings. On forewing, a russet-brown smear along trailing edge and row of black spots near outer edge. Antennae strongly feathered in male. Dark f. *obscura* is widespread. See Great Prominent. **FS** Mid May-July. **Hab** BWd.

Tawny Prominent *Harpyia milhauseri* Rare immigrant S **FW** 21-24mm. Forewing pale grey. In trailing half, two thick parallel blackish streaks, and thick dark outer cross-line. Faint, light brown outer central cross-band. Hindwing whitish, with prominent black blotch at trailing corner. Antennae feathered except at tip. **FS** May-June. **Hab** Wd.

Great Prominent *Peridea anceps* Local S,WC,(NW) **FW** 23-32mm. Forewing with complex grey, dull yellow and brown marbling an greenish tint. Dark brown dashes near outer edge. Hindwing yellowish white, protruding when at res Uncommon f. *fusca* is blackish brown. Antennae slightly feathered in male. See Lobster Moth, Larg Dark Prominent. **FS** Late April-June. **Hab** BWd.

Dilobinae

Figure of Eight *Diloba caeruleocephala* Commo S,C,(N,Ir) **FW** 15-19mm. Forewing grey. Inner whit central mark resembles an '8'. Antennae feathered in male. Figure of Eighty and Poplar Lutestring (p.2 have broader forewing, different FS, outer central mark resembles an eight and antennae not feathere **FS** September-November. **Hab** H Sc Wd G.

Thaumetopoeidae

Processionary moths

Pine Processionary *Thaumetopoea pityocamp* Possible rare immigrant S **FW** M 16-17mm F 18-22mm. Dark central crescent on greyish forewing See Oak Processionary. Pale Eggar (p.14) lacks central crescent mark on forewing. Larvae of both these species of processionary moth cause severe allergic reactions. **FS** May-July. **Hab** CWd.

Oak Processionary *Thaumetopoea processio* Immigrant S; import; resident in Channel Islands **FW** M 14-16mm F 16-17mm. Similar to Pine Processionary, but forewing base pale and central crescent mark small, cross-lines smoother. **FS** Late July-September. **Hab** BWd G.

Lymantriidae Tussock moths

Furry, medium to large moths. Males have feathe antennae. Most are nocturnal, coming to light, especially males. They do not feed. Larval hairs of some species can cause severe skin irritation.

Reed Tussock *Laelia coenosa* Former resident S extinct **FW** 16-21mm. Forewing pale buff in male unmarked or with outer line of small blackish dot Antennae black, strongly feathered. Wings plain whitish in female. See White Satin. **FS** July-Augus **Hab** Wt.

Scarce Vapourer *Orgyia recens* RDB EC **FW** M 13-17mm. Similar to Vapourer, but wings i male dark chocolate brown. Forewing with elongated orange-brown blotches, white spots near forewing tip, and fine whitish pattern near base. Female with rudimentary wings, dark grey. **FS** Jun July; (August-October). Male flies by day. Female sedentary, remaining on cocoon. **Hab** A Wt Wd H

Vapourer *Orgyia antiqua* Common T **FW** M 12-17mm. Male with orange-brown wings, indistinct darker cross-lines and conspicuous white spot nea trailing corner. Female with rudimentary wings, lig grey-brown. See Scarce Vapourer. **FS** In south, July-October. In north, September-October. Male flies by day and at night, occasionally coming to light. Female sedentary, remaining on cocoon. **Hab** Ub.

Marbled Brown
Drymonia dodonaea
f. *nigrescens*

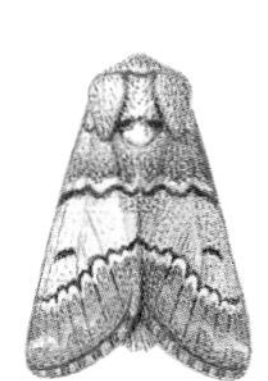

Lunar Marbled Brown
Drymonia ruficornis

Dusky Marbled Brown
Gluphisia crenata vertunea

Small Chocolate-tip
Clostera pigra

Scarce Chocolate-tip
Clostera anachoreta

Chocolate-tip
Clostera curtula

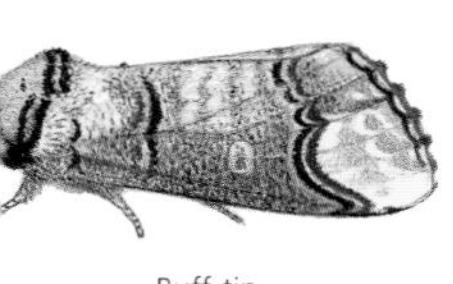

Buff-tip
Phalera bucephala

Lobster Moth
Stauropus fagi
f. *obscura*

Tawny Prominent
Harpyia milhauseri

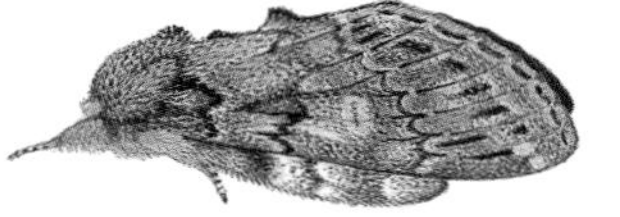

Great Prominent
Peridea anceps

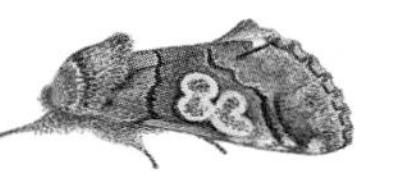

Figure of Eight
Diloba caeruleocephala

umetopoeidae Processionary moths

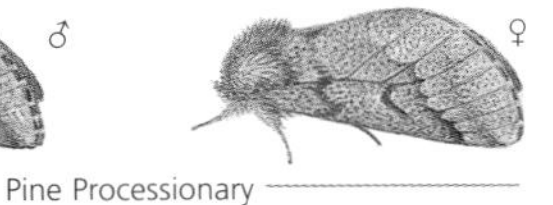

♂ ♀

Pine Processionary
Thaumetopoea pityocampa

♂ ♀

Oak Processionary
Thaumetopoea processionea

ıantriidae Tussock moths

Reed Tussock
Laelia coenosa

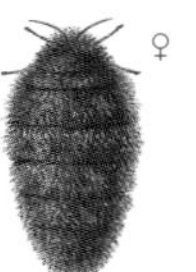

♂ ♀

Scarce Vapourer
Orgyia recens

♂ ♀

Vapourer
Orgyia antiqua

Dark Tussock *Dicallomera fascelina* Local S,WC,N,(Ir) **FW** 18-28mm. Front legs are stretched well forward when at rest. Forewing grey, finely peppered with black. Black cross-lines usually edged with small orange-brown blotches. Antennae grey. **FS** July-August. **Hab** A Up Sd Sh.

Pale Tussock *Calliteara pudibunda* Common S,C,Ir **FW** M 21-22mm, F 27-31mm. Resting posture as Dark Tussock. Usually paler, forewing cross-lines less intense and not edged orange-brown. Antennae brown in male. Female larger, usually without dark central shading. Melanic f. *concolor*, with blackish-grey forewing and dark grey hindwing, is frequent in parts of southern England. See Dark Tussock. **FS** May-June. **Hab** Ub.

Brown-tail *Euproctis chrysorrhoea* Local S, SE, EC **FW** M 16-20mm, F 18-19mm. Uppersides of wings usually slightly silky and pure white, although sometimes male has a few tiny black dots near trailing corner of forewing. In male, upperside of abdomen white at base, otherwise deep chocolate-brown, or rusty-brown. Female has large, bulbous, dark brown tuft of hair at tip of abdomen. Often raises or curls abdomen into view if disturbed, as does similar Yellow-tail. **FS** July-August; (October). **Hab** Sc H G.

Yellow-tail *Euproctis similis* Common S,C,(N,Ir) **FW** M 16-22mm, F 17-23mm. Not dissimilar to Brown-tail but slightly slimmer, with more rounded wings. Male has one or more blackish spots near trailing corner of forewing, and occasionally near base. Female larger, with un-feathered antennae, and with at most faint dark spots near trailing corner of forewing. Abdomen white with golden yellow tip, larger (but not bulbous) in female. See also White Satin Moth. **FS** July-August; (recently October). **Hab** Ub.

White Satin Moth *Leucoma salicis* Local S,EC,(WC,N,Ir) **FW** 18-27mm. Wings broad, plain white, with strong silky sheen. Legs ringed black and white. Tip of abdomen white. Antennae grey. Black V Moth has central black V on broader forewing. See also Reed Tussock (female) and Yellow-tail. **FS** July-August. **Hab** H Sc BWd G.

Black V Moth *Arctornis l-nigrum* Immigrant; occasional transitory resident S,E **FW** 19-27mm. Wings greenish white when freshly emerged, quickly fading to white, semi-transparent with slight silky sheen. Forewing broad with thin black central mark usually V-shaped, but may be shallo Antennae in male orange-brown. See White Satin Moth. **FS** Late June-July. **Hab** H.

Black Arches *Lymantria monacha* Local S,(C) **FW** M 18-20mm, F 20-28mm. Forewing usually white, with numerous irregular or jagged black cross-lines, sometimes merged into a broad centr band, and central V-mark. Abdomen with pink banding, which may be faint on dark examples. Female larger, with distinctly pointed abdomen. Infrequent f. *eremita* has forewing sooty grey, oft with cross-lines obscured. Gypsy Moth lacks pink abdomen; male is distinctly brown, female is mor thickset, and forewing broader with less irregular wing markings and very blunt abdomen. **FS** Late July-August. **Hab** Wd.

Gypsy Moth *Lymantria dispar* Immigrant; form resident S **FW** M 20-24mm, F 31-35mm. Male h broad, deep brown forewing, wavy cross-lines an a dark central, roughly V-shaped mark. Sometime diffuse paler cross-bands. Creamy white female similarly marked, but much larger, with very blun abdomen, dark brown towards tip. See Black Arches. **FS** July-August. Male comes to light, and also flies by day. Female apparently does not usu fly far from the cocoon. **Hab** AWt (Ub in mainlan Europe).

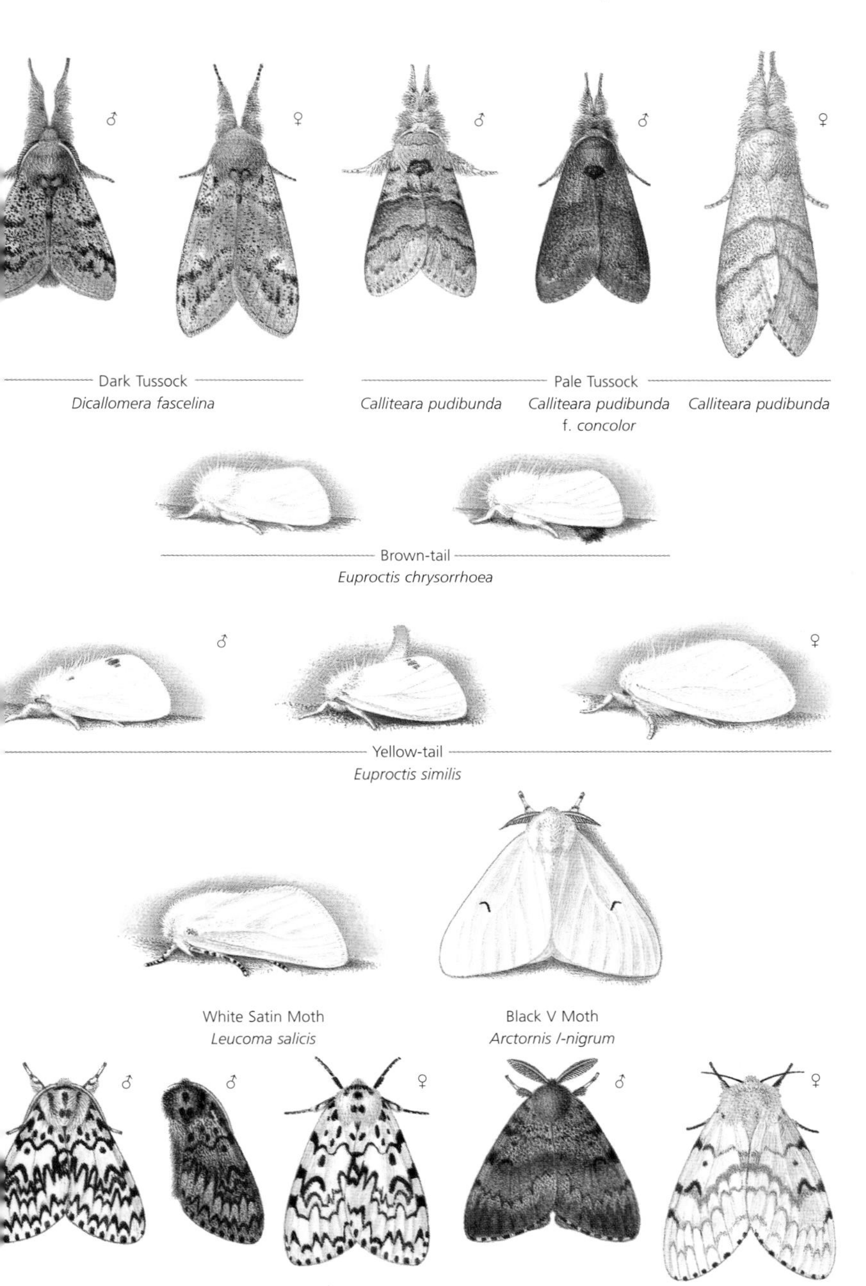
♂
♀
♂
♂
♀
Dark Tussock
Dicallomera fascelina
Pale Tussock
Calliteara pudibunda
Calliteara pudibunda f. *concolor*
Calliteara pudibunda
Brown-tail
Euproctis chrysorrhoea
♂
♀
Yellow-tail
Euproctis similis
White Satin Moth
Leucoma salicis
Black V Moth
Arctornis l-nigrum
♂
♂
♀
♂
♀
Black Arches
mantria monacha
Lymantria monacha f. *eremita*
Lymantria monacha
Gypsy Moth
Lymantria dispar

Arctiidae Tigers, ermines, footmen

Tigers and ermines are often brightly banded or spotted. Footmen are more slender and generally less colourful. Most arctiids are nocturnal and come to light (unless stated). Many do not feed, but some come to flowers and sugar.

Lithosiinae

Round-winged Muslin *Thumatha senex* Local S,C,(N),Ir **FW** 10-11mm. Wings very broad and rounded, creamy brown, slightly translucent. Forewing with dark central dot and two cross-rows of dark dots or dashes. Hindwing with small dark central spot. See Muslin Footman. **FS** Late June-late August. **Hab** Wt Sd Gr Up.

Dew Moth *Setina irrorella* Na. S,NW,Ir **FW** 11-18mm. Forewing triangular, leading edge straight in male, orange-yellow with three cross-rows of small black spots. Female smaller, with narrower forewing. **FS** June-July. Male flies by day and at night. **Hab** Cl Sh CGr.

Rosy Footman *Miltochrista miniata* Local S,(C) **FW** 12-15mm. Rounded forewing salmon-pink (rarely yellow). Fine, very wavy black central cross-line. **FS** Mid June-early August. **Hab** BWd.

Muslin Footman *Nudaria mundana* Local T **FW** 10-12mm. Similar to Round-winged Muslin, but wings semi-transparent. Forewing narrower, with two dark, roughly V-shaped cross-lines. Hindwing plain. **FS** Late June-early August. **Hab** Gr H G Wd.

Red-necked Footman *Atolmis rubricollis* Local S,WC,(N),Ir **FW** 15-18mm. Wings plain black. Collar red. Abdomen yellow on tip and on underside. **FS** June-July. Sometimes flies around treetops in sunshine. **Hab** Wd.

Four-dotted Footman *Cybosia mesomella* Local S,(C,N) **FW** 13-16mm. Forewing broad, white with leading and outer edges yellow, sometimes dull yellow (f. *flava*), with black dot near leading and trailing edges. **FS** Mid June-early August. Easily disturbed by day. **Hab** A Up Gr Wt Wd.

Dotted Footman *Pelosia muscerda* RDB E **FW** 13-16mm. Forewing soft grey-brown. 5-6 small black spots, in two separate rows. See Small Dotted Footman. **FS** Mid July-August. **Hab** Wt.

Small Dotted Footman *Pelosia obtuse* RDB E **FW** 12-14mm. Not unlike Dotted Footman. Forewing shorter and browner with one roughly V-shaped row of small black central spots. **FS** July. **Hab** Wt.

Orange Footman *Eilema sororcula* Local S **FW** 13-16mm. Forewing orange-yellow, leading edge straight in basal half, then strongly curved towards tip. Yellow forms of Dingy and Buff Footman are larger; forewing leading edge more evenly curved. **FS** Late May-June. **Hab** BWd.

Dingy Footman *Eilema griseola* Common S,(C,Ir) **FW** 15-18mm. Forewing broad, rounded. Leading edge strongly curved, in grey form with pale, narrow, often indistinct stripe. Hindwing grey-brown. In frequent f. *stramineola* forewing plain straw-yellow. See Common, Buff and Orang Footman. **FS** July-August. **Hab** Wt Gr Wd.

Hoary Footman *Eilema caniola* Nb. SW,(Ir) **FW** 15-17mm. Forewing narrow, silky, very pale gre with pale orange-yellow stripe along leading edge or white with stripe very faint (f. *lacteola*). Hindwir white. See Scarce Footman, Common Footman. **FS** Late July-early September. **Hab** Cl Sh Gr.

Pigmy Footman *Eilema pygmaeola pygmaeola* RDB E,SE; ssp. *pallifrons* RDB SE **FW** 10-15mm. Ssp. *pygmaeola* forewing narrow, silky greyish-white. Hindwing with distinct and often extensive grey smear in leading half. Rests with wings held close to body. Ssp. *pallifrons* has straw-yellow forewing. Micro-moth *Crambus perlella* has long palps, and rests with shiny forewings steeply arched. **FS** Mid July-August. **Hab** Sd Sh.

Scarce Footman *Eilema complana* Local S,C,Ir; **Northern Footman** f. *sericea* RDB WC
Scarce Footman: FW 15-18mm. Very similar to Common Footman, but orange-yellow stripe on leading edge of forewing reaches tip without narrowing. Rests with wings held tightly around body. Hindwing pale straw, sometimes with grey smear. **Northern Footman: FW** 14-17mm. Slight smaller, with narrower forewing, stripe on leading edge often narrowed before tip. Grey smear, ofte extensive, on hindwing. **FS** July-August. **Hab** Scar Footman Ub. Northern Footman AWt.

Buff Footman *Eilema depressa* Local S,(C,Ir) **FW** 15-17mm. Forewing in male greyish white, fringes orange-yellow. Hindwing pale with diffuse dark border. Forewing in female yellowish brown brownish grey with distinct orange stripe on leadi edge, and hindwing grey-brown. F. *unicolor* has forewing plain orange-yellow. Dingy Footman has broader, more rounded forewing. See also Comm Footman, Orange Footman. **FS** July-August. **Hab** Wd Sc.

Common Footman *Eilema lurideola* Common S,C,(N,Ir) **FW** 14-17mm. Forewing leaden grey. Well-defined yellow stripe on leading edge narrow toward tip. Hindwing pale straw. Rests with forew ings gently curled over body. See Scarce, Northern and Hoary Footman. See also Dingy Footman, wit broader forewing, and dark female Buff Footman which is brownish (both with grey-brown hind-wing). **FS** July-August. **Hab** Ub.

Four-spotted Footman *Lithosia quadra* Na; immigrant. SW,Ir **FW** M 18-22 F 20-26mm. Large. In male, black and yellow blotches at base grey forewing. Female unmistakable, with two da brown spots on yellow forewing. **FS** July-Septemb **Hab** BWd.

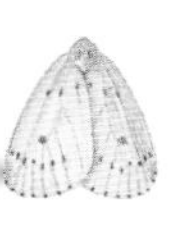
ound-winged Muslin
Thumatha senex

Dew Moth
Setina irrorella

Rosy Footman
Miltochrista miniata
f. *flava*

Muslin Footman
Nudaria mundana

Red-necked Footman
Atolmis rubricollis

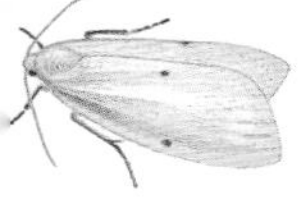
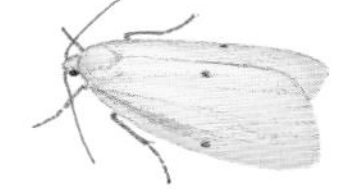
Four-dotted Footman
Cybosia mesomella
f. *flava*

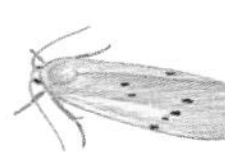
Dotted Footman
Pelosia muscerda

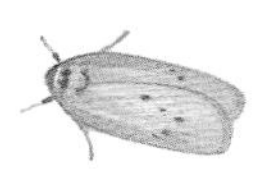
Small Dotted Footman
Pelosia obtusa

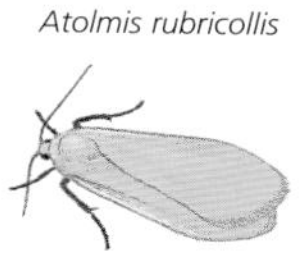
Orange Footman
Eilema sororcula

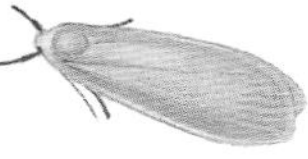

Dingy Footman
Eilema griseola
f. *stramineola*

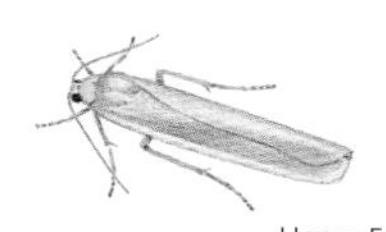
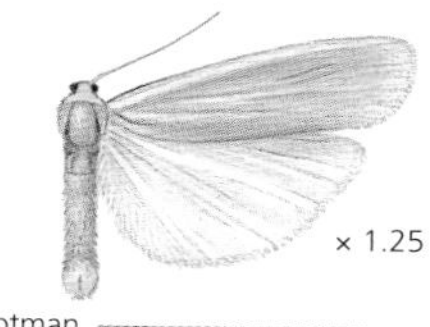

Hoary Footman
Eilema caniola

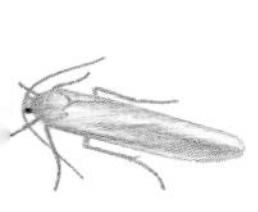

Pigmy Footman
'ema pygmaeola pygmaeola | *Eilema pygmaeola pallifrons*

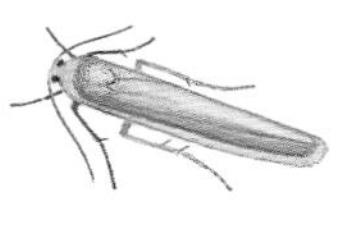

Scarce Footman
Eilema complana

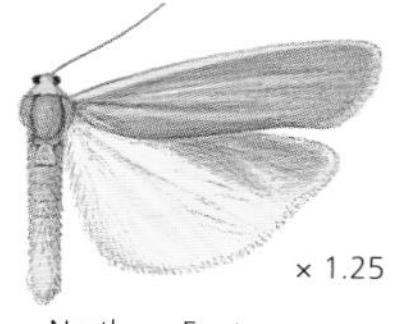

Northern Footman
Eilema complana f. *sericea*

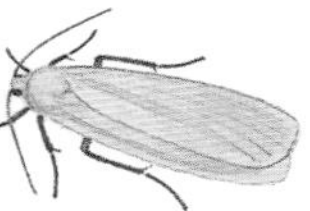

Buff Footman
Eilema depressa

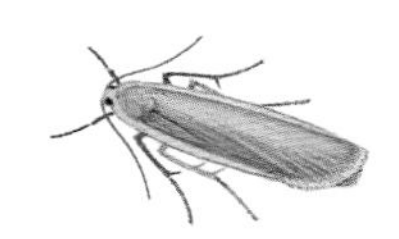
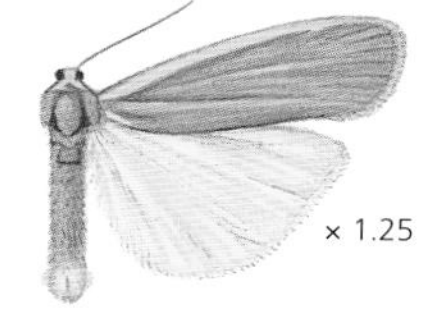

Common Footman
Eilema lurideola

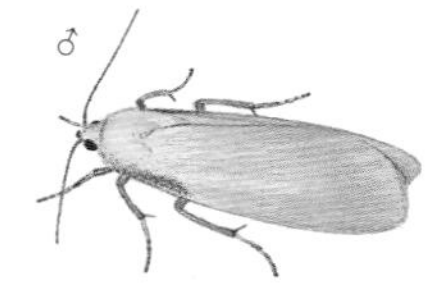

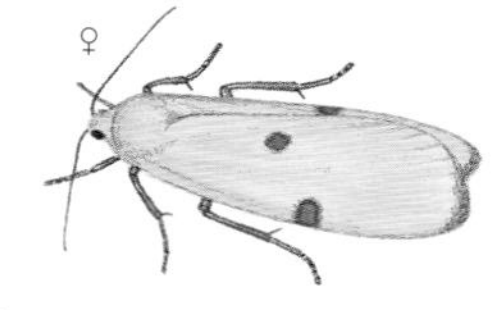

Four-spotted Footman
Lithosia quadra

Arctiinae

Feathered Footman *Spiris striata* Uncertain (4+ records from 19th century). **FW** 15-22mm. Forewing yellow, in male usually with numerous black stripes. Female usually plainer, stripes restricted to outer edges and central crescent reduced to two small dots. Hindwing usually orange-yellow, with black central crescent and variable black border, or less often almost entirely black. Male has feathered antennae. **FS** May-August. Active by day. **Hab** A Wd.

Speckled Footman *Coscinia cribraria* ssp. *bivittata* RDB S; ssp. *arenaria* Immigrant **FW** 15-18mm. Rests with forewings wrapped closely around body and folded, so that tips appear pointed. Ssp. *bivittata*: Forewing greyish-white with cross-rows of blackish spots, sometimes merged, and blackish streaks, their extent variable. Some examples are extensively clouded. Hindwing grey with whitish fringes. Ssp. *arenaria*: Has dark markings highly reduced. Similar micro-moths lack dark streaks. **FS** July-August. Can be disturbed by day. **Hab** A.

Crimson Speckled *Utetheisa pulchella* Immigrant S,(T) **FW** 15-22mm. Forewing creamy white, with intricate pattern of pink or red and black spots. Sometimes red spots are merged into cross-bands, and occasionally black spots are reduced to tiny dots. Hindwing white, with irregular black border and often small dark central marks. **FS** March-October, mainly from July onwards. Easily disturbed by day, flies freely in sunshine and at night.

Beautiful Utetheisa *Utetheisa bella* Rare immigrant/import **FW** 22mm. Similar to Crimson Speckled but usually with irregular orange or pink bands and blotches on forewing and ground-colour of hindwing pink. [Not illustrated.]

Wood Tiger *Parasemia plantaginis plantaginis* Local T,(rare SE); ssp. *insularum* Shetland, Orkney, northern mainland Scotland **FW** 17-20mm. Unmistakable. Ssp. *plantaginis*: Variable. In female, black basal markings on hindwing more extensive. In northern England and parts of Scotland, males frequently with ground-colour whitish (f. *hospita*). Ssp. *insularum*: Male has ground-colour of hindwing darker orange-yellow and black basal markings more extensive. **FS** Late May-July. Easily disturbed by day from low vegetation. Male flies in sunshine. Female active in late afternoon and after dark. **Hab** A Up CGr Sc Wd.

Garden Tiger *Arctia caja* Common T **FW** 28-37mm. Unmistakable. Dark brown blotches on forewing highly variable, but extreme examples with blotches almost entirely absent or almost covering wings are rare in the wild. Forms with ground-colour of hindwing and abdomen yellow or sooty-brown are very rare. If disturbed, displays hindwings and produces a clear yellow fluid from two ducts just behind the head. **FS** July-August. Flies late at night. **Hab** Ub.

Cream-spot Tiger *Arctia villica* ssp. *britannica* Local S **FW** 25-32mm. Forewing black, with creamy-white blotches, including one at base. Thorax black with white shoulders. Hindwing with ground-colour yellow. Upperside of abdomen largely bright red, but yellowish near base. Variable but extreme examples with spots highly reduced or greatly enlarged are rare. See Scarlet Tiger (very rarely with hindwing yellow), which is more slender with forewing iridescent, and lacking white blotch at base. **FS** Late May-early July. Sometimes found at rest by day. **Hab** C Gr H A Wd.

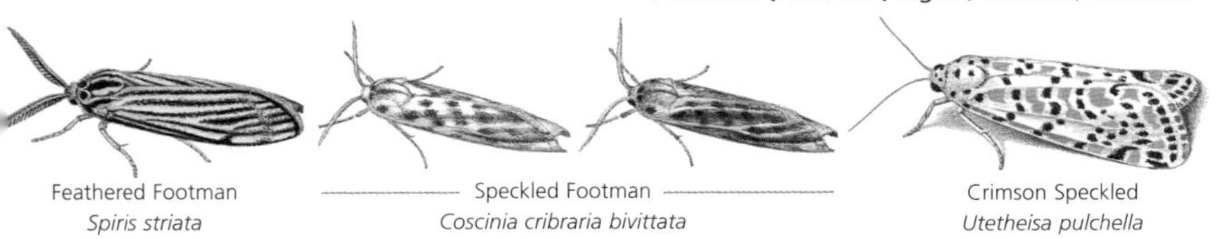

Feathered Footman
Spiris striata

Speckled Footman
Coscinia cribraria bivittata

Crimson Speckled
Utetheisa pulchella

Wood Tiger

Parasemia plantaginis plantaginis

f. *hospita*

Garden Tiger
Arctia caja

Arctia caja
f. *petriburgensis*

Arctia caja
f. *lutescens*

Arctia caja
f. *fumosa*

Cream-spot Tiger
Arctia villica britannica

Clouded Buff *Diacrisia sannio* Local T
FW M 19-22mm F 17-20mm. Unmistakable. Male often with pink along leading and trailing edge of forewing. Forewing much narrower and orange in female, with orange-red veins. Blackish clouding on hindwing highly variable, generally more extensive in female. **FS** June-July; (rarely late August). Male easily disturbed by day and flies in sunshine and at night. Female seems to fly little, but is sometimes found at rest. **Hab** A Up CGr Wd.

White Ermine *Spilosoma lubricipeda* Common T **FW** 18-23mm. Scattered white spots and dots on forewing highly variable in extent, sometimes arranged into cross-rows, less often forming streaks along veins. Hindwing with central black spot and usually further spots near outer edge. In southern half of Britain, forewing usually white with creamy tint and hindwing white. In Scotland and Ireland (and occasionally further south) forewing creamy buff or brown and hindwing creamy white. Abdomen yellow above, with dark spots and whitish tip. See Water Ermine, Buff Ermine and female Muslin Moth. **FS** Mid May-late July; (in southern England, September-October). Usually flies late in the night. **Hab** Ub.

Buff Ermine *Spilosoma luteum* Common S,C,(N),Ir **FW** 17-22mm. Forewing yellowish-buff to whitish buff, hindwing slightly paler. Extent of black spots on forewing highly variable, sometimes forming streaks. A row of rather elongated spots from tip to trailing edge, often broken but usually complete on underside. Abdomen yellow above, with dark spots. A form with mainly black wings, is very rare in the wild. See White Ermine and male Muslin Moth (Ireland). **FS** Mid May-July. **Hab** Ub.

Water Ermine *Spilosoma urticae* Nb. S,E,(SW) **FW** 18-21mm. Very like an unusually plain White Ermine, but with forewing pure white, and without central black spot on hindwing. Forewing usually with just one or two central black dots, and sometimes a short row near tip, or entirely plain. See also Muslin Moth. **FS** June-July. **Hab** Wt.

Muslin Moth *Diaphora mendica* Common S,C,(N),Ir **FW** M 14-17mm F 17-19mm. Forewing broad, with a variable pattern of black spots. In England, Wales and Scotland, male is grey-brown or sooty-grey, in Ireland creamy white or buff. Female has white, slightly translucent wings and whitish abdomen with black spots. White, Water and Buff Ermines are generally larger, with opaque wings and abdomen largely yellow. **FS** Late April-June. Male is nocturnal. Female is active by day, flies in sunshine, and may be found crawling over low vegetation. **Hab** Ub.

Ruby Tiger *Phragmatobia fuliginosa* ssp. *fuliginosa* Common S,C,Ir; ssp. *borealis* Common N (Scotland) **FW** 14-19mm. Thickset with rather thinly-scaled wings. Forewing pinkish brown or deep pink, with one or two small dark central marks. Hindwing bright pink (very rarely yellow) with highly variable sooty-grey shading. Ssp. *borealis* forewing darker, sometimes dull brown. Hindwing sooty-grey, often with pink streak along trailing edge. Moths from northern England and Ireland are intermediate. **FS** Ssp. *fuliginosa* Mid April-June; mid July-early September. Ssp. *borealis* May-July. Sometimes flies by day. **Hab** Ub.

Jersey Tiger *Euplagia quadripunctaria* Nb.; suspected immigrant SW **FW** 28-33mm. Black and creamy-white striped markings on forewing, and hindwing with red, orange or yellow ground-colour. Variation is usually slight, and examples with entirely black forewings or more extensively white are unusual. **FS** Mid July-early September, usually from early August. Active by day, visiting flowers. Also flies at night. **Hab** C H G.

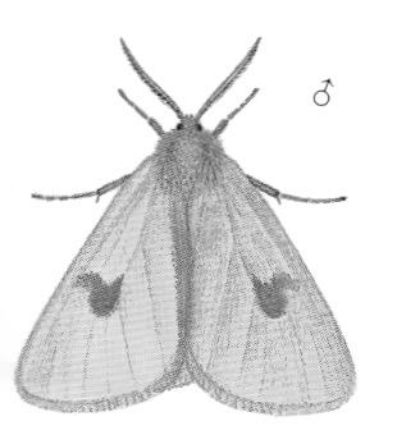

Clouded Buff
Diacrisia sannio

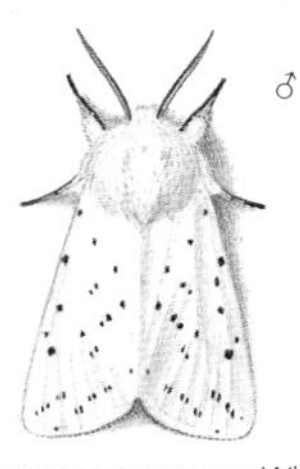

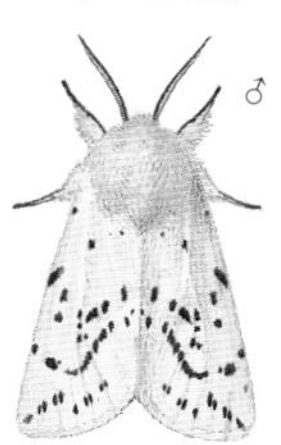

White Ermine
Spilosoma lubricipeda

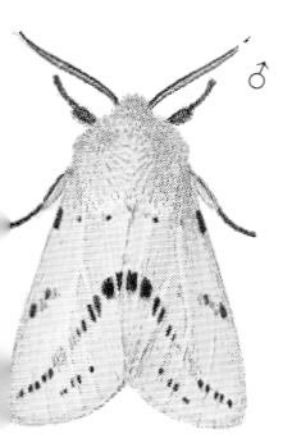

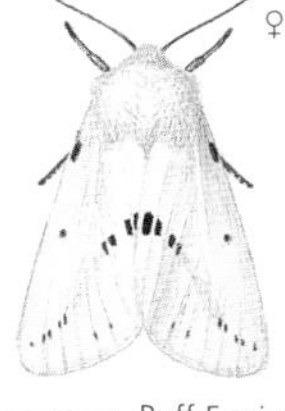

Buff Ermine
Spilosoma luteum

Water Ermine
Spilosoma urticae

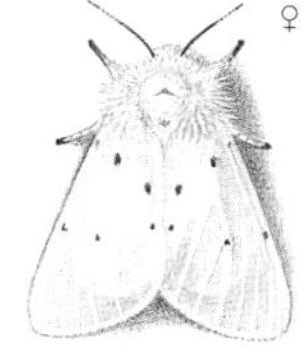

Muslin Moth
Diaphora mendica

Ruby Tiger
Phragmatobia fuliginosa fuliginosa
Phragmatobia fuliginosa borealis

Jersey Tiger
Euplagia quadripunctaria

f. *lutescens*

Scarlet Tiger *Callimorpha dominula* Local SW,S,(SE) **FW** 23-27mm. Unmistakable, with white and yellow spots and blotches on iridescent black forewing and largely red hindwing. Rarely, outer forewing spots reduced or absent and hindwing extensively black or hindwing yellow. See Cream-spot Tiger. **FS** June-July. Flies by day, and often seen at rest. Also flies at night. **Hab** Wt Gr C G.

Cinnabar *Tyria jacobaeae* Common S,C,(N) **FW** 17-23mm. Unmistakable. Very rarely has yellow instead of red markings, or forewing is red with black leading and outer edge, or wings are entirely black. Burnet moths (p.8), also black and red and active by day, are more thickset with much narrower forewing and long, thickened antennae. **FS** Mid May-early August. Easily disturbed by day and flies in sunshine. Also flies at night. **Hab** Ub.

Ctenuchidae

Syntominae

Nine-spotted *Amata phegea* Suspected rare immigrant **FW** 18-22mm. Unlike any moth resident in the British Isles, with slender, inky blue-black wings and white spots, two yellow bands on abdomen and white-tipped antennae. Two very similar species occur in mainland Europe, could possibly occur as immigrants, and examination of genitalia is required to confirm their identity. **FS** June-July. Flies only by day and visits flowers. **Hab** Gr Wd.

Nolidae Black arches

Small, whitish or grey moths, which are easily mistaken for micro-moths. Forewings rather rounded, with basal and central scale tufts (easily lost). Wings held fairly flat when at rest. All are nocturnal and come to light, less often to sugar.

Small Black Arches *Meganola strigula* Na. S **FW** 9-11mm. Similar to Least Black Arches, but with broader, greyer forewing (also note later flight season). Outer area seldom noticeably darker, and usually with small but distinct blackish streaks, roughly arranged into a cross-row. Hindwing also darker, grey-brown. **FS** Late June-early August. **Hab** BWd.

Kent Black Arches *Meganola albula* Nb. S **FW** 10-11mm. Ground-colour of forewing white, with smooth appearance like polished flint due to soft, tawny-brown or grey-brown markings. These are variable in extent and may be reduced to a narrow central cross-band. A plain white form has also been recorded. Scarce Black Arches is smaller, with fine cross-lines, often edged with darker, frequently blackish scales. **FS** Late June-early August. Sometimes disturbed by day. **Hab** C CGr Wd.

Short-cloaked Moth *Nola cucullatella* Common S,C **FW** 8-10mm. Sharply demarcated dark base of grey (or less often darker grey-brown) forewing gives the appearance of a short cloak when moth is at rest. **FS** June-July. **Hab** H Wd Sc G

Least Black Arches *Nola confusalis* Local S,C,(N,Ir) **FW** 9-11mm. Forewing rather narrow, usually whitish with fine, black cross-lines, inner-most elbowed or V-shaped. A narrow, dark outer central cross-band, often shaped like a question mark, and outer area often darker. In f. *columbina*, found in Epping and Hainault Forests, Essex, fore-wing grey-brown and markings obscure. See Small Black Arches, Scarce Black Arches, Jersey Black Arches. **FS** May-June. **Hab** BWd O G.

Scarce Black Arches *Nola aerugula* Immigrant; transitory resident S,E **FW** 8-9mm. Forewing white variably clouded with brown or grey-brown. Slightly wavy, fine black or brown cross-line beyond middle on some examples rather faint. Least Black Arches flies earlier and outer black cross-line is strongly curved. See also Kent Black Arches. **FS** Late June-early August. Has been found at rest on grass stems after dark. **Hab** Sd.

Jersey Black Arches *Nola chlamitulalis* Rare immigrant (one record, Jersey) **FW** 7-10mm. Forewing with bold blackish-brown blotches near outer edge and tawny band along outer edge, otherwise whitish with faint markings. Closest in shape to Least Black Arches, but forewing more pointed and angular. **FS** July. [Not illustrated.]

♂

Scarlet Tiger
Callimorpha dominula

Scarlet Tiger
f. *bimacula* *Callimorpha dominula* f. *rossica*

Cinnabar
Tyria jacobaeae *Tyria jacobaeae* f. *flavescens* *Tyria jacobaeae* f. *coneyi*

tenuchidae

Nine-spotted *Amata phegea*

olidae Black arches

Small Black Arches
Meganola strigula

Kent Black Arches
Meganola albula

Short-cloaked Moth
Nola cucullatella

Least Black Arches
Nola confusalis

Scarce Black Arches
Nola aerugula

All Nolidae shown × 1.25

Noctuidae

Mostly medium-sized and stout-bodied, resting with the trailing edges of forewings brought together or overlapping, covering the hindwings. Largely nocturnal, coming to light, flowers, over-ripe fruit, other natural sources of sugar and artificial baits (unless stated). Forewing usually with conspicuous central kidney-shaped and oval marks.

Noctuinae Darts, yellow underwings and clays

Forewings usually held flat over body and strongly overlapping.

Square-spot Dart *Euxoa obelisca* ssp. *grisea* Nb. S,W,N **FW** 14-18mm. Forewing grey-brown or brown, ground-colour rather uniform. Very similar to some forms of White-line Dart, with pale streak along leading edge of forewing (often darker in female). No black arrowheads before outermost cross-line. Outer central cross-line close to or merging with kidney-mark. See White-line Dart, which has ground-colour usually less uniform. If in doubt, genitalia should be examined. See also Coast Dart. **FS** Early August-early October. **Hab** Cl (very locally Up inland).

White-line Dart *Euxoa tritici* Common T **FW** 13-17mm. Very variable. Forewing blackish grey, dark brown, lighter grey, pale brown or sandy, often with pale streak along leading edge. Short, dark arrowheads (less often blotches) inside outermost cross-line; outer central cross-line usually arcs quite widely around kidney. Tends to be paler, brighter, and sandy or grey on coastal sand-dunes and sandy heathland, and dark and strongly marked on peaty moorland. See Square-spot Dart, Coast Dart, Garden Dart, Heath Rustic (p.106). **FS** Mid July-August. **Hab** A Up Sd Cl Gr Wd.

Garden Dart *Euxoa nigricans* Common T **FW** 15-18mm. Similar in size and shape to White-line Dart, but plainer and browner or black (especially in north), without arrowheads before outermost cross-line or pale streak along leading edge. See also Square-spot Rustic (p.106), which has broader forewing (in male), and Coast Dart. **FS** July-mid September. **Hab** G H Ar Gr.

Coast Dart *Euxoa cursoria* Nb. E,WC,N,Ir **FW** 14-18mm. Forewing straw and white to dark grey and brown, usually with at least a sandy tint. Darker forms are more frequent in north. Very similar to White-line Dart and equally variable; forewing slightly narrower, slightly more tapered and usually more rounded. On forewing underside, kidney large and blurred, with blurred dark band beyond. In White-line Dart, underside usually darker, kidney small and crescent-like and no darker band. See also Garden Dart, Square-spot Dart, Sand Dart. **FS** Late July-early September. **Hab** Sd.

Wood's Dart *Agrotis graslini* Jersey **FW** 15-20mm. Most like the sandy form of Archer's Dart, with central dart-mark long and blunt, and antennae feathered in male, but forewing more pointed and hindwing pure white. Archer's Dart has hindwing marked with grey (may only be slight). See also Spalding's Dart. **FS** In mainland Europe, August-October. **Hab** Sd.

Light Feathered Rustic *Agrotis cinerea* Nb. S,C,(Ir) **FW** 13-17mm. Distinguished by lack of dart-mark in centre of forewing and reduction of oval and kidney-mark, the former being tiny or absent. Forewing variable in colour, with fine, dark, irregular cross-lines. Forewing narrower in smaller female. Light chalky or bluish-grey (southern England and south Wales). Darker, slate-grey, brown or blackish, usually with cross-lines strongly evident (Derbyshire, Warwickshire and Forest of Dean, Gloucestershire). **FS** May-June. **Hab** CGr Cl Sh.

Archer's Dart *Agrotis vestigialis* Local T **FW** 14-18mm. Forewing rather angular, sandy, whitish or grey, boldly marked. Long bullet-shaped dart-mark and a row of short, dark arrowheads towards outer edge. Shoulders usually paler than rest of thorax. Shows strong habitat variation. On inland heaths (e.g. Dorset, Hampshire and Surrey) often particularly dark, with silvery grey markings. Paler, sandy or whitish on coastal sand-dunes. Antennae feathered in male. See Wood's Dart, Spalding's Dart, Sand Dart. **FS** July-September. **Hab** Sd A Gr.

Turnip Moth *Agrotis segetum* Common T **FW** 16-21mm. Forewing pale sandy brown, darker brown (occasionally grey) to black. Kidney, oval and central dart-mark hollow-centred or dark, obscure in darkest examples. Hindwing with slight mother-of-pearl effect, in male usually gleaming white; darker individuals, especially female, have darker veins and marginal shading. Dark stripe on front of collar thin or absent. Antennae feathered to two-thirds in male. See Heart and Club and Heart and Dart. Pearly Underwing (p.104) is usually larger, and forewing lacks prominent dart-mark. Hindwing has strong mother-of-pearl effect, and is darker than in male Turnip Moth. See also Crescent Dart, Great Dart. **FS** In southern and central Britain, May-June; August-October. In north, May-July; (autumn). **Hab** Ub.

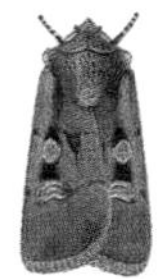

Square-spot Dart
Euxoa obelisca grisea

White-line Dart
Euxoa tritici

White-line Dart
Euxoa tritici

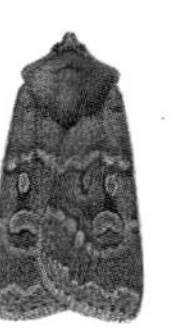
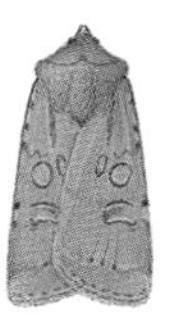

Garden Dart
Euxoa nigricans

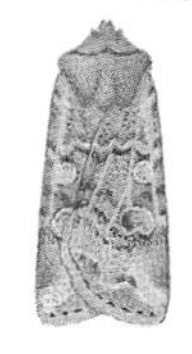

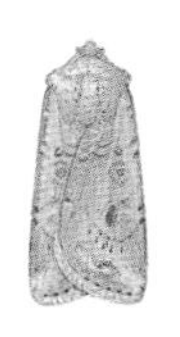

Coast Dart
Euxoa cursoria

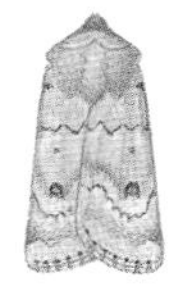
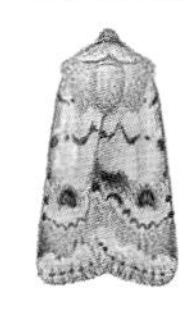

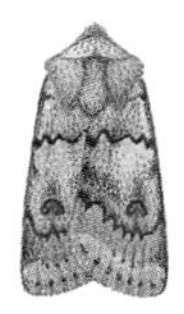

Light Feathered Rustic
Agrotis cinerea

Archer's Dart
Agrotis vestigialis

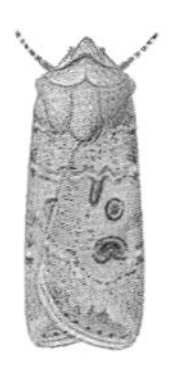

Turnip Moth
Agrotis segetum

Wood's Dart
Agrotis graslini

Heart and Club *Agrotis clavis* Common S,(C,N,Ir) **FW** 14-18mm. Forewing pale straw, greyish brown or pale brown, often flecked or clouded with brown, dark brown or black. Stockier than Turnip Moth and Heart and Dart; central dart usually shorter and thicker. Antennae feathered to two-thirds in male. See also Crescent Dart, Great Dart. **FS** Mid June-early August. **Hab** Sd Gr.

Heart and Dart *Agrotis exclamationis* Common T **FW** 15-19mm. Thick blackish stripe on front of collar. Forewing usually rather plain, pale- or greyish brown to dark brown or blackish. Central mark solid, usually dart-like. Antennae not visibly feathered in male. Sometimes central marks joined, distorted, blurred or formed into streaks. See Heart and Club, Turnip Moth, Great Dart, Black Collar. **FS** Mid May-late August; (in south, September-October). **Hab** Ub.

Crescent Dart *Agrotis trux* ssp. *lunigera* Local SW,WC,Ir **FW** 16-19mm. Forewing rather angular, leading edge straight. Oval small, pale with dark outline. Forewing in male pale to dark grey-brown, dusted or clouded dark brown; in female blackish. Antennae slightly feathered in male. Heart and Club has more rounded forewing tip, darker hindwing and more strongly feathered antennae. See also Turnip Moth, Great Dart. **FS** July-August. **Hab** Cl.

Dark Sword-grass *Agrotis ipsilon* Immigrant T **FW** 15-25mm. Forewing brown or blackish brown. Thick black dart extending outwards from kidney, and two smaller outer darts. Pearly Underwing lacks black darts. See also Red Sword-grass, Sword-grass (p.118). **FS** Recorded in every month, but most frequent July-October. **Hab** Ub.

Spalding's Dart *Agrotis herzogi* Rare immigrant SW (one record) **FW** 15-17mm. Somewhat like a pale male Shuttle-shaped Dart, with flattened, elongated oval. Forewing much more angular, more than in Archer's Dart. Dark arrowheads near outer edge, but streakier than Archer's Dart. Antennae not visibly feathered in male. Wood's Dart has forewing more pointed and antennae feathered in male. **FS** Recorded in November.

Shuttle-shaped Dart *Agrotis puta* ssp. *puta* Common S,C,(Ir); ssp. *insula* Scilly **FW** 12-16mm. Pale oval elongated into a shuttle, pointed at both ends. Forewing in male pale greyish brown, kidney dark brown. In female dark brown or blackish. Ssp. *insula* forewing brighter and more contrasting, dark brown form frequent in male. See Flame. **FS** At least two generations, April-October. **Hab** Ub.

Sand Dart *Agrotis ripae* Nb. S,C,NE,Ir **FW** 14-18mm. Forewing sandy, cream or greyish, markings smaller and daintier than other darts. Leading edge straight. See Coast Dart, with more rounded forewing, held closer to body at rest. See also Archer's Dart. **FS** June-July. **Hab** Sd.

Great Dart *Agrotis crassa* Immigrant S; possible former resident; resident Channel Islands **FW** 16-18mm. Stout, forewing broad, pale browr to blackish. Kidney large. Inner central cross-line projecting sharply outwards near trailing edge. Da arrowheads before outermost cross-line. Antenna feathered in male. Heart and Dart, Turnip Moth and Heart and Club are smaller and slighter, with narrower forewing, kidney smaller and antennae less strongly feathered in male. **FS** July-Septembe

Flame *Axylia putris* Common T **FW** 14-16mm. Forewing pale straw-yellow, sometimes tinged reddish brown. Dark brown streak along leading edge. Kidney mark and thorax dark brown, oval small and round. Rests with wings tightly folded around body. **FS** June-July; (September). **Hab** Ub.

Portland Moth *Actebia praecox* Nb.; immigrant **FW** 17-21mm. Forewing long, slender, silvery gree closely overlapped at rest. **FS** Mid July-September. **Hab** Sd A RSh.

Eversmann's Rustic *Actebia fennica* Rare imm grant S,C,N **FW** 16-18mm. Forewing long, narro dark purplish grey; in male broad orange-yellow streak in trailing half. Oval and kidney conspicuou pale-outlined. Small black arrowheads before oute most cross-line. **FS** July-August.

Black Collar *Ochropleura flammatra* Rare immi- grant S,C,N **FW** 19-21mm. Collar black, tinged with grey in female. Forewing milky-brown; sinuo black streak, sometimes broken, from base to pale oval. Oval and kidney pale. Wings held close to body when at rest. Heart and Dart is smaller with dark kidney and oval, narrower black mark on collar, and lacking basal streak. **FS** May-Septembe

Flame Shoulder *Ochropleura plecta* Common T **FW** 12-15mm. Forewing rich reddish brown or purplish brown; bright, straw-coloured band alonç leading edge. Hindwing glossy yellowish white. Se Radford's Flame Shoulder. **FS** In south, April-June; July-September. In north, late May-July. **Hab** Ub.

Radford's Flame Shoulder *Ochropleura leucogaster* Immigrant S **FW** 13-16mm. Like Flam Shoulder but forewing longer, duller, less reddish; oval and kidney usually smaller, black streak projec sharply beyond kidney (also sometimes on worn Flame Shoulder). Hindwing cleaner white, with no yellowish gloss. Contrast greater between dark thorax, pale collar and white hairs around front er of abdomen. **FS** In mainland Europe, May onward British records late September-November.

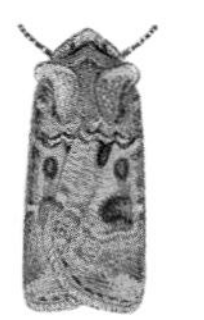

Heart and Club
Agrotis clavis

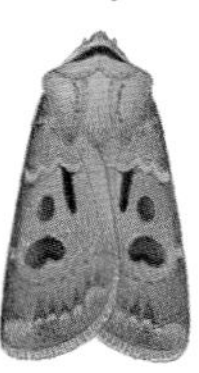

Heart and Dart
Agrotis exclamationis

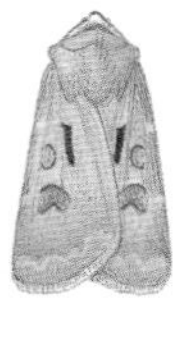

Heart and Dart
Agrotis exclamationis

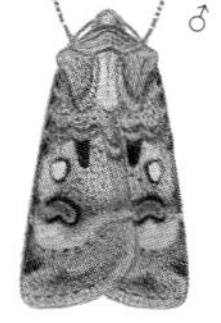
♂
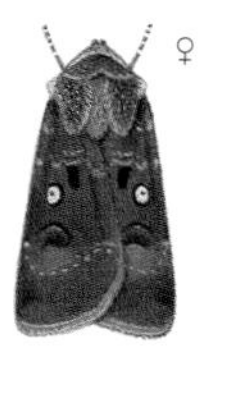
♀

Crescent Dart
Agrotis trux lunigera

Dark Sword-grass
Agrotis ipsilon

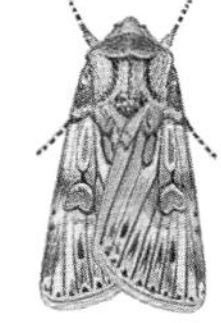

Spalding's Dart
Agrotis herzogi

♂
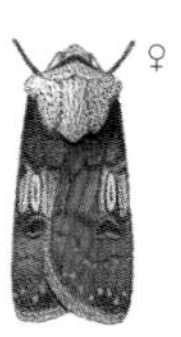
♀

♂
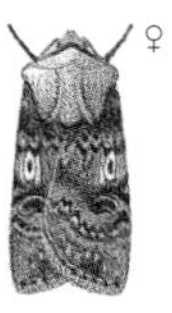
♀

Shuttle-shaped Dart
Agrotis puta puta *Agrotis puta insula*

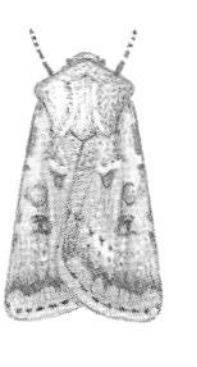
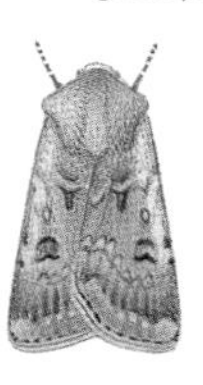

Sand Dart
Agrotis ripae

Great Dart
Agrotis crassa

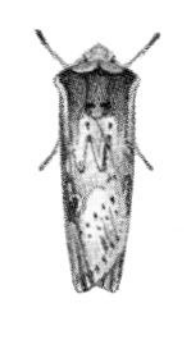

The Flame
Axylia putris

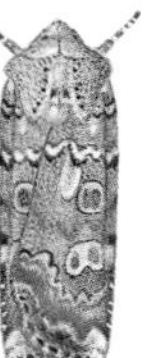

'rtland Moth
ebia praecox

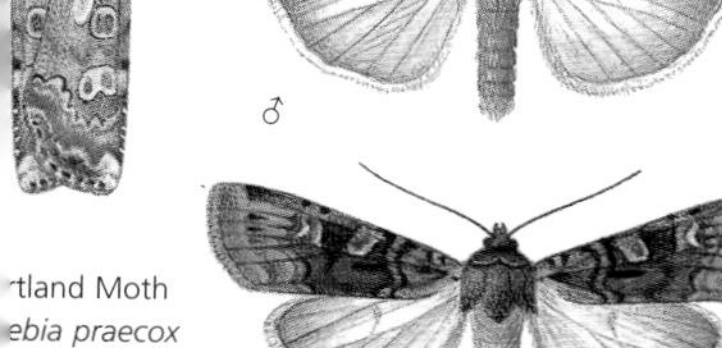
♂
♀

Eversmann's Rustic
Actebia fennica

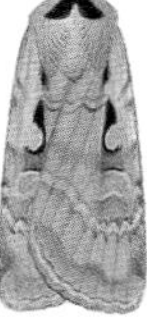

Black Collar
Ochropleura flammatra

Flame Shoulder
Ochropleura plecta

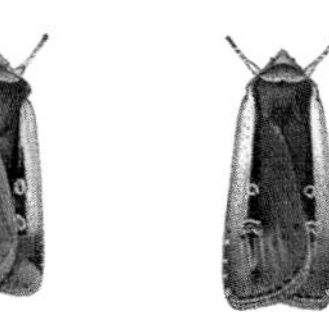

Radford's Flame Shoulder
Ochropleura leucogaster

Northern Rustic *Standfussiana lucernea* Local S,WC,N,Ir **FW** 17-21mm. Forewing dark brownish grey, heavily dusted pale yellowish brown or greyish brown, to blackish with very faint markings. Markings soft, blurred and indistinct. Hindwing dark with chalky-white fringes. Underside of fore- and hindwing often with dark grey bands or almost entirely dark grey. See Dotted Rustic, Stout Dart, Grey, Brindled Ochre (p.116). **FS** Late June-September. Flies in late afternoon sunshine and at night. **Hab** Cl Up.

Dotted Rustic *Rhyacia simulans* Local T **FW** 17-21mm. Forewing dull yellowish brown, with cross-row of dark dots beyond kidney and fine dark cross-lines, inner central one doubled. F. *suffusa* smaller, darker, more obscurely marked (Hebrides, Orkney, Shetland and NW Ireland). Hindwing grey-brown. Stout Dart is mousy brown, lacks black dots beyond kidney, usually has black basal streak, and hindwing whitish. See also Northern Rustic. **FS** In England, late June-July, aestivating then active late August-early October. In Scotland, July-early September. Often enters outbuildings. **Hab** H Wd Gr Up.

Southern Rustic *Rhyacia lucipeta* Suspected rare immigrant (one record, SE) **FW** 24-29mm. Somewhat like Dotted Rustic and some forms of Northern Rustic but much larger, with golden yellow markings on forewing and greenish tint when fresh. **FS** Recorded July. [Not illustrated.]

Large Yellow Underwing *Noctua pronuba* Common T **FW** 21-26mm. Forewing long, rather narrow, with small black pip-mark on leading edge near tip. In male, rather plain dark reddish- or blackish brown, or warm brown, marbled pale brown or grey, with pale streak along leading edge. Female rather uniform light brown or brownish grey, flecked with darker scales, or reddish brown. Hindwing with narrow black outer band, no central mark or clouding near base. Lunar Yellow Underwing is smaller; hindwing has dark central crescent. **FS** June-October or November. **Hab** Ub.

Lunar Yellow Underwing *Noctua orbona* Nb. S,C,N,(Ir) **FW** 17-20mm. Forewing rather narrow, with well defined black mark on leading edge near tip. Hindwing with central crescent. See Lesser Yellow and Large Yellow Underwings. **FS** Late June-September, aestivating in July, reappearing from late August. **Hab** Gr Wd.

Lesser Yellow Underwing *Noctua comes* Common T **FW** 16-21mm. Forewing usually rather broad, outermost cross-line dark, thickened at leading edge, often forming roughly triangular mark, but not a well-defined black mark. Pale or dark greyish- or reddish brown. In northern Scotland, often blackish with hindwing darkened. On Scilly and Lundy Islands often with bold dark cross-lines. Hindwing with narrow black border and dark central crescent. See Lunar Yellow and Least Yellow Underwings. **FS** June-October. **Hab** Ub.

Broad-bordered Yellow Underwing *Noctua fimbriata* Common T **FW** 22-27mm. Stout forewing angular, hindwing orange-yellow with broad black border. Forewing in male reddish brow to olive green; female pale brown, light green or pale reddish brown. Uncommonly mahogany (both sexes). **FS** July-September. Emerges in July, aestivates and becomes active again in August and September. **Hab** Wd H G.

Langmaid's Yellow Underwing *Noctua janthina* Immigrant **FW** 16-18mm. Very similar to Lesser Broad-bordered Yellow Underwing. Upperside forewing usually darker, but otherwise indistinguishable. On hindwing, black border generally broader, extending along leading edge unbroken, in Lesser Broad-bordered stopping befo leading edge or extending diffusely along it, usuall broken. On underside forewing of Langmaid's, outer edge of black area smooth or diffuse (toothe effect may be suggested) and may extend close to outer edge, with area beyond dull brown. In Lesser Broad-bordered, outer edge of black area usually distinctly toothed, ending well before outer edge and area beyond yellowish brown. In borderline cases, examination of genitalia is necessary. **FS** Early July-August.

Lesser Broad-bordered Yellow Underwing *Noctua janthe* Common T **FW** 16-20mm. Collar delicate light green when freshly emerged, fading to light brown. Forewing deep purplish brown or (less commonly) reddish brown, clouded blue-grey. Oval and kidney partly outlined in white, all other markings usually obscure. Hindwing without central dark crescent. Black border broad and base streaked blackish. See Langmaid's Yellow Underwing. **FS** Mid July-early September. **Hab** Ub.

Least Yellow Underwing *Noctua interjecta* ssp. *caliginosa* Common S,C,(Ir) **FW** 14-17mm. Forewing rich reddish brown, sometimes extensivel blackish. On hindwing, inner edge of black border wavy, base streaked blackish. Sometimes a small dark central crescent. Lesser Yellow Underwing is usually larger, hindwing with large central crescent straighter black border and usually yellow at base. **FS** July-August. **Hab** Ub.

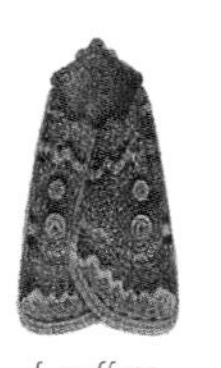

f. *suffusa*

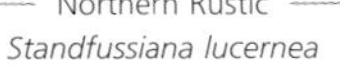
Northern Rustic
Standfussiana lucernea

Dotted Rustic
Rhyacia simulans

Large Yellow Underwing
Noctua pronuba

Lunar Yellow Underwing
Noctua orbona

Lesser Yellow Underwing
Noctua comes

Scilly specimen

Hebrides specimen

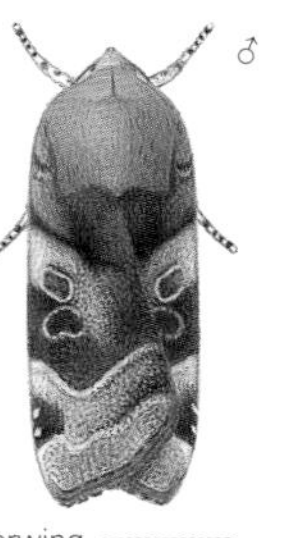

Broad-bordered Yellow Underwing
Noctua fimbriata

underside

Langmaid's Yellow Underwing
Noctua janthina

underside

Lesser Broad-bordered Yellow Underwing
Noctua janthe

Least Yellow Underwing
Noctua interjecta caliginosa

Stout Dart *Spaelotis ravida* Local S,C
FW 18-22mm. Forewing rather narrow, mousy grey-brown, usually with reddish tint along leading edge, sometimes more extensive. Usually a long black streak from base. Hindwing dirty white, slightly darker around outer margin. See Dotted Rustic, Northern Rustic. **FS** June-July, aestivating in outbuildings or under loose bark, then August-September. **Hab** Gr Wt.

Double Dart *Graphiphora augur* Common T
FW 18-21mm. Forewing broad, rather plain, light brown to mousy or dark grey-brown, sometimes slightly reddish tinted. Markings simply outlined in blackish. **FS** June-mid August. **Hab** BWd Sc H Wt G.

Rosy Marsh Moth *Coenophila subrosea* RDB WC **FW** 17-22mm. Forewing rather broad; dark bar between and before oval and kidney. Rosy-pink in male, clouded light grey, female with strong silvery bloom. Antennae feathered in male. Hindwing whitish with diffuse darker border. Purple and Ingrailed Clays have small blackish central spot. Ingrailed Clay is usually smaller, with more angular forewing. Purple Clay has uniformly grey hindwing. Both have un-feathered antennae. **FS** Late July-August. **Hab** AWt.

Cousin German *Protolampra sobrina* Na. N
FW 14-17mm. Forewing pink and silvery grey to dark reddish grey. Markings indistinct. Kidney darker in trailing half. Purple Clay, Barred Chestnut and Ingrailed Clay have small dark central dot. Dark northern Neglected Rustic usually has longer, more angular forewing with kidney more distinctly darker in trailing half. See also Dotted Clay. **FS** Late July-August. **Hab** Up.

Autumnal Rustic *Eugnorisma glareosa* Common T **FW** 15-16mm. Black anvil-shaped mark between pale oval and kidney, and smaller black marks near base. Forewing narrow, angular, cold whitish grey. Sometimes pale orange-brown (Kent), pink-tinged (most often in west), or darker (in Scotland). Grey-black f. *edda* mainly Shetland, also Orkney and occasionally south to Aberdeen. Dark Shetland Ingrailed Clay is usually brownish black rather than greyish black. **FS** August-October. **Hab** Ub.

Plain Clay *Eugnorisma depuncta* Nb. N,WC, (EC,SW) **FW** 16-20mm. Forewing broad, pale yellowish brown. Two bold blackish, broken cross-lines in basal half. **FS** July-early September. **Hab** BWd.

True Lover's Knot *Lycophotia porphyrea* Common T **FW** 12-15mm. Forewing usually reddish brown, sometimes deep pinkish- or purplish brown, less often greyish brown or grey-black. Variegated, with fine black and white markings. Hindwing greyish. See Heath Rustic, with pale streak along leading edge, and Beautiful Yellow Underwing. **FS** June-August. Sometimes active by day. **Hab** A M.

Pearly Underwing *Peridroma saucia* Immigra possible transitory resident T **FW** 19-23mm. Forewing brown, variably marbled, clouded or flecked lighter or darker, sometimes with reddish brown. Hindwing whitish, with strong mother-of-pearl sheen; veins and outer margin dark. Grey stripe on thorax. See Turnip Moth, Dark Sword-grass. **FS** January-December. Most frequen September-October.

Ingrailed Clay *Diarsia mendica mendica* Common T; ssp. *thulei* Shetland; ssp. *orkneyensis* Orkney **FW** 13-17mm. Ssp. *mendica* in south, forewing pale straw, yellowish orange, orange-brown or reddish brown; central black dot and small black arrowhead or crescent-marks along outer edge. In north, usually smaller, darker, forewing often narrower, sometimes clouded pink or grey, often lacking central dot. Ssp. *orkney-ensis* and *thulei* often darker, forewing narrower, grey-brown, pinkish brown, reddish brown, or blackish. See Small Square-spot, Purple Clay, Barre Chestnut, Rosy Marsh Moth (cf. ssp. *mendica*). Autumnal Rustic f. *edda* (cf. ssp. *thulei*). **FS** In sou June-July. In north, July-August. **Hab** In south, usually Wd. In north, also M Up.

Barred Chestnut *Diarsia dahlii* Local N,C,(SE,Ir **FW** 15-18mm. Forewing rather broad, leading ed strongly curved. Dark central dot. Male orange- or reddish brown, clouded and banded purplish brown, oval and kidney inconspicuous, sometimes darker between. See Ingrailed Clay, Small Square-spot. Female deep pinkish-red, dark reddish- or purplish-brown. Kidney pale or pale outlined. See Purple Clay, which is blackish between oval and kidney. See also Square-spotted Clay. **FS** August-September. **Hab** BWd A M.

Purple Clay *Diarsia brunnea* Common T
FW 16-20mm. Forewing quite broad, rather plain, pinkish brown to dark, purplish brown. Kidney pale outlined, or pale and conspicuous. Blackish between oval and kidney. Dark central dot. Northern Ingrailed Clays are usually orange-tinted and marbled. See also female Barred Chestnut, Rc Marsh Moth, Square-spotted Clay. **FS** June-Augus **Hab** Wd A M.

Small Square-spot *Diarsia rubi* Common T
FW 12-16mm. Forewing pinkish brown, variably banded and clouded reddish brown or dark browr Central black dot. Outside of outer central cross-line dark-edged with very fine, short dark streaks extending outwards, or a band. Second-generatio moths are often smaller and darker. Paler, brighter in north. See Fen Square-spot. Northern Ingrailed Clays are usually more marbled. See also male Barred Chestnut. **FS** In England, Wales and Ireland May-early June; August-September. In Scotland, June-July. **Hab** Ub.

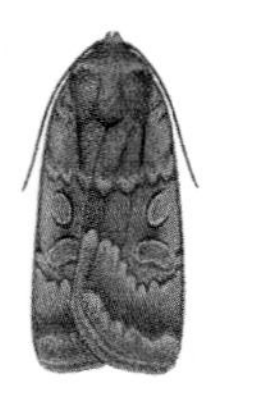

Stout Dart
Spaelotis ravida

Double Dart
Graphiphora augur

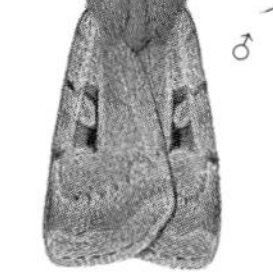

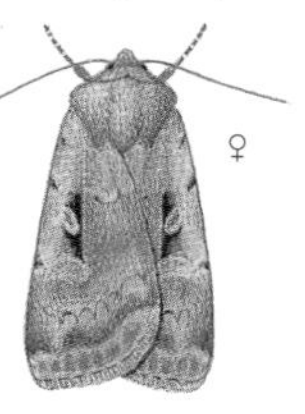

Rosy Marsh Moth
Coenophila subrosea

Cousin German
Protolampra sobrina

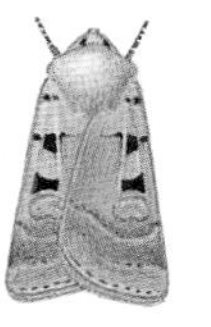

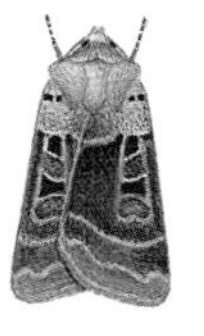
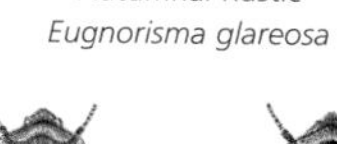

Autumnal Rustic
Eugnorisma glareosa

Plain Clay
Eugnorisma depuncta

True Lover's Knot
Lycophotia porphyrea

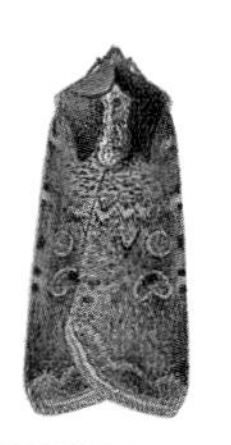

Pearly Underwing
Peridroma saucia

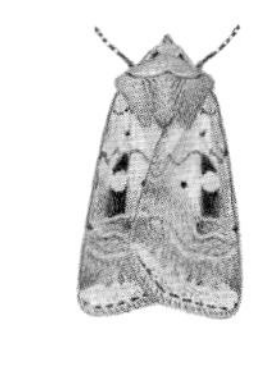

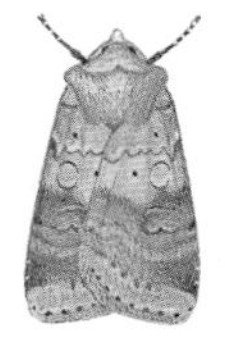

Ingrailed Clay
Diarsia mendica mendica

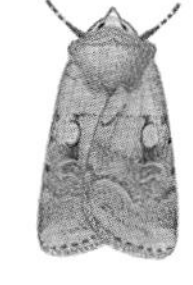

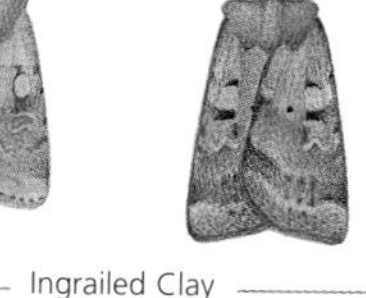

Ingrailed Clay
Diarsia mendica mendica

D. m. thulei

Barred Chestnut
Diarsia dahlii

Purple Clay
Diarsia brunnea

2nd generation

Scottish specimen

Small Square-spot
Diarsia rubi

Fen Square-spot *Diarsia florida* Local EC,WC **FW** 15-17mm. Similar to southern Small Square-spot; larger, paler and pinkish buff (also note flight season). **FS** Late June-July. **Hab** Wt.

Northern Dart *Xestia alpicola* ssp. *alpina* Na. N,(Ir) **FW** 15-17mm. Thickset. Forewing broad. Brown, grey or blackish, often with thick black streaks, especially in basal half. Often variegated with reddish and/or grey. **FS** Late June-August. **Hab** Up.

Setaceous Hebrew Character *Xestia c-nigrum* Common T **FW** 14-19mm. Forewing grey-brown or grey. Pale straw-yellow triangular blotch contrasts with adjacent black, roughly saddle-shaped mark. Collar pale. See Triple-spotted Clay. **FS** In south, May-July; August-October. In northern England and Scotland, July-August. **Hab** Ub.

Triple-spotted Clay *Xestia ditrapezium* Local S,WC,N,(Ir) **FW** 17-19mm. Similar to Double Square-spot. Forewing usually narrower, darker; reddish brown or purplish brown to purplish black. Hindwing tends to be paler and less uniform. See also Square-spotted Clay. **FS** Late June-early August. **Hab** BWd, G.

Double Square-spot *Xestia triangulum* Common T **FW** 17-19mm. Forewing quite broad, grey-brown. Bold black blocks either side of pale oval and kidney, bold black mark on leading edge near tip. See Triple-spotted Clay, Square-spotted Clay. **FS** June-early August. **Hab** Ub.

Ashworth's Rustic *Xestia ashworthii* Na. WC **FW** 16-20mm. Forewing light to dark ashen grey. Diffuse dark blotches either side of pale oval and kidney and diffuse black dash on leading edge near tip. Fine dark wavy cross-lines. **FS** Mid June-August. **Hab** Up.

Dotted Clay *Xestia baja* Common T **FW** 17-21mm. Forewing reddish brown or warm greyish brown, sometimes pink-tinged. Two sharp black marks at leading edge near tip, otherwise rather plain with weak markings. Usually a small black dot near base, centrally placed. Neglected Rustic and Cousin German lack sharp black marks near leading edge. **FS** Late July-late August. **Hab** Ub.

Square-spotted Clay *Xestia rhomboidea* Nb. S,(C,N) **FW** 17-20mm. Forewing rather broad, dark grey-brown. A black block either side of oval and kidney, and usually centrally. Outer central cross-line pale, outermost cross-band thick, dark and irregular, not forming black mark at leading edge. See Triple-spotted Clay, Double Square-spot, Purple Clay, female Barred Chestnut. **FS** Late July-August. **Hab** BWd.

Neglected Rustic *Xestia castanea* Local T **FW** 16-18mm. Kidney dark-outlined, blackish in trailing half. Forewing rather plain; very fine black wavy cross-lines or dots. In south, light greyish brown or reddish brown, sometimes pinkish. Further north, usually pink or reddish, darkest in northern Scotland. Pale Square-spot Rustics have kidney pale-outlined. Dark Square-spot Rustics brown. See als Cousin German, Dotted Clay. **FS** August-September. **Hab** A Wd M.

Six-striped Rustic *Xestia sexstrigata* Common T **FW** 15-17mm. Forewing warm brown. Veins a fine cross-lines dark brown. Oval and kidney pale, dark-outlined. **FS** July-August. **Hab** Ub.

Square-spot Rustic *Xestia xanthographa* Common T **FW** 14-17mm. Forewing light grey-brown (sometimes reddish) to dark or blackish brown. Kidney pale or pale-outlined, rather squar obscured in some dark examples. Oval evident, other markings usually weak. See Neglected Rusti Garden Dart (p.98), Brown Rustic (p.128). **FS** Late July-early October. **Hab** Ub.

Heath Rustic *Xestia agathina agathina* Local T; ssp. *hebridicola* Hebrides **FW** 14-16mm. Ssp. *agathina*: Forewing rather variegated, light greyish- or reddish brown, dark grey or blackish. Oval small, whitish, usually elongated. Inner centr cross-line deeply zigzagged. Male antennae slight feathered. Ssp. *hebridicola*: Whitish grey. White-li Dart (p.98) is not reddish, oval less elongated, ma antennae not feathered. See also True Lover's Knc **FS** Late August-September. **Hab** A M.

Gothic *Naenia typica* Local T **FW** 17-22mm. Forewing very broad, rounded, brownish grey; ve and cross-lines whitish. Bordered and Feathered Gothics have narrower forewing. **FS** June-July. **Hab** Wd Wt H G.

Great Brocade *Eurois occulta* Nb. N; immigran T **FW** 24-27mm. Residents have forewing blackis variably marbled grey, black streak or spot at base Immigrants are grey. Grey Arches is smaller, rests with wings less overlapping, forewing leading ed more arched, basal streak absent. **FS** Residents Ju early August. Immigrants late July-September. **Hab** AWt Wd M.

Green Arches *Anaplectoides prasina* Common **FW** 20-25mm. Forewing green, fading to yellowis grey. Variably marbled white, brown and black. Thorax green, with rusty red tuft. **FS** June-July. **Hab** BWd.

Red Chestnut *Cerastis rubricosa* Common T **FW** 14-17mm. Forewing angular, leading edge straight. Rich reddish brown to dark purplish brov variably dusted light grey. Markings pale, indistinc Usually reddish in southern England. Predominate dark in north and in upland habitats. See White-marked. **FS** Late February-April. In northern Britai April-May. **Hab** Ub.

White-marked *Cerastis leucographa* Local S,C **FW** 14-16mm. Similar to (southern) Red Chestnut but slightly smaller. Oval and kidney distinct, crea white, kidney dark in trailing third. Outer central cross-line very fine, blackish, finely scalloped or formed of white-tipped dashes. Leading edge ver slightly curved. **FS** Late March-April. **Hab** BWd.

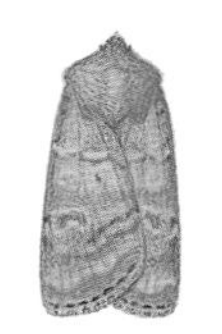

Fen Square-spot
Diarsia florida

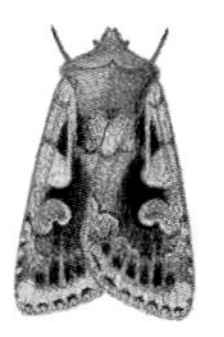

Northern Dart
Xestia alpicola alpina
Cumbrian specimen

Setaceous Hebrew Character
Xestia c-nigrum

Triple-spotted Clay
Xestia ditrapezium

Double Square-spot
Xestia triangulum

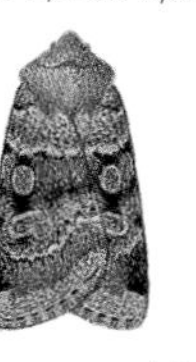
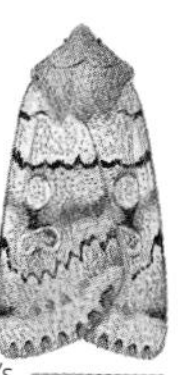

Ashworth's Rustic
Xestia ashworthii

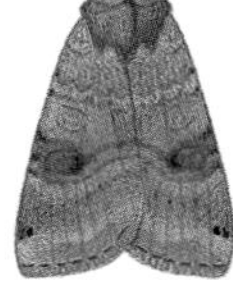

Dotted Clay
Xestia baja

Square-spotted Clay
Xestia rhomboidea

Neglected Rustic
Xestia castanea

Six-striped Rustic
Xestia sexstrigata

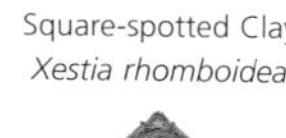

Square-spot Rustic
Xestia xanthographa

Heath Rustic
Xestia agathina agathina

Gothic
Naenia typica

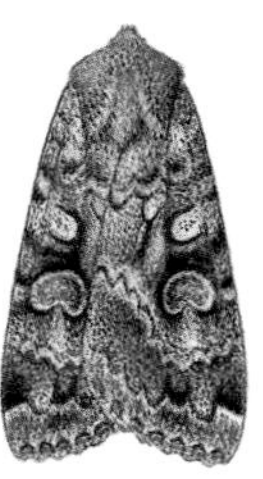

Great Brocade
Eurois occulta

Green Arches
Anaplectoides prasina

Red Chestnut
Cerastis rubricosa

White-marked
Cerastis leucographa

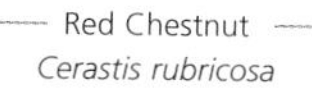

Hadeninae Brocades, quakers and leaf-eating wainscots

Beautiful Yellow Underwing *Anarta myrtilli* Common T **FW** 10-12mm. Forewing reddish brown, or greyish, intricately marbled whitish. Small central white blotch. See True Lover's Knot. **FS** In the south, late April-August (two overlapping generations). In the north, June-July. Active by day, flying low over heather in sunshine. **Hab** A M.

Small Dark Yellow Underwing *Anarta cordigera* Na. NE **FW** 10-12mm. Forewing dark grey. Kidney quite large, white, conspicuous. **FS** Late April-May or mid June. Active only by day, in sunshine. **Hab** Up.

Broad-bordered White Underwing *Anarta melanopa* RDB N **FW** 11-13mm. Forewing grey, oval and kidney black. **FS** Mid May-June. Active only by day, flying low over the ground. **Hab** Up.

Nutmeg *Discestra trifolii* Common S,C,(N,Ir) **FW** 14-18mm. Forewing narrow at base, leading edge straight. Pale to dark grey-brown or sandy, usually dusted with grey. Kidney quite large, trailing half dark. Outermost cross-line forms distinct W. See White Colon, which is usually larger and stockier. Dusky Brocade (f. *obscura*) (p.132) is larger, forewing broader. Confused (p.132) is browner, kidney edged whitish. All have forewing base broader. **FS** In south, April-June; August-September. From Midlands north, June-July. **Hab** G R Gr Wd.

Shears *Hada plebeja* Common T **FW** 14-17mm. Forewing quite angular, leading edge straight; whitish grey, sandy, pale to dark brownish grey, or blackish. Whitish, branched central mark, sometimes reduced, highlighted by dark marks nearby. See Brindled Green (p.120). **FS** Late May-early July; (in south, August). **Hab** Gr A Sd Wd.

Pale Shining Brown *Polia bombycina* pRDB S **FW** 19-23mm. Forewing pale brown with reddish shine when fresh (probable immigrants are greyer). Kidney large, outer edge outlined white. Outermost cross-line slightly wavy, with variable dark brown edging, forming dash at trailing corner. See Scarce Brindle, Large Nutmeg (p.132). **FS** Early June-mid July. **Hab** Gr Ar Wd.

Silvery Arches *Polia trimaculosa* Nb. S,C,N **FW** 21-25mm. Forewing grey, lustrous, marbled. Inner edging of outermost cross-line black, well-defined. No dash at trailing corner. Reddish tinted (southern England), darker silvery grey or bluish (Scotland). Thorax with reddish tufts. See Pale Shining Brown, Grey Arches. **FS** June-July. **Hab** A M Wd.

Grey Arches *Polia nebulosa* Common T **FW** 21-26mm. Forewing whitish to dark grey (rarely black), not lustrous, leading edge strongly curved. Blackish dash or arrow in trailing corner. Dark inner edging on outermost cross-line irregular, variable. See Silvery Arches. **FS** June-July. **Hab** Wd.

Feathered Ear *Pachetra sagittigera* ssp. *britan-nica* Former resident; presumed extinct S **FW** 17-20mm. Forewing light brown with dark central hoof-shaped mark. Oval and kidney pale. Roughly square whitish blotch on trailing edge. S Bordered Gothic. **FS** Mid May-late June. **Hab** CG

White Colon *Sideridis albicolon* Nb. S,C,NE,Ir **FW** 17-20mm. Forewing grey-brown, with grainy texture. Trailing outer edge of kidney with white spots. Outermost cross-line whitish, broken, not forming central W. See Cabbage Moth, Crescent Striped (p.130), Dusky Brocade (p.132), Nutmeg **FS** Late May-June; (in south, July-August). **Hab** Sd Sm Sh A.

Bordered Gothic *Heliophobus reticulata* ssp. *marginosa* pRDB S,EC; ssp. *hibernica* Ir **FW** 17-19mm. Forewing veins and cross-lines whitish. Ssp. *marginosa* light brown, ssp. *hibern* darker (south coast of Ireland). Feathered Gothic (FS August-September) has cross-lines brown, leading edge straight and antennae feathered in male. See Gothic, Beautiful Gothic (smaller), Feathered Ear. **FS** May-July. **Hab** CGr.

Cabbage Moth *Mamestra brassicae* Commo T **FW** 14-22mm. Forewing dark brownish grey blackish grey, usually with paler brown blotches Kidney conspicuously outlined chalky white. Outermost cross-line forming distinct pale W in centre. See White Colon, Dark Brocade (p.120). **FS** May-October (usually three generations). In north, June-July. **Hab** Ub.

Dot Moth *Melanchra persicariae* Common S,C,(N),Ir **FW** 16-21mm. Forewing rather broa glossy black. Prominent white kidney. **FS** Late Ju August. **Hab** Ub.

Broom Moth *Melanchra pisi* Common T **FW** 16-20mm. Forewing pale to dark reddish- purplish brown, sometimes marbled with grey brownish yellow, tinged pink or dusted purplish grey. Outermost cross-line conspicuous, creamy white, irregular, often broken, often forming bl in trailing corner. **FS** Late May-July. **Hab** Ub.

Beautiful Brocade *Lacanobia contigua* Loc T **FW** 16-19mm. Forewing greyish white, clou grey, pink- or orange-brown, and blackish. Pale blotches form diagonal band (sometimes indist from leading edge or pale oval to trailing corne broken by cross-line, forming V when at rest. See Pale-shouldered Brocade, Dog's Tooth, Ligh Brocade. **FS** June-July. **Hab** A M Wd.

Light Brocade *Lacanobia w-latinum* Local S **FW** 18-21mm. Forewing grey, sometimes pink-tinged. Markings bold, clear-cut. Broad, unifor light grey outer cross-band. See Beautiful Broc Dusky Brocade (p.132), Saxon (p.130). **FS** May-mid July. **Hab** Gr A Sc Wd.

hindwings

Beautiful Yellow Underwing
Anarta myrtilli

Small Dark Yellow Underwing
Anarta cordigera

Broad-bordered White Underwing
Anarta melanopa

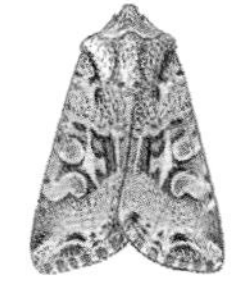
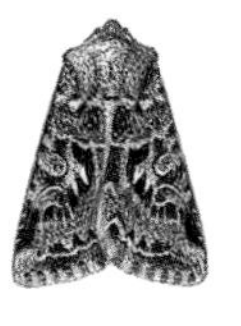
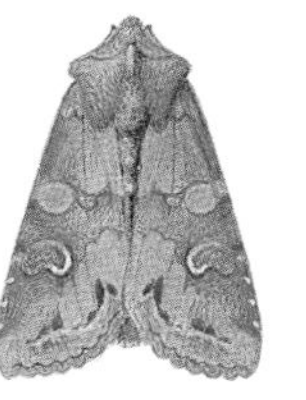

Nutmeg
Discestra trifolii

Shears
Hada plebeja

Pale Shining Brown
Polia bombycina

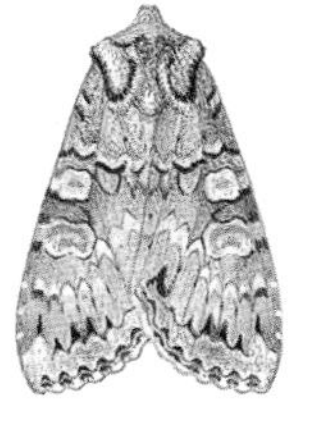
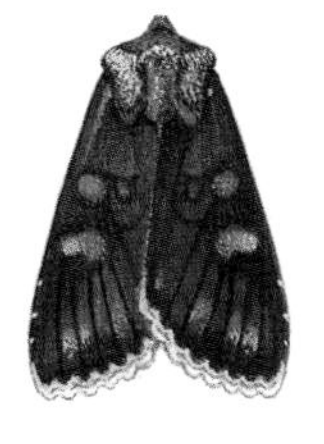

Silvery Arches
Polia trimaculosa

Grey Arches
Polia nebulosa

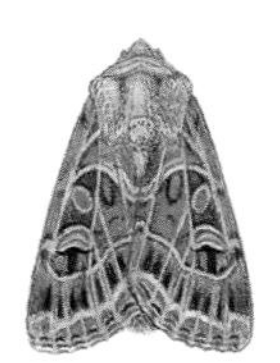
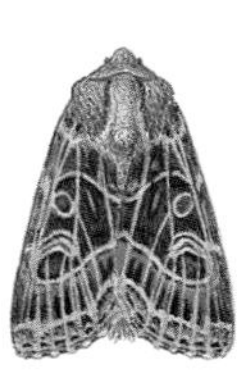
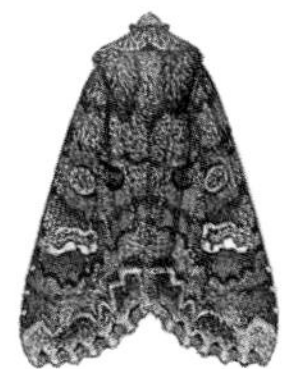

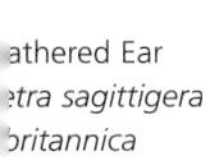

athered Ear
etra sagittigera britannica

White Colon
Sideridis albicolon

Bordered Gothic
Heliophobus reticulata marginosa
Heliophobus reticulata hibernica

Cabbage Moth
Mamestra brassicae

Dot Moth
Melanchra persicariae

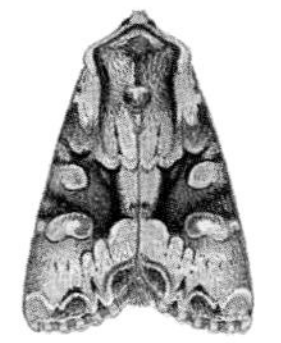

Broom Moth
Melanchra pisi

Beautiful Brocade
Lacanobia contigua

Light Brocade
Lacanobia w-latinum

Pale-shouldered Brocade *Lacanobia thalassina* Common T **FW** 16-20mm. Forewing reddish brown with pale dusting or light greyish brown. Pale basal patch and black streak. Black line with short arm between central cross-lines forms outline of a tooth-mark. See Dog's Tooth, Beautiful Brocade, Dusky Brocade (p.132). Dark Brocade (p.120) lacks pale basal patch. **FS** May-July; (in south, August). **Hab** Wd Sc M.

Dog's Tooth *Lacanobia suasa* Local S,C,(N,Ir) **FW** 15-20mm. Forewing grey-brown, clouded with sandy brown, or entirely dark grey-brown. Central solid or outlined tooth-mark. See Pale-shouldered Brocade, Dusky Brocade (p.132), Bright-line Brown-eye, Dingy Shears (p.130). **FS** In southern England, May-early July; late July-early September. Further north, June-July. **Hab** Gr Wt Sm M.

Bright-line Brown-eye *Lacanobia oleracea* Common T **FW** 14-19mm. Forewing rather uniform warm brown, slightly dusted white. Orange blotch in kidney, fine pure white outer cross-line forming a W. See Dog's Tooth. **FS** May-late July; (in south, August-September). **Hab** Ub.

Splendid Brocade *Lacanobia splendens* Recent immigrant S Forewing pinkish brown. Kidney and oval whitish or whitish outlined. Kidney dark grey in trailing third. Outermost cross-line whitish, forming a W. **FS** June-July.

Glaucous Shears *Papestra biren* Local SW,WC,N,Ir **FW** 15-18mm. Forewing rather narrow, tapered, ash-grey, often marked with yellowish white, especially outermost cross-line. Kidney large, rounded, whitish. **FS** May-July. **Hab** M.

Broad-barred White *Hecatera bicolorata* Common T **FW** 13-15mm. Forewing white or greyish white. Broad blackish central cross-band. **FS** Late May-July; (in south, August). **Hab** Gr.

Small Ranunculus *Hecatera dysodea* pRDB SE,SWales,(C) **FW** 14-15mm. Forewing greenish grey. A scattering and outer row of orange spots. Broad darker central cross-band. Feathered and Large Ranunculus (p.120) are larger (and later FS). **FS** June-early August. **Hab** Gr R G.

Campion *Hadena rivularis* Common T **FW** 14-16mm. Very like Lychnis. Forewing broader, marbled purplish pink when fresh. Kidney and oval usually joined, or kidney extended towards oval (on Lychnis, nearly always separate, kidney rarely extended). Pale outermost cross-line zigzagged, ending at trailing corner (on Lychnis, curved in trailing half, reaching trailing edge). **FS** In southern England, late May-June; August-September. Further north, May-June only. **Hab** Gr.

Tawny Shears *Hadena perplexa perplexa* Common S,C,(N) **Pod Lover** ssp. *capsophila* Local (Protected on Man) W,Ir **FW** 13-15mm. **Tawny Shears:** Forewing rather broad, leading edge straight. Whitish, pale straw, tawny or dull brown. Markings sharply defined. Central tooth- or bullet-mark, arrowheads before outermost cross-line. Hindwing white, border darker. See Sand Dart (p.100) (larger, hindwing border rarely darker), Viper's Bugloss. **Pod Lover:** Dull brownish grey Lychnis is larger, forewing broader. See also Ba Marbled Coronet. **FS** May-July; (in south, Augu **Hab** Gr.

Viper's Bugloss *Hadena irregularis* Former dent; presumed extinct E **FW** 14-15mm. Forew sandy brown, marbled warm brown. Fine wavy blackish cross-lines. No central bullet- or tooth-mark. See Tawny Shears, Dusky Sallow (p.134) **FS** Late May-July. **Hab** Gr.

Barrett's Marbled Coronet *Hadena lutea* ssp. *barrettii* Nb. SW,Ir **FW** 15-19mm. Forewir markings rather indistinct, warm brown, yellov or greyish brown. Obscure pale central blotch. Lychnis and Pod Lover (smaller) have finer, crisp markings. See also Grey. **FS** Early June-August. **Hab** Cl Sh.

Varied Coronet *Hadena compta* Common SE,S,EC **FW** 13-15mm. Similar to Marbled Co but white central forewing cross-band complet not diagonal, and tip grey. **FS** June-July; (Septer **Hab** G CGr.

Marbled Coronet *Hadena confusa* Local T **FW** 14-16mm. Forewing blackish in S, C and E England. Central white blotches, sometimes forming broken diagonal central cross-band. W blotch at tip. Further north and west, often tin dark olive green, blotches dull yellow, in Orkne and Shetland often reduced or absent. See Var Coronet. **FS** Late May-early July; (in south-east England, August). **Hab** CGr G.

White Spot *Hadena albimacula* RDB S **FW** 15-17mm. Forewing dark brown. White straight-edged central blotch, fine wavy narrov white-edged black cross-lines, white spots at b See Marbled Coronet, Cameo (p.120). **FS** May (August-September). **Hab** CGr Sh Cl.

Lychnis *Hadena bicruris* Common T **FW** 14-17mm. Forewing quite broad, dark gre brown. Fine, quite crisp, straw-white markings dark, solid, square or tooth-like central mark. S Campion, Barrett's Marbled Coronet, Pod Love **FS** In south, late May-July; August-September. Midlands north, June-July. **Hab** Ub.

Grey *Hadena caesia* ssp. *mananii* RDB (Protect on Man) NW,Ir **FW** 15-17mm. Forewing grey-b (Man) or blue-grey (S Ireland). Clouded, markin indistinct. In Barrett's Marbled Coronet forewing broader, with pale central blotch. See also North Rustic (p.102). **FS** Late May-August. **Hab** Cl.

Silurian *Eriopygodes imbecilla* RDB Wales **FW** 10-13mm. Forewing rather narrow, especi in female. Kidney pale, narrow, oval absent. Fi dark cross-lines. Male ranges from reddish- to brown or fawn. Female smaller, darker reddish brown. **FS** June-July. Sometimes active by day. **Ha**

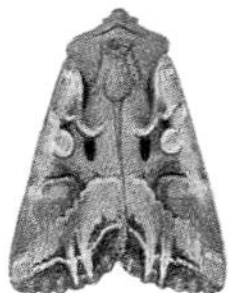

Pale-shouldered Brocade
Lacanobia thalassina
f. *humeralis*

Dog's Tooth
Lacanobia suasa
f. *dissimilis*

Bright-line Brown-eye
Lacanobia oleracea

ndid Brocade
obia splendens

Glaucous Shears
Papestra biren

Broad-barred White
Hecatera bicolorata

Small Ranunculus
Hecatera dysodea

Campion
Hadena rivularis

Viper's Bugloss
Hadena irregularis

Tawny Shears
Hadena perplexa perplexa

Pod Lover
Hadena perplexa capsophila

Barrett's Marbled Coronet
Hadena luteago barrettii

Varied Coronet
Hadena compta

Marbled Coronet
Hadena confusa

White Spot
Hadena albimacula

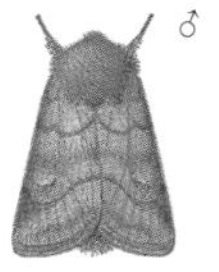

Lychnis
lena bicruris

Grey
Hadena caesia mananii

♂ ♂ ♀

Silurian
Eriopygodes imbecilla

Antler Moth *Cerapteryx graminis* Common T **FW** 12-17mm. Forewing light to dark olive brown or reddish-tinged, with dull texture. Elongated, branched, creamy white central antler-like mark, sometimes reduced. Black streaks, sometimes reduced or absent. Antennae slightly feathered in male. **FS** Mid July-mid September. Often active by day, especially in north. **Hab** Gr.

Hedge Rustic *Tholera cespitis* Common T **FW** 15-19mm. Rather thickset. Forewing quite broad, leading edge straight. Rather uniformly blackish brown. Oval, kidney and cross-lines pale. Whole wing is finely dusted with golden yellow. Kidney-mark sometimes extends to a point in direction of oval. Male has slightly feathered antennae. See Straw Underwing (p.128). **FS** August-September. **Hab** Gr.

Feathered Gothic *Tholera decimalis* Common S,C,(N),Ir **FW** 16-22mm. Forewing quite broad, leading edge straight. Dull grey-brown with straw-white streaks along veins. Cross-lines dark. Antennae feathered in male. See Bordered Gothic, Gothic. **FS** Late August-September. **Hab** Gr.

Pine Beauty *Panolis flammea* Common S,C,N,(Ir) **FW** 15-16mm. Forewing rather narrow and tapering. Orange-brown, reddish brown or brick red, sometimes variegated greenish grey. Large, whitish, rather elongated kidney-mark. Rests with wings folded tightly against body. **FS** March-May. **Hab** CWd G.

Silver Cloud *Egira conspicillaris* Na. W,SW **FW** 16-18mm. Most frequent form unmistakable, with forewing extensively blackish. Paler forms not unlike Pale Pinion (p.118) but shoulders not strongly projecting and hindwing white with dark veins. Rests with forewing creased, so tip appears to project more strongly. **FS** Mid April-late May. **Hab** Gr H Sc Wd O.

Small Quaker *Orthosia cruda* Common S,C,(N,Ir) **FW** 12-15mm. Forewing rather uniform pale to dark pastel brown, greyish or reddish-tinged, or delicately frosted whitish. Kidney narrow. Pale outer cross-line and sometimes further blackish cross-lines. Hindwing grey. See Blossom Underwing, Common Quaker. **FS** Late February-early May. **Hab** BWd H G.

Blossom Underwing *Orthosia miniosa* Local; suspected immigrant S,WC,(Ir) **FW** 15-17mm. Forewing warm sandy or pinkish brown, markings softly defined, fringe pinkish. Kidney rather narrow. Central cross-lines evident, darker brown, finely scalloped or wavy. Central band usually darker. Hindwing pinkish white. See Small Quaker. See also Common Quaker, Orange Upperwing (p.122). **FS** Early March-late April. **Hab** BWd Sc.

Northern Drab *Orthosia opima* Local T **FW** 15-17mm. Stocky, thorax very furry. Forewing tapered, angular. Leading edge straight. Cold light grey, yellowish grey (saltmarshes in south-east England), warm dark grey or brown, or greyish black. Central band usually evident, darker. See Lead-coloured and Clouded Drabs. **FS** April-May. **Hab** Gr A Wt CGr Sd Sm.

Lead-coloured Drab *Orthosia populeti* Local S,C,N,(Ir) **FW** 15-17mm. Forewing with tip quite rounded, leading edge slightly curved. Fairly uniform leaden grey, or blackish grey. Oval and kidney quite large, rounded. Antennae visibly fea ered in male. Outermost cross-line often with sm brown or black marks, especially centrally. Easily overlooked. Clouded Drab is usually larger, with forewing usually less rounded at tip. Pale forms are less uniform, and kidney darker in trailing ha Antennae not feathered to the naked eye in mal See also Common Quaker and Northern Drab. **FS** March-April. **Hab** BWd H G.

Powdered Quaker *Orthosia gracilis* Commor **FW** 15-19mm. Forewing rather sharp-tipped, rat plain, with powdered or grainy texture. Sandy wh sandy grey, bright orange- or reddish brown, dar grey-brown tinged pink or mauve, to blackish. O a curved outer central cross-row of blackish dots. Pale in much of lowlands. In New Forest and Somerset mainly reddish brown. Often darker and pinkish in Scotland, Ireland and parts of Wales. S Clouded Drab. **FS** April-May. **Hab** Wt BWd H Sc.

Common Quaker *Orthosia cerasi* Common T **FW** 13-17mm. Forewing with tip quite rounded, leading edge slightly curved. Sandy, orange-brow greyish- to blackish brown. Oval and kidney larg rounded, pale-outlined. See Small Quaker, Blossc Underwing, Vine's Rustic (p.140). **FS** March-May (sometimes in mild spells in late autumn and winter). **Hab** Ub.

Clouded Drab *Orthosia incerta* Common T **FW** 16-20mm. Forewing rather variable in shape usually rather sharp-tipped. Leading edge slightly curved. Blackish, or dark reddish brown with obscure markings, pale brown, reddish or light grey, blotched, clouded, dusted, or flecked darke Trailing half of kidney darker (in paler forms). Outermost cross-line usually with dark blotches. Antennae not visibly feathered in male. See Powdered Quaker (outermost cross-line without dark blotches). See also Northern Drab, Lead-coloured Drab, Twin-spotted Quaker. **FS** Early March-May, sometimes earlier. **Hab** Ub.

Twin-spotted Quaker *Orthosia munda* Common S,C,(N),Ir **FW** 17-20mm. Forewing rat broad, leading edge curved. Sandy, reddish- or p greyish brown. Two roughly central black (or bro spots on pale outermost cross-line, sometimes fa occasionally absent. Antennae visibly feathered in male. See Clouded Drab (blotches rather than sp on outermost cross-line). **FS** March-April, someti earlier. **Hab** BWd.

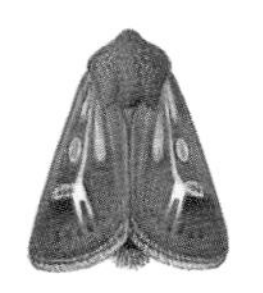

Antler Moth
Cerapteryx graminis

Hedge Rustic
Tholera cespitis

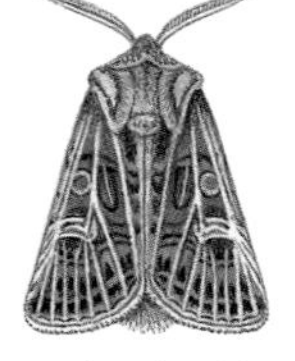

Feathered Gothic
Tholera decimalis

Pine Beauty
Panolis flammea

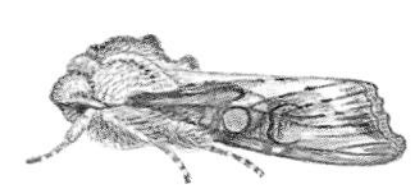

Silver Cloud
Egira conspicillaris

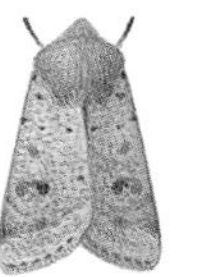
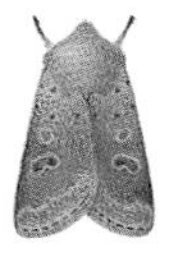

Small Quaker
Orthosia cruda

Blossom Underwing
Orthosia miniosa

Essex specimen

Northern Drab
Orthosia opima

Lead-coloured Drab
Orthosia populeti

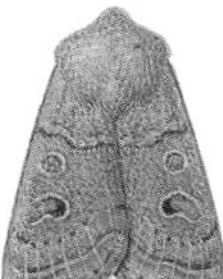

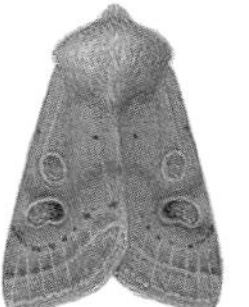
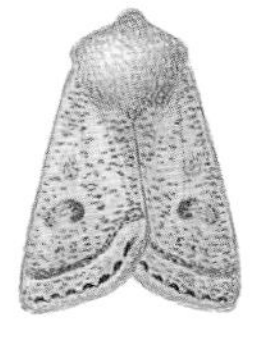

Powdered Quaker
Orthosia gracilis

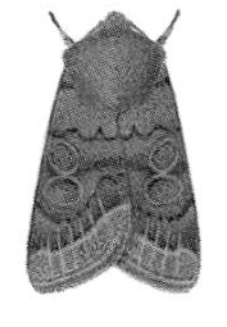
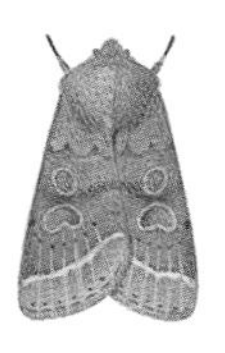

Common Quaker
Orthosia cerasi

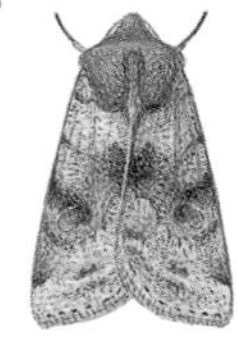
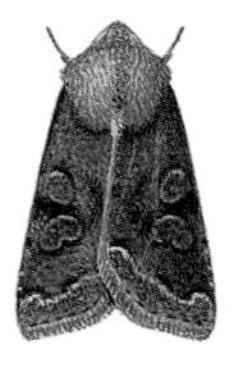

Clouded Drab
Orthosia incerta

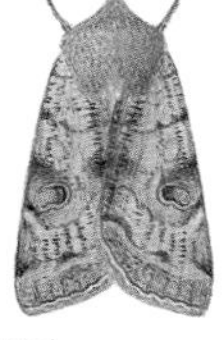

Clouded Drab
Orthosia incerta

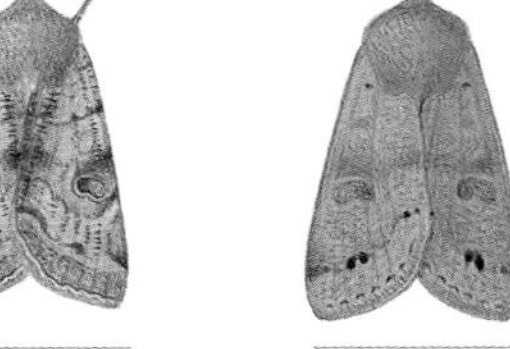
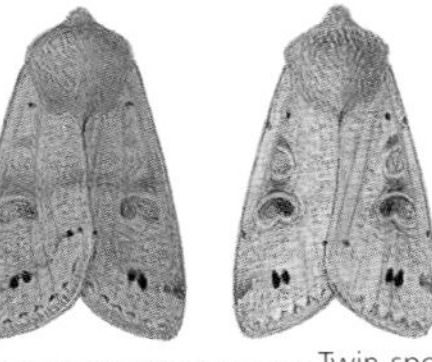
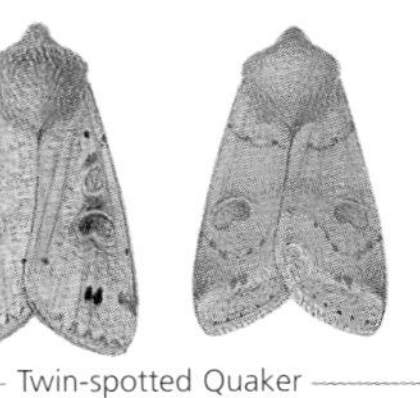
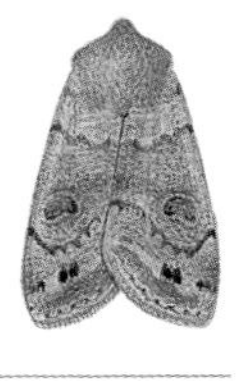

Twin-spotted Quaker
Orthosia munda

Hebrew Character *Orthosia gothica* Common T **FW** 15-17mm. Forewing usually greyish-, reddish- or purplish brown. Central black saddle-mark, sometimes divided, distorted, or paler and indistinct (usually on moorland in north). **FS** In south, March-early May. In north and in Ireland, April-early June. **Hab** Ub.

Double Line *Mythimna turca* Nb. SW,WC,(SE) **FW** 18-23mm. Forewing broad, rich sandy brown. Kidney narrow, slit-like, white, dark-outlined. **FS** June-August. **Hab** BWd Gr.

Brown-line Bright-eye *Mythimna conigera* Common T **FW** 15-17mm. Forewing orange-brown. White tear-shaped mark at trailing end of kidney. Inner central cross-line V-shaped. **FS** Late June-August. **Hab** Gr.

Clay *Mythimna ferrago* Common T **FW** 15-18mm. Thickset. Forewing quite broad, pinkish brown, light olive or dull sandy brown. White tear-shaped mark at trailing end of kidney. Male with broad black band on underside of abdomen. See White-point. **FS** Late June-early August. **Hab** Ub.

White-point *Mythimna albipuncta* Immigrant S,C,Ir; recent colonist S **FW** 14-17mm. Similar to Clay but smaller. Forewing orange-brown or pinkish brown. White central spot round. Male with broad black band on underside of abdomen. **FS** May-November, peaking July-September. **Hab** Gr.

Delicate *Mythimna vitellina* Immigrant S(T); resident Channel Islands **FW** 12-14mm. Forewing angular, pale yellow to orange-brown, or orange-red. Cross-lines fine, dark brown, inner and central lines jagged. Oval and kidney narrow. Kidney often with dark dot at trailing end. **FS** April-November, peaking August-October. **Hab** Gr.

Striped Wainscot *Mythimna pudorina* Local S,C,Ir **FW** 16-19mm. Forewing with leading edge curved. Softly marked, pale straw, streaked pink or pale brown and blackish. Fringes pink. **FS** June-July. **Hab** Wt.

Southern Wainscot *Mythimna straminea* Local S,(C),Ir **FW** 14-18mm. Very like Smoky and Common Wainscot. Forewing tip often hooked, outer edge usually quite straight. Light greyish straw, often tinged pinkish brown. Hindwing whitish, slightly to moderately dusted grey, veins dark. Short black central dashes along veins, sometimes faint. Forewing underside plain pale straw with small dark kidney, or slightly streaked or dusted grey centrally. See also Mathew's Wainscot. **FS** July-August. **Hab** Wt.

Smoky Wainscot *Mythimna impura* Common T **FW** 14-18mm. Forewing straw. Central vein whitish, brown streak adjacent. Outer edge usually rounded. Hindwing grey, or whitish lightly clouded grey. Forewing underside extensively blackish. See Southern and Common Wainscots. **FS** June-August; (occasionally September-October in south). **Hab** Gr.

Common Wainscot *Mythimna pallens* Common T **FW** 14-17mm. Similar to Smoky Wainscot, forewing rather more tapered, outer edge usually straighter. Straw or pale reddish brown (infrequently heavily streaked brown). Hindwing whitish, sometimes slightly dusted grey, less often extensively. Underside usually largely plain, sometimes black streaks on forewing. See also Southern and Mathew's Wainscots. **FS** In south, June-July; August-October. Elsewhere, July-August. **Hab** Gr.

Mathew's Wainscot *Mythimna favicolor* Nb. S,SE **FW** 16-18mm. Forewing similar in shape to Common Wainscot, deep sandy orange or straw. Central vein not or faintly paler, dark central streak faint. Hindwing white, streaked grey. See also Southern Wainscot. **FS** Mid June-late July. **Hab** Sm.

Shore Wainscot *Mythimna litoralis* Nb. S,C,(N),I **FW** 15-18mm. Forewing sandy. Conspicuous dark-edged white central streak. Hindwing white. **FS** Late June-late August; (occasionally October). **Hab** Sd.

L-album Wainscot *Mythimna l-album* Nb.; immigrant S **FW** 15-16mm. Forewing straw, bold dark streaks and dashes, clear white central L-mark. Hindwing brownish white, veins brown. See Shoulder-striped and Devonshire Wainscots. **FS** July mid September-late October. **Hab** Gr (C).

White-speck *Mythimna unipuncta* Immigrant T; probable transitory resident S, Channel Islands **FW** 18-21mm. Forewing tapered. Pale to dark sandy brown. Dark streak from tip. White central dot, central vein sometimes white. Faint orange oval and kidney. Hindwing grey, veins blackish. **FS** All year, peaking August-October. **Hab** Gr (C).

Obscure Wainscot *Mythimna obsoleta* Local S,EC,(WC) **FW** 15-18mm. Forewing dull straw, with fine blackish streaks and dusting. Central vein whitish, sometimes with small white spot. Blackish dots form weak outer cross-line. Hindwing whitish, dusted and streaked grey. See Shoulder-striped and Devonshire Wainscots. **FS** May-mid July. **Hab** Wt.

Shoulder-striped Wainscot *Mythimna comm* Common S,C,NE,Ir **FW** 16-19mm. Forewing light brown. Long black basal streak. Central vein whitis from base. Hindwing grey-brown. See Devonshire, L-album and Obscure Wainscots. **FS** Late May-late July. **Hab** Wt Gr Wd.

Devonshire Wainscot *Mythimna putrescens* N SW **FW** 14-17mm. Not unlike L-album Wainscot. Forewing less angular, lacking central white L, hindwing white. See also Shoulder-striped and Obscure Wainscots. **FS** July-September. **Hab** Gr (C).

Cosmopolitan *Mythimna loreyi* Immigrant S,(C,I **FW** 16-17mm. Forewing angular, straw. Broad brown central streak and dark wedge from tip, often merged. Small white central spot. Hindwing pure white. See White-speck. **FS** May-November, peaking September-October. **Hab** Gr (C).

Flame Wainscot *Mythimna flammea* Na. SE, S **FW** 14-18mm. Forewing narrow, tapered, leading edge strongly curved. Greyish-straw, pinkish tinge Central vein whitish, long brown central streak. **FS** Mid May-early July. **Hab** Wt.

Hebrew Character
Orthosia gothica

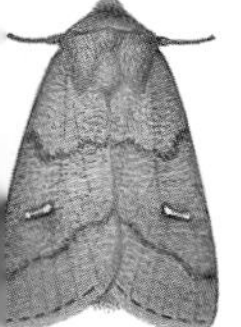

Double Line
Mythimna turca

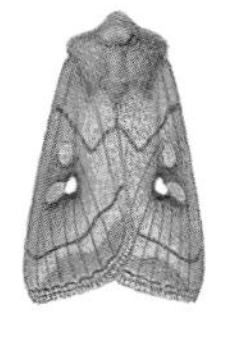

Brown-line Bright-eye
Mythimna conigera

Clay
Mythimna ferrago

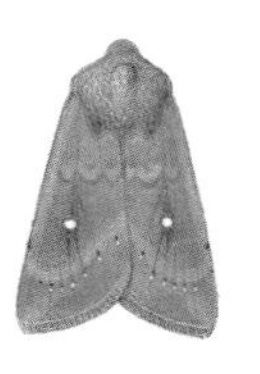

White-point
Mythimna albipuncta

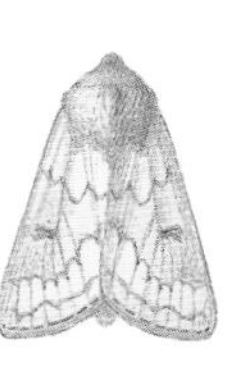

Delicate
Mythimna vitellina

:triped Wainscot
thimna pudorina

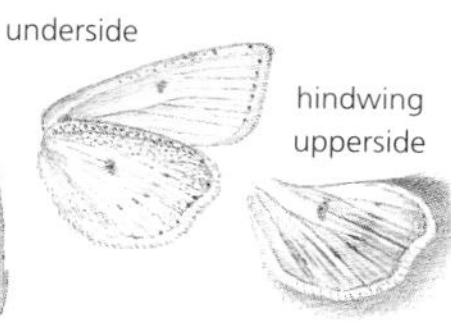

Southern Wainscot
Mythimna straminea

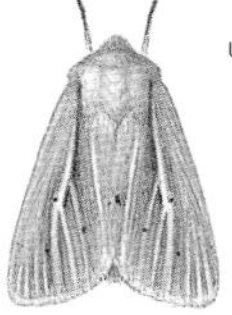

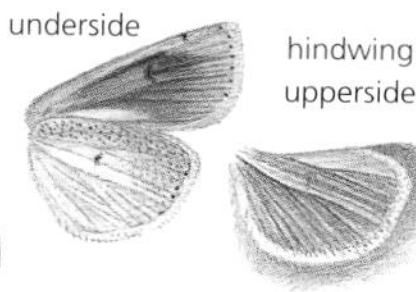

Smoky Wainscot
Mythimna impura

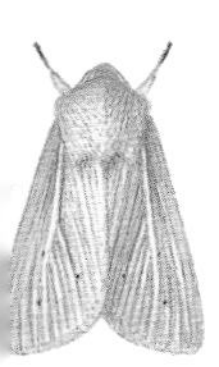

Common Wainscot
Mythimna pallens

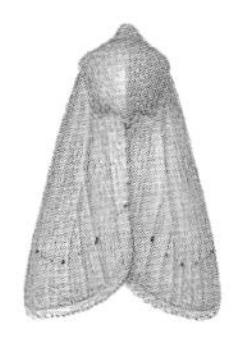

Mathew's Wainscot
Mythimna favicolor

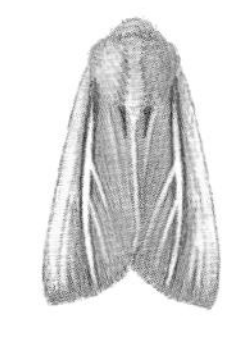

Shore Wainscot
Mythimna litoralis

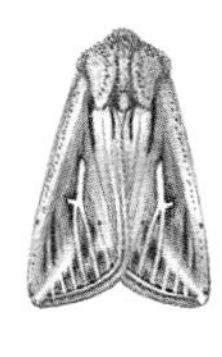

L-album Wainscot
Mythimna l-album

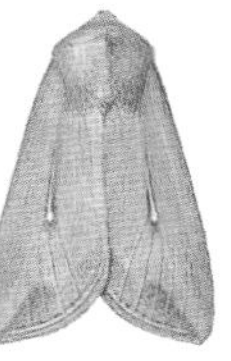
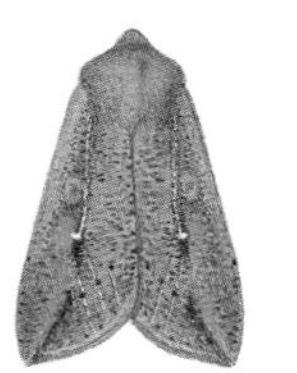

White-speck
Mythimna unipuncta

Obscure Wainscot
Mythimna obsoleta

Shoulder-striped Wainscot
Mythimna comma

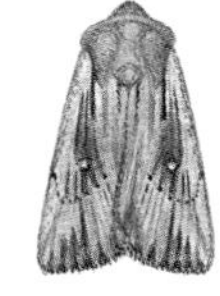

Devonshire Wainscot
Mythimna putrescens

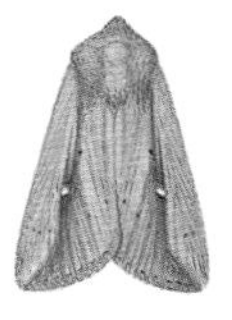

Cosmopolitan
Mythimna loreyi

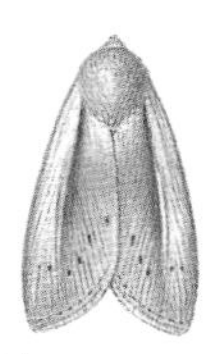

Flame Wainscot
Mythimna flammea

Cuculliinae

Sharks, pinions, shoulder-knots, chestnuts, sallows and allies

Resting postures of species in this group are varied. The following nine species (sharks) have thorax with forward-pointing crest, reminiscent of a shark's dorsal fin, and rest with wings closed tightly against the body. Forewing rather narrow, tapered with leading edge strongly arched toward tip.

Wormwood *Cucullia absinthii* Nb. S,C,Ir **FW** 16-19mm. Forewing grey. Bold blackish blotches, spots in kidney and in doubled, figure-of-eight-like oval, and dashes on outer edge. See Cudweed, Scarce Wormwood. **FS** July, occasionally to mid August. **Hab** R.

Scarce Wormwood *Cucullia artemisiae* Rare immigrant S; suspected import **FW** 16-19mm. Not unlike Cudweed, but forewing narrower, cross-lines distinct. Trailing edge grey, black streaks absent. See Wormwood, Cudweed. **FS** In mainland Europe, June-July.

Chamomile Shark *Cucullia chamomillae* Local S,C,(N,Ir) **FW** 19-23mm. Forewing grey-brown, tinged and streaked pale brown, grey and blackish. Fine blackish streaks near outer edge, extending into fringes. Hindwing grey in male, darker brownish grey in female. **FS** April-May. **Hab** Gr Ar.

Shark *Cucullia umbratica* Common T **FW** 22-26mm. Similar to Chamomile Shark, but usually larger. Forewing greyer, black streaks not extending into fringes. Pale brown streak through faint pale oval and kidney. Hindwing in male whitish with veins dark. **FS** Late June-August. **Hab** Gr H Wt Sd Sh G.

Star-wort *Cucullia asteris* Nb. S,C **FW** 19-23mm. Not unlike Mullein, but forewing grey, oval and kidney distinct and fringes smooth. See Mullein. **FS** Mid June-early August. **Hab** Sm BWd.

Cudweed *Cucullia gnaphalii* ssp. *occidentalis* Former resident; presumed extinct SE **FW** 17-19mm. Forewing grey-brown. Black line on trailing edge, outer central cross-line forms scythe-shaped mark near trailing edge. Oval and kidney with dark grey spots inside. Black streak in trailing corner, and sometimes near outer edge. See Scarce Wormwood, Wormwood. **FS** Late May-mid July. **Hab** Wd.

Striped Lychnis *Shargacucullia lychnitis* Na. S **FW** 18-21mm. Similar to Mullein, but on average smaller and paler. Forewing with oval and kidney sometimes discernible, pale. Central spot on hind-wing underside usually smaller and fainter, sometimes absent. **FS** June-July. **Hab** CGr.

Water Betony *Shargacucullia scrophulariae* Rare immigrant S **FW** 18-22mm. Very similar to Mullein and Striped Lychnis, and only reliably distinguished by examination of genitalia. **FS** In mainland Europe, May-June.

Mullein *Shargacucullia verbasci* Common S,C,(Ir) **FW** 19-24mm. Forewing yellowish brown, broad dark brown stripe along leading and trailing edge. Oval and kidney absent. Fringes scalloped. See Star-wort, Striped Lychnis, Water Betony. **FS** Late April-May. **Hab** Gr Sc H Wt Sh G.

Toadflax Brocade *Calophasia lunula* RDB SE **FW** 14-15mm. Forewing quite broad, grey-brown. Black streaks in outer half. Kidney small, narrow, oval very small, both white. Fringe banded. **FS** Late May-July; August. **Hab** Sh Gr (C).

Antirrhinum Brocade *Calophasia platyptera* Suspected rare immigrant SE **FW** 12-15mm. Like Toadflax Brocade in shape, but slightly smaller. Forewing narrower, grey finely streaked dark grey. Oval and kidney absent. Blackish blotch near centre of trailing edge. [Not illustrated.]

Minor Shoulder-knot *Brachylomia viminalis* Common S,C,N,(Ir) **FW** 13-15mm. Forewing whitish- to blackish grey, sometimes pinkish red along leading edge and around oval and kidney. Black streak at base, beside short diagonal black streak. Antennae slightly feathered in male. Minor (pp.132-134) lack basal streaks. See also Union Rustic (p.132). **FS** July-August. **Hab** Wd Wt G.

Beautiful Gothic *Leucochlaena oditis* RDB S **FW** 14-16mm. Forewing dark brown, sometimes purplish or greyish. White lines like crazy paving; oval and kidney whitish or golden. Bordered Gothic (p.108) is much larger. **FS** Late August-mid October. **Hab** Gr (C).

Sprawler *Asteroscopus sphinx* Common S,C,(Ir) **FW** 17-22mm. Thorax stout and very furry. Forewing broad, usually grey or grey-brown with long black basal streak and streaky pattern. Antennae feathered in male. Dark olive brown f. *fusca* most frequent in central southern England, increasing elsewhere. **FS** Late October-early December. Does not feed. **Hab** BWd.

Rannoch Sprawler *Brachionycha nubeculosa* RDB N **FW** 20-24mm. Thickset. Forewing broad, quite rounded. Grey or brown and blackish. Kidney large, slightly distorted, its trailing edge white. **FS** March-mid April. **Hab** BWd.

Brindled Ochre *Dasypolia templi* Local N,C,SW,(Ir) **FW** 18-23mm. Thickset. Forewing rough-scaled. Greenish brown, heavily dusted and marked dull yellow and grey, or paler, yellowish brown. Hindwing dirty yellowish brown. Some Northern Rustics (p.102) are similar, but usually noticeably silky and hindwing dark grey with chalk white fringes. **FS** Late August (in north)-October. Female reappearing April-May. Does not feed. **Hab** Gr M Wt Sd.

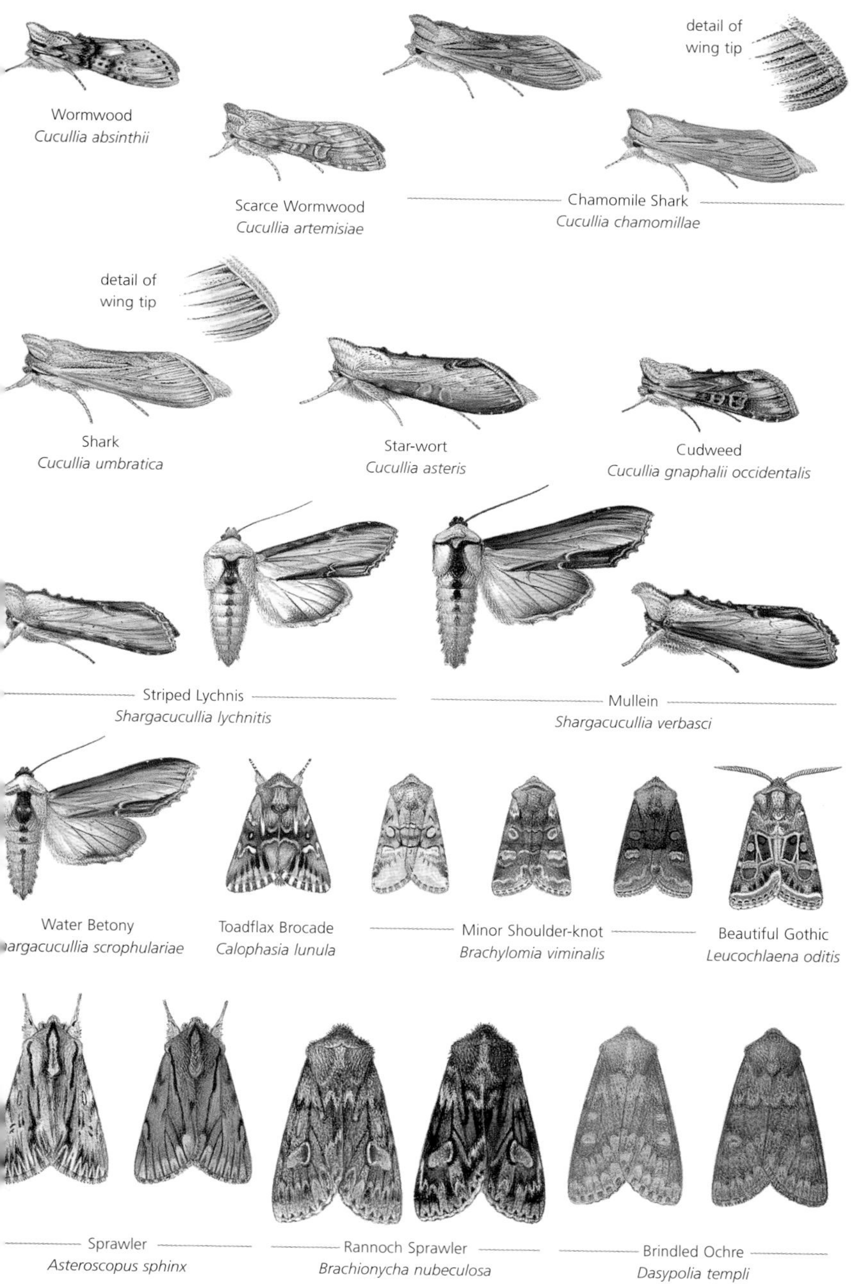

Wormwood
Cucullia absinthii

Scarce Wormwood
Cucullia artemisiae

Chamomile Shark
Cucullia chamomillae

Shark
Cucullia umbratica

Star-wort
Cucullia asteris

Cudweed
Cucullia gnaphalii occidentalis

Striped Lychnis
Shargacucullia lychnitis

Mullein
Shargacucullia verbasci

Water Betony
argacucullia scrophulariae

Toadflax Brocade
Calophasia lunula

Minor Shoulder-knot
Brachylomia viminalis

Beautiful Gothic
Leucochlaena oditis

Sprawler
Asteroscopus sphinx

Rannoch Sprawler
Brachionycha nubeculosa

Brindled Ochre
Dasypolia templi

Feathered Brindle *Aporophyla australis* ssp. *pascuea* Nb. S,Ir **FW** 14-17mm. Forewing rather narrow, usually grey, less often dark brown. Black basal and outer streaks, often fine dark jagged cross-lines. Hindwing white. See Deep-brown Dart (cf. dark form) **FS** Late August-early October. **Hab** C.

Deep-brown Dart *Aporophyla lutulenta* Common S,C **FW** 15-18mm. Forewing dull brownish- or greyish black. Markings grey-brown, often obscure. Hindwing in male white, sometimes with central row of blackish dots or dashes; in female, dark grey. Antennae of male slightly feathered. See Northern Deep-brown Dart, Black Rustic, Feathered Brindle. **FS** September-October. **Hab** Gr A Sd Wd.

Northern Deep-brown Dart *Aporophyla lueneburgensis* Common N,WC,Ir **FW** 15-17mm. Like Deep-brown Dart, but slightly smaller, forewing blackish, or heavily dusted cold grey. Black dots or dashes on hindwing of male, often pronounced. See also Black Rustic. **FS** Early August-mid September. **Hab** Gr M.

Black Rustic *Aporophyla nigra* Common N,S,WC,(EC) **FW** 17-21mm. Forewing black, glossy. Outer edge of kidney usually whitish. Antennae not visibly feathered. See Deep-brown Dart and Northern Deep-brown Dart. **FS** September-October. **Hab** Ub.

Golden-rod Brindle *Lithomoia solidaginis* Local N,WC **FW** 18-21mm. Forewing grey, slightly hooked, tip blunt. Brown stripe along leading edge. Kidney large, conspicuous. Rests with wings folded around body, rear end raised. See Sword-grass. **FS** August-September. **Hab** M Sc Wd.

Tawny Pinion *Lithophane semibrunnea* Local S,(C) **FW** 16-20mm. Forewing narrow, tawny brown, and darker brown, mainly in trailing half. Trailing corner with solid blackish bar, parallel with trailing edge, cut by pale flattened S-mark. Thorax with central crest. Shoulders protruding like ears. See Pale Pinion. **FS** October-November, reappearing March-May. **Hab** BWd G.

Pale Pinion *Lithophane hepatica* Local S,C,Ir **FW** 17-20mm. Similar to Tawny Pinion, but slightly broader, usually paler forewing. Often a brown or blackish bar, central in trailing half. Trailing corner with two small brown elliptical marks. Hindwing grey-brown. See also Silver Cloud. **FS** October-November, reappearing March-May. **Hab** BWd.

Grey Shoulder-knot *Lithophane ornitopus* ssp. *lactipennis* Common S,WC,Ir **FW** 17-19mm. Forewing light grey. Black basal antler-mark. Kidney often marked with light brown. See Grey Chi. **FS** September-November, reappearing February-April. **Hab** BWd.

Conformist *Lithophane furcifera furcifera* Immigrant S,C; ssp. *suffusa* Resident, Wales, presumed extinct **FW** 17-20mm. Thin black roughly central bar, not reaching beyond kidney. Base with pale patch, thick black antler-mark. Kidney reddish brown. Ssp. *furcifera* forewing smooth slaty-grey. Ssp. *suffusa* blackish grey. See Nonconformist, Softly's Shoulder-knot. **FS** September-October, reappearing March-May.

Softly's Shoulder-knot *Lithophane consocia* Rare immigrant S **FW** 18-20mm. Similar to Conformist ssp. *furcifera*. Forewing dark grey, pattern usually more contrasting, with darker grey speckling and stronger whitish variegation. May require genitalia examination for confirmation. **FS** September-November, reappearing March-May.

Nonconformist *Lithophane lamda* Immigrant S **FW** 17-20mm. Simlar to Conformist ssp. *furcifera* and Softly's Shoulder-knot but forewing grey with central bar longer, often thicker, extending beyond kidney. **FS** September-October, reappearing in spring.

Blair's Shoulder-knot *Lithophane leautieri* ssp. *hesperica* Common S,C,(N,Ir) **FW** 17-20mm. Forewing narrow, grey. Long straight black basal streak. Kidney, hindwing and underside sometimes pinkish. **FS** September-November. **Hab** G H CWd.

Red Sword-grass *Xylena vetusta* Local N,W,(S), **FW** 24-29mm. Rests with wings creased, closed tightly around body. Forewing with leading half straw or buff, contrasting sharply with rich mahogany or blackish brown trailing half. Long black sword-like streak beyond kidney (not always visible when moth at rest). Lower part of hind leg dark red-brown. See Sword-grass, Dark Sword-gras (p.100). **FS** September-November, reappearing March-May. **Hab** M Up Wd Wt.

Sword-grass *Xylena exsoleta* Nb. N,C,(Ir) **FW** 24-29mm. Like Red Sword-grass, but forewing pattern not strongly contrasting, straw-buff marble with grey, mainly in trailing half. Sword-marks usually shorter. Lower half of hind leg pale above. See also Golden-rod Brindle, Dark Sword-grass (p.100). **FS** September-October, reappearing March May. **Hab** M Up Wd.

Early Grey *Xylocampa areola* Common T **FW** 15-18mm. Forewing grey, marbled blackish grey, sometimes pinkish. Oval and kidney pale, wit additional pale oval, the three often joined. **FS** March-May. **Hab** BWd Sc H G.

Double-spot Brocade *Meganephria bimaculos* Uncertain (few records, last in 1949) **FW** 22-26mr Forewing broad, straw-buff, marked brown. Kidney large, bulbous, pale. Hindwing with dark blotch ne centre and near trailing edge. [Not illustrated.]

Green-brindled Crescent *Allophyes oxyacan-thae* Common T **FW** 17-20mm. Forewing brown variably marked metallic green, or dark brown. Kidney large, bulbous. Black basal mark resemblin loaded crossbow. White crescent on outer central cross-line in trailing half. **FS** September-November **Hab** BWd Sc H G.

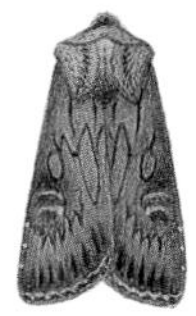

Feathered Brindle
Aporophyla australis pascuea

Deep-brown Dart
Aporophyla lutulenta

Northern Deep-brown Dart
Aporophyla lueneburgensis

Black Rustic
Aporophyla nigra

Golden-rod Brindle
Lithomoia solidaginis

Tawny Pinion
Lithophane semibrunnea

Pale Pinion
Lithophane hepatica

Grey Shoulder-knot
Lithophane ornitopus lactipennis

ftly's Shoulder-knot
ithophane consocia

Conformist
Lithophane furcifera suffusa
Lithophane furcifera furcifera

Nonconformist
Lithophane lamda

ir's Shoulder-knot
hophane leautieri hesperica

Red Sword-grass
Xylena vetusta

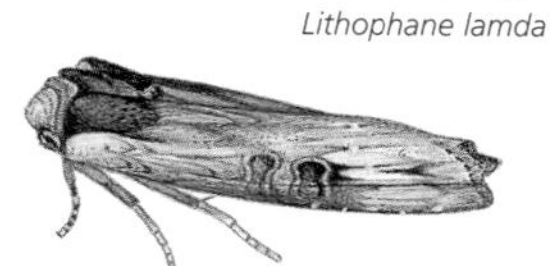

Sword-grass
Xylena exsoleta

Early Grey
Xylocampa areola

Green-brindled Crescent
Allophyes oxyacanthae

Oak Rustic *Dryobota labecula* Immigrant; recent colonist S; resident Channel Islands **FW** 12-15mm. Forewing rather blunt, brown or blackish. Kidney orange or white (f. *albomacula*). Short black basal streak. See Common and Lesser Common Rustics (cf. f. *albomacula*) (p.134). **FS** October-December. **Hab** Wd G.

Merveille du Jour *Dichonia aprilina* Common T **FW** 18-23mm. Forewing broad, leading edge curved, bright lichen green. Black markings may form blotches or central band. Extreme examples are largely black, but oval and broad kidney green. See Scarce Merveille du Jour. **FS** September-October. **Hab** BWd.

Brindled Green *Dryobotodes eremita* Common T **FW** 15-17mm. Forewing dull green, greenish black or grey, strongly variegated with black, white and brown, or more obscurely marked. Small, variable pale central blotch, bordered with black along its rear and outer edges, nearly always with small outward projection at its trailing corner. Shears (p.108) has two projections on central blotch and is never green. **FS** August-mid October. **Hab** BWd H G.

Beautiful Arches *Blepharita satura* Possible former resident, presumed extinct or rare immigrant S **FW** 19-23mm. Forewing broad, leading edge curved. Dark brown marbled reddish brown, especially outer area, oval and kidney. Thick central bar and rather short basal streak black. Thorax with reddish crest. See Dark Brocade. **FS** In mainland Europe, July-October. **Hab** In mainland Europe, Wd A.

Dark Brocade *Blepharita adusta* Common T **FW** 18-21mm. Forewing rather angular, grey-brown, brown (sometimes tinged reddish), or blackish brown. Darker examples lightly dusted grey. Kidney with outer edge whitish, often wavy. Central bar black, variable, sometimes thin, reduced. Base not distinctly paler, with black streak. Outermost cross-line jagged with distinct central W. If central bar reduced or absent, see Cabbage Moth (p.108) (lacks basal streak), Northern Arches and Exile (stouter, cross-lines thicker, forewing more blunt). See also Dusky Brocade (p.132) (forewing less angular, greyer), Pale-shouldered Brocade, Beautiful Brocade (p.108), Bedrule Brocade. **FS** Late May-early August. **Hab** In south, A CGr Wt Wd. In north, M Up Sd.

Bedrule Brocade *Blepharita solieri* Suspected rare immigrant N (one record) **FW** 16-19mm. Resembles Dark Brocade, but slightly smaller and more tawny brown. Hindwing whitish in male with darker border, dark in female (greyish white in Dark Brocade). **FS** In mainland Europe, August-September.

Grey Chi *Antitype chi* Common N,C,(S),Ir **FW** 15-19mm. Forewing greyish white, light or dark grey, or greyish green. Black mark in centre of forewing, often resembling Greek letter Chi, or anvil-shaped, thickened to form solid bar, or reduced. See Grey Shoulder-knot. **FS** August-September. **Hab** Ub.

Flame Brocade *Trigonophora flammea* Immigrant; transitory resident S **FW** 20-23mm. Forewing purplish brown, tinged violet when fresh. Kidney large, pale straw, with pointed extension. Pale straw streak along trailing edge. Two very similar species occur in France: *T. crassicornis* (antennae with longer fine filaments) and *T. jodia* (noticeably smaller). **FS** September-early November.

Large Ranunculus *Polymixis flavicincta* Local S,EC **FW** 17-22mm. Forewing quite broad, rough-textured, delicate greenish grey or whitish, usually with golden orange freckling, particularly on outermost cross-line and around kidney. Hindwing whitish or grey, with thick darker central line. Antennae not feathered. See Black-banded, Feathered Ranunculus, Small Ranunculus. **FS** September-October. **Hab** G Gr A.

Cameo *Polymixis gemmea* Suspected rare immigrant S **FW** 16-20mm. Forewing olive brown with greenish component, strongly variegated white. Oval and kidney large, white. Whitish, dark-edged hoof-shaped mark adjoining outer edge of thickly white inner central cross-line. See White Spot (p.110) (usually smaller, lacking greenish tint). **FS** In mainland Europe, July-September.

Black-banded *Polymixis xanthomista* ssp. *statices* Na. SW,(WC,Ir) **FW** 16-18mm. Similar to Large Ranunculus, but usually smaller, forewing narrower with dark central cross-band, (sometimes ill-defined) passing between pale oval and kidney. Hindwing with fine, almost continuous dark line on outer margin, without central line, in male white, in female grey-brown. Antennae not feathered. See also Feathered Ranunculus. **FS** Mid August-early October. **Hab** Cl.

Feathered Ranunculus *Polymixis lichenea lichenea* Local. S,C,(N,Ir); ssp. *scillonea* Scilly **FW** 15-18mm. Ssp. *lichenea*: Forewing rather delicate greyish green, often dusted and freckled whitish grey, sometimes tinged yellowish or brownish. Hindwing with bold, black dashes on outer margin, sometimes with dark central line, whitish in male, grey in female. Antennae feathered in male. Ssp. *scillonea*: Forewing darker green, often strongly freckled blackish, sometimes with extensive whitish markings. **FS** Late August-early October. **Hab** C.

Oak Rustic
Dryobota labecula

f. *albomacula*

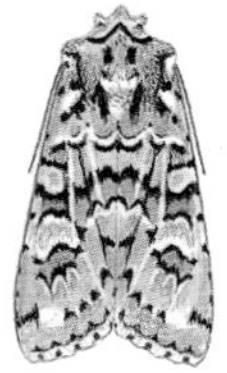

Merveille du Jour
Dichonia aprilina

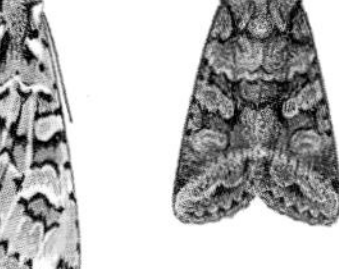

Brindled Green
Dryobotodes eremita

Beautiful Arches
Blepharita satura

Dark Brocade
Blepharita adusta

Dark Brocade
Blepharita adusta

♂

Bedrule Brocade
Blepharita solieri

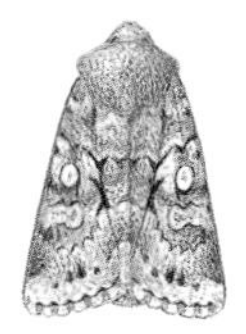

Grey Chi
Antitype chi

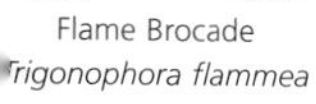

Flame Brocade
Trigonophora flammea

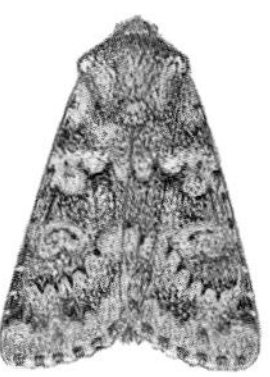

Large Ranunculus
Polymixis flavicincta

Cameo
Polymixis gemmea

Black-banded
Polymixis xanthomista statices

♂
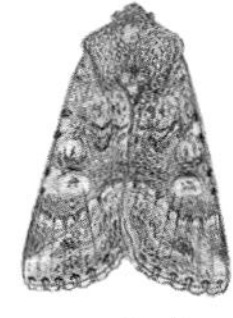

Feathered Ranunculus
Polymixis lichenea lichenea

P. l. scillonea

Satellite *Eupsilia transversa* Common T
FW 17-20mm. Forewing rich reddish brown, or dull brown, sometimes with bluish or purplish sheen when fresh. Rather small kidney and two adjacent dots white, orange or orange-brown. Fringes scalloped. **FS** Late September-May. **Hab** Ub.

Orange Upperwing *Jodia croceago* RDB S
FW 14-17mm. Forewing with tip pointed, orange. White dashes on leading edge. Thick dark brown or blackish central cross-line, right-angled at trailing end of kidney. Outer central cross-row of blackish dots. Hindwing white with rather faint irregular pinkish-grey central cross-line and central spot. See Orange Sallow, Blossom Underwing (p.112). **FS** Early September-early November, reappearing February-mid May. **Hab** BWd Sc.

Chestnut *Conistra vaccinii* Common T
FW 14-15mm. Outer edge of forewing rounded, tip usually rather blunt. Orange-brown or deep chestnut brown. Rather plain or with distinct pale or dark (even blackish) cross-lines and bands, pale veins and/or pale dusting. Kidney usually with solid blackish spot in trailing third. See Dark Chestnut, Dotted Chestnut, Red-headed Chestnut.
FS Late September-May. **Hab** BWd Sc H G.

Dark Chestnut *Conistra ligula* Common S,C,(N,Ir) **FW** 13-15mm. Similar to Chestnut, but forewing usually narrower, very slightly hooked or pointed. Rather shiny, usually dark chestnut or dark chocolate brown, or blackish brown, less often paler chestnut brown. Rather plain or with distinct pale outer band and cross-lines. **FS** October-February. **Hab** BWd H G.

Dotted Chestnut *Conistra rubiginea* Nb. SW,S **FW** 15-17mm. Forewing light chestnut-orange to almost brick-red, extensive black spots (rarely reduced), trailing third of kidney black. See Chestnut. **FS** October-November, reappearing March-May. **Hab** Wd Sc A H.

Red-headed Chestnut *Conistra erythrocephala* Rare immigrant; transitory resident S **FW** 16-17mm. Forewing with outer edge rounded, rather uniform grey-brown tinged reddish, reddish brown, or dark reddish brown with streak along leading edge. Oval, kidney and outer cross-band pale. Kidney with black spots, mainly in trailing third, or black ring. Usually a dark wedge on leading edge near wing tip. See Chestnut. **FS** September-November, reappearing March-April. **Hab** Wd Sc.

Brick *Agrochola circellaris* Common T
FW 14-19mm. Forewing reddish-, pinkish- or greyish brown. Trailing third of kidney blackish. Wavy cross-lines and bands, and sometimes veins, dark grey or brown, outermost cross-line usually with dark inner shading. Hindwing grey, broad brownish white wedge along leading edge. See Yellow-line Quaker, Dusky-lemon Sallow, Pale-lemon Sallow. **FS** Late August-early December. **Hab** BWd Sc H G.

Red-line Quaker *Agrochola lota* Common T
FW 15-18mm. Forewing grey, sometimes with pinkish flush. Outermost cross-line reddish brown, fairly straight, notched near leading edge. Trailing third of kidney intensely black. **FS** September-mid November. **Hab** Wd Sc Wt H G.

Yellow-line Quaker *Agrochola macilenta* Common T **FW** 14-16mm. Forewing pale yellowish brown, sometimes tinged grey or pink. Outermost cross-line almost straight, notched near leading edge. Trailing third of kidney blackish or as ground-colour. See Brick, Red-line Quaker. **FS** September-November. **Hab** Wd A M H Sc G.

Southern Chestnut *Agrochola haematidea* RDB S,SE **FW** 14-15mm. Forewing distinctly pointed, deep reddish brown. Dark grey or blackish shading along trailing edge extending into dark outer cross-band. See Beaded Chestnut. **FS** Late September-mid November. Mainly active in first hour of darkness. **Hab** A.

Flounced Chestnut *Agrochola helvola* Common T **FW** 16-18mm. Forewing angular, rather broad, quite pointed. Chestnut brown, rather softly marked. Broad dark reddish brown or purplish brown bands near base and outer margin. Hindwing grey with narrow band around outer margin, fringes, and wedge along leading edge all pale. See Beaded Chestnut. **FS** September-October. **Hab** BWd Sc A M.

Brown-spot Pinion *Agrochola litura* Common S,C,N **FW** 14-17mm. Forewing reddish-, dark purplish- or greyish brown. Basal half often distinctly paler. Short diagonal dash near tip, marks along leading edge and partial basal cross-line all intensely black. See Beaded Chestnut (lacks intensely black marks). **FS** Late August-October. **Hab** BWd A Wt Sc H G.

Beaded Chestnut *Agrochola lychnidis* Common S,C,(N),Ir **FW** 15-18mm. Forewing chestnut- or reddish brown, brownish white, greyish yellow, grey-brown or blackish. Rather plain or with clear cross-lines and/or pale veins. Kidney usually narrow oval small, usually elongated. Usually a dark diagonal dash or wedge on leading edge near tip. Hindwing uniformly grey, sometimes with small obscure central spot. See Brown-spot Pinion, Lunar Underwing, Southern Chestnut, Flounced Chestnut. **FS** September-early November. **Hab** Ub.

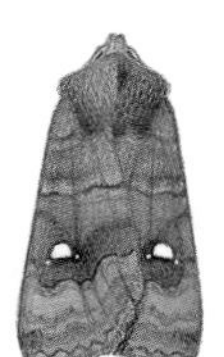

Satellite
Eupsilia transversa

Orange Upperwing
Jodia croceago

Chestnut
Conistra vaccinii

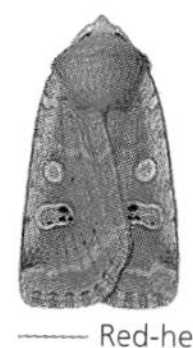
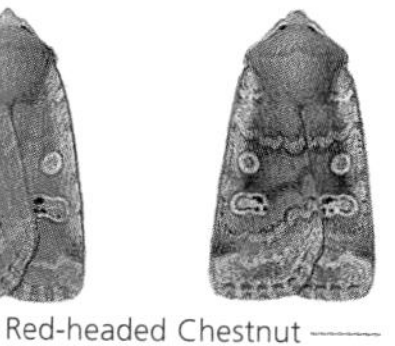

Dark Chestnut
Conistra ligula

Dotted Chestnut
Conistra rubiginea

Red-headed Chestnut
Conistra erythrocephala

Brick
Agrochola circellaris

Red-line Quaker
Agrochola lota

Yellow-line Quaker
Agrochola macilenta

Southern Chestnut
Agrochola haematidea

Flounced Chestnut
Agrochola helvola

Brown-spot Pinion
Agrochola litura
f. *rufa-pallida*

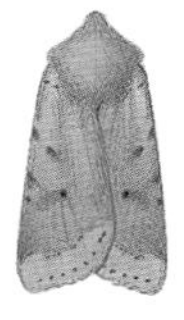

Beaded Chestnut
Agrochola lychnidis

Centre-barred Sallow *Atethmia centrago* Common T **FW** 15-18mm. Forewing quite broad, slightly hooked. Orange-yellow, with broad pinkish red or pinkish brown central band, paler in leading half, but kidney dark. Uniformly orange, reddish and purplish forms are rare. **FS** August-September. **Hab** BWd H G.

Lunar Underwing *Omphaloscelis lunosa* Common S,C,(N),Ir **FW** 14-17mm. Forewing grey, yellowish- or reddish brown, or blackish, sometimes distinctly banded, tip rather blunt. Outer cross-row of black spots, black dash on leading edge near tip. Veins frequently pale. Hindwing usually whitish, with dark central crescent and outer blotches or band. Less often extensively clouded grey. Beaded Chestnut has uniformly grey hindwing, forewing tip usually less blunt, outer black spots absent, and kidney and oval narrower. **FS** Late August-mid October. **Hab** Gr G.

Orange Sallow *Xanthia citrago* Common S,C,N **FW** 15-17mm. Forewing rather broad, tip slightly hooked, orange-yellow or dull orange, with fine speckling and veins orange-red (less often brown). Thick dark fairly straight diagonal central cross-line, passing between oval and kidney, touching kidney. Outer central cross-line solid. Hindwing plain yellowish white. See Orange Upperwing. **FS** August-early October. **Hab** BWd G.

Barred Sallow *Xanthia aurago* Common S,C,(N) **FW** 14-16mm. Forewing pinkish red or purplish brown. Broad, usually yellow or orange-yellow (less often deep- or reddish orange) wavy-edged central band. **FS** September-early November. **Hab** BWd H Sc G.

Pink-barred Sallow *Xanthia togata* Common T **FW** 13-16mm. Head and shoulders dark pinkish brown, rest of thorax yellow. Forewing slightly hooked, bright orange-yellow, markings deep pink or reddish brown. An outer central cross-band, its inner edge elbowed at kidney, sometimes broken into scalloped lines. See Sallow. **FS** In south, September-October. In north, August-September. **Hab** BWd Sc H G.

Sallow *Xanthia icteritia* Common **FW** 14-17mm. Head and thorax yellow. Forewing slightly hooked, yellow or orange-yellow. Markings irregular, reddish brown, dark brown or pinkish, often reduced. Sometimes forewing almost plain yellow. Hindwing white. See Pink-barred Sallow, Dusky-lemon Sallow, Angle-striped Sallow. **FS** In south, September-October. In north, August-September. **Hab** BWd Sc H G.

Dusky-lemon Sallow *Xanthia gilvago* Local S,C,(N) **FW** 15-18mm. Forewing tip not hooked. Dull orange-yellow or orange-brown, variably and irregularly banded, marked and clouded blackish grey or (less often) dark brown. Hindwing whitish, sometimes streaked grey-brown in trailing third. See Pale-lemon Sallow, Sallow, Brick. **FS** Late August-early October. **Hab** BWd H G.

Pale-lemon Sallow *Xanthia ocellaris* Na. SE,S **FW** 18-19mm. Forewing slightly hooked. Dull orange-brown, most often rather uniform. Less frequently marked with dark brown. Hindwing whitish, streaked grey-brown in trailing third. See Dusky-lemon Sallow, Brick. **FS** September-October. **Hab** H G.

Acronictinae Daggers

Scarce Merveille du Jour *Moma alpium* RDB S **FW** 17-20mm. Forewing lichen-green with white streaks. Cross-lines black, irregular, blotchy, strongest near base and outer edge. Kidney narrow black. See Merveille du Jour. **FS** Early June-mid July. **Hab** BWd.

Poplar Grey *Acronicta megacephala* Common T **FW** 17-20mm. Forewing broad, light grey, heavily and coarsely dusted blackish, or largely blackish. Diffuse pale patch beyond kidney. Hindwing whitish in male with dark outer shading, grey in female. Veins often blackish grey, especially in outer half. See Knot Grass (with narrower forewing), Sycamore, Coronet. **FS** Late May-early August. **Hab** BWd Sc H G.

Sycamore *Acronicta aceris* Local S,C **FW** 18-22mm. Forewing broad, grey, finely dusted dark grey and brownish. Less often dark grey (frequently in London). Pale outer central cross-line in shape of question-mark, even on dark examples. Area beyond kidney not noticeably paler (cf. Poplar Grey). Hindwing whitish in male, grey in female, with veins strongly dark and outer shading. See Poplar Grey, Sweet Gale Moth. **FS** Mid June-early August. **Hab** G H BWd Sc.

Miller *Acronicta leporina* Common T **FW** 16-21mm. Forewing whitish, finely dusted grey (sometimes densely). Less often pure white (in parts of Scotland). Markings rather sparse. Black crescent forms inner edge of otherwise pale kidney. Outer cross-line thickened towards trailing edge, sometimes forming short dagger mark. **FS** Late May-early August. **Hab** BWd Sc G.

Alder Moth *Acronicta alni* Local S,C,Ir **FW** 16-19mm. Forewing grey or dark grey-brown (frequently in London and elsewhere). Blackish clouding covering all or most of trailing half, extending to leading edge centrally. Long thick black streak at base and trailing corner. **FS** May-June. **Hab** BWd.

Centre-barred Sallow
Atethmia centrago

Lunar Underwing
Omphaloscelis lunosa

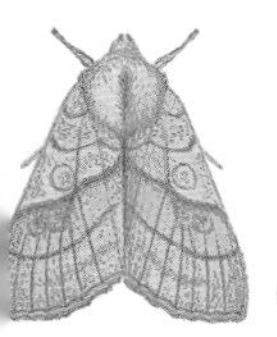

Orange Sallow
Xanthia citrago

Barred Sallow
Xanthia aurago

Pink-barred Sallow
Xanthia togata

Sallow
Xanthia icteritia

Dusky-lemon Sallow
Xanthia gilvago

Pale-lemon Sallow
Xanthia ocellaris

carce Merveille
du Jour
Moma alpium

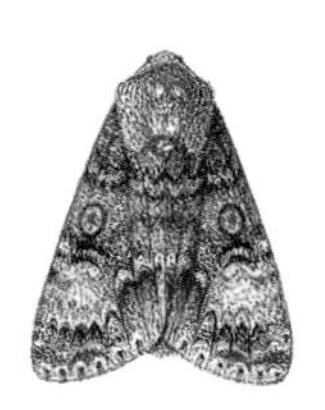

Poplar Grey
Acronicta megacephala

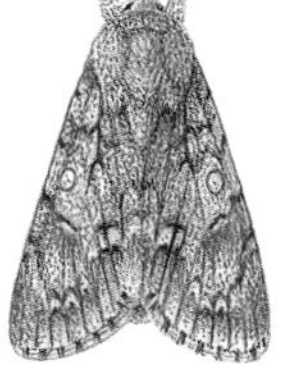

Sycamore
Acronicta aceris
f. *infuscata*

Miller
Acronicta leporina
f. *grisea* f. *melanocephala*

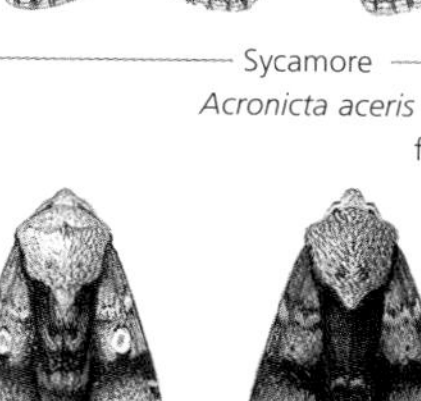

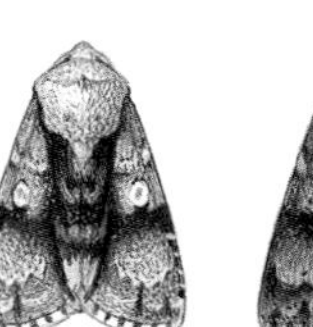

Alder Moth
Acronicta alni
f. *suffusa*

Dark Dagger *Acronicta tridens* Common S,C,(N) **FW** 17-20mm. Only separable with certainty from Grey Dagger on genitalia. Tends to have slightly shinier forewing, in male often narrower. Sometimes tinged brownish or pink. **FS** Mid May-July; (September-October). **Hab** Ub.

Grey Dagger *Acronicta psi* Common T **FW** 17-20mm. Forewing grey. Markings clear black. Long dagger mark near trailing corner, long straight branched basal streak and fine edging between largely pale oval and kidney. See Dark Dagger. Very light and very dark grey examples tend to be Grey Dagger. See also Scarce Dagger. **FS** Mid May-August; (September-October). **Hab** Ub.

Marsh Dagger *Acronicta strigosa* Rare immigrant; former resident S **FW** 13-15mm. Forewing grey, clouded darker grey. Three thick black streaks in trailing half. **FS** Late June-early July. **Hab** Sc H.

Light Knot Grass *Acronicta menyanthidis menyanthidis* Local C,(N,S),Ir; ssp. *scotica* Local N **FW** 16-20mm. Ssp. *menyanthidis* quite thickset, forewing quite rounded, grey or very dark grey. Oval very small, without black dot inside. Ssp. *scotica* slightly larger, usually more boldly-marked, hindwing browner. See Scarce Dagger, Sweet Gale Moth. **FS** Late May-mid July. **Hab** M AWt A.

Scarce Dagger *Acronicta auricoma* Rare immigrant; former resident S **FW** 16-17mm. Forewing grey, clouded darker grey. Black dagger mark near trailing corner and long black basal streak. Oval with dark spot inside. See Light Knot Grass (plainer, more thickset), Knot Grass, Grey Dagger. **FS** May-early June; mid July-August. **Hab** BWd.

Sweet Gale Moth *Acronicta euphorbiae* ssp. *myricae* Na. N,Ir **FW** 14-16mm. Forewing grey, finely dusted darker. Basal streak weak or absent. Lacking dagger mark or conspicuous white spots near trailing corner. Hindwing white in male, grey in female. See Knot Grass, Light Knot Grass, also Sycamore (larger). **FS** Late April-early June; (in Ireland, July-August). **Hab** M Sc H.

Knot Grass *Acronicta rumicis* Common T **FW** 16-20mm. Forewing grey, irregularly dusted and indistinctly marked blackish, or largely blackish. 1-2 distinct chalky white spots in trailing half at roughly two-thirds and broken white outermost cross-line. Short black basal streak. Dagger mark absent from trailing corner. Hindwing grey-brown. See Scarce Dagger, Poplar Grey, Sweet Gale Moth, Coronet. **FS** In south, May-June; August-early September. From Midlands north, May-July. **Hab** Ub.

Reed Dagger *Simyra albovenosa* Nb. S **FW** 16-20mm. Forewing very pointed, whitish-straw or reddish-straw, with long dark blackish basal and outer central streaks. Hindwing pure white. See Blair's Wainscot (p.138). **FS** May-July; August-early September. Does not seem to feed. **Hab** Wt.

Coronet *Craniophora ligustri* Local S,C,N,(Ir) **FW** 17-19mm. Forewing quite broad, blunt, texture smooth. Appears blackish, but actually marbled brownish purple and dark olive green, with wavy black cross-lines. Outer edge of kidney and patch beyond usually white or whitish, but white markings vary and may be absent. See Poplar Grey, Knot-grass. **FS** June-July. **Hab** BWd H Sc.

Bryophilinae Lichen feeders

Tree-lichen Beauty *Cryphia algae* Immigrant, recent colonist S,(C) **FW** 10-13mm. Forewing with basal (and outer) area usually largely green, less frequently yellow or brownish. Central band usually contrastingly darker, brownish, often blackish along its inner and trailing edge. Obscurely marked Marbled Green forms *impar* and *westroppi* are usually predominantly greyish. **FS** July-September.

Marbled Beauty *Cryphia domestica* Common S,C,(N),Ir **FW** 12-14mm. Forewing rather narrow, rounded. Greyish or greenish white, marbled greenish or dull orange, or extensively green. Inner central cross-line extends from leading to trailing edge. See Marbled Green. **FS** July-August. **Hab** G H Wd.

Marbled Grey *Cryphia raptricula* Immigrant S **FW** 12-14mm. Forewing narrow. From light grey with well-defined markings to obscurely marked blackish grey. Sometimes broadly streaked reddish brown. Strongly curved outer central cross-line, sometimes pale-edged. Hindwing brownish white. **FS** In northern Europe, July-August.

Marbled Green *Cryphia muralis muralis* Local S,Ir **FW** 12-15mm. Similar to Marbled Beauty. Usually larger, forewing broader, more angular. Inner central cross-line stops before trailing edge and basal cross-line curves around to almost meet it, often forming pale cloverleaf-shaped blotch. Forewing greenish white, lichen-green, olive green, greyish, yellowish or brownish. Markings bold to faint. See also Tree-lichen Beauty. F. *impar* (Cambridge and Gloucester) forewing brownish- or greenish grey, irregularly dusted and blotched blackish. F. *westroppi* (Ireland) smaller, markings often indistinct but extremely variable. **FS** July-August. **Hab** Cl G H.

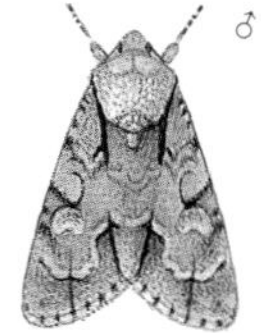
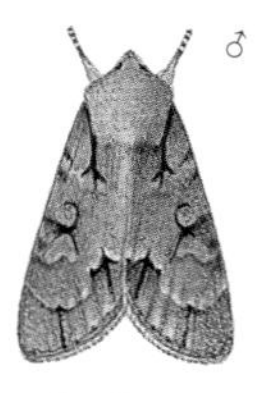
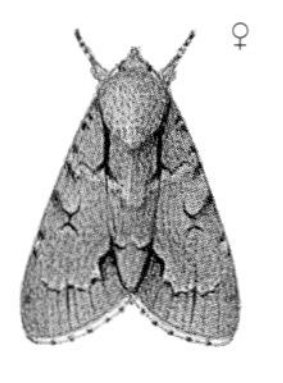

♂ ♂ ♀ ♂ ♀

Dark Dagger
Acronicta tridens

Grey Dagger
Acronicta psi

Marsh Dagger
Acronicta strigosa

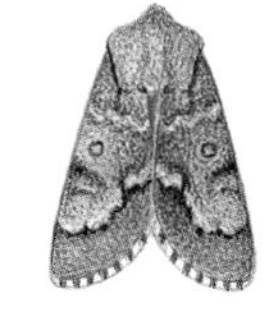

Light Knot Grass
Acronicta menyanthidis menyanthidis

Acronicta menyanthidis scotica

Scarce Dagger
Acronicta auricoma

Sweet Gale Moth
Acronicta euphorbiae myricae

Knot Grass
Acronicta rumicis
f. *salicis*

Reed Dagger
Simyra albovenosa

Coronet
Craniophora ligustri
f. *coronula*

Tree-lichen Beauty
Cryphia algae

Marbled Beauty
Cryphia domestica

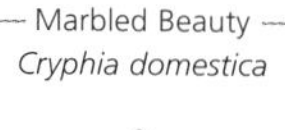

Marbled Grey
Cryphia raptricula

Marbled Green
Cryphia muralis muralis

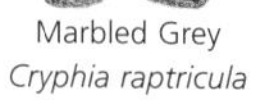

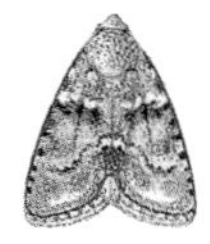

Marbled Green
Cryphia muralis muralis f. *impar*

Amphipyrinae Arches, brindles, minors, rustics and allies

Forewings usually held in shallow, tent-like fashion, sometimes slightly overlapping.

Copper Underwing *Amphipyra pyramidea* Common S,C,(N),Ir **FW** 21-26mm. Very similar to Svensson's Copper Underwing. Forewing broad. Brown or blackish brown (in Svensson's brown, often less brightly marked). Inner central cross-line forms two V-marks in trailing half, usually roughly level (in Svensson's trailing V usually protrudes further out). Crucially, on hindwing underside copper restricted to outer third, ending abruptly at dark cross-band, basal two-thirds clear pale straw, speckled grey-brown streak along leading edge. In Svensson's, copper extends to base in trailing half, grey-brown speckling extensive, with basal third not or hardly paler. **FS** July-October. **Hab** BWd Sc H G.

Svensson's Copper Underwing *Amphipyra berbera* ssp. *svenssoni* Common S,C,Ir **FW** 21-26mm. See Copper Underwing. **FS** Late July-mid September. **Hab** BWd Sc H G.

Mouse Moth *Amphipyra tragopoginis* Common T **FW** 16-18mm. Forewing shiny, mousy brown. Almost plain with three dark central spots. Often runs rapidly, mouse-like, to cover. **FS** July-October. **Hab** Ub.

Old Lady *Mormo maura* Local S,C,(N),Ir **FW** 30-36mm. Unmistakable, large. Forewing and hindwing very broad, dark brown. Forewing sometimes pink-tinged. **FS** July-September. **Hab** Wt G H Sc Wd.

Bird's Wing *Dypterygia scabriuscula* Local S,C,(SW) **FW** 16mm. Forewing chocolate-brown. Pale brown patch in trailing corner, with moth at rest resembling a pair of bird's wings. **FS** Late May-July; (in south, August-September). **Hab** BWd H Sc A G.

Brown Rustic *Rusina ferruginea* Common T **FW** M 16-18mm, F 14-16mm. Forewing blunt, light to dark brown, broader in male (with feathered antennae). 5-6 small whitish spots along leading edge. Female smaller with narrower, more rounded forewing. Female Square-spot Rustic (p.106) lacks whitish spots on leading edge. **FS** June-July. **Hab** Ub.

Guernsey Underwing *Polyphaenis sericata* Channel Islands **FW** 17-20mm. Forewing greyish green, leading edge curved. Fine, dark, white-edged cross-lines, the outer central deeply scalloped. Hindwing orange with broad dark brown border. See Straw Underwing, Orache Moth. **FS** June-August. **Hab** C.

Straw Underwing *Thalpophila matura* Common S,C,(N,Ir) **FW** 17-20mm. Forewing quite broad, with leading edge straight. Grey-brown, brown or dark brown, sometimes marked reddish or dusted white. Hindwing straw yellow, border brown. See Guernsey Underwing, Hedge Rustic (p.112). **FS** Late July-August. **Hab** Ub.

Orache Moth *Trachea atriplicis* Rare immigrant; former resident S; resident Channel Islands **FW** 20-22mm. Forewing grey-brown, strongly marbled green. Conspicuous oblique central pinkish-white flash. See Guernsey Underwing. **FS** June-August. **Hab** Wt Gr.

Small Angle Shades *Euplexia lucipara* Common T **FW** 14-17mm. Forewing dark brown, tinged pinkish brown. Kidney bright, straw yellow. Rests with forewings creased, horizontal, head slightly down. **FS** June-July; (in southern England, September). **Hab** Ub.

Angle Shades *Phlogophora meticulosa* Commc Immigrant T **FW** 21-25mm. Unmistakable. Rests li Small Angle Shades. Usually olive green and pinkis brown when fresh, fading to brown. **FS** All year, mainly May-June; August-October. Often seen at rest by day, sitting openly. **Hab** Ub.

Purple Cloud *Actinotia polyodon* Immigrant S **FW** 13-15mm. Forewing brown, marbled pinkish purple, without cross-lines. Broad streaks and jagged outer marks pale straw. Kidney large, pale; oval absent. **FS** Recorded May-June and August.

Pale-shouldered Cloud *Actinotia hyperici* Rare immigrant S **FW** 12-16mm. Forewing grey, cloude whitish and indistinctly with brown, notably beyonc kidney. Oval and kidney whitish. Base with large whitish patch in leading half and long black streak. **FS** In mainland Europe 2-3 generations, May-Octobe

Berber *Pseudenargia ulicis* Suspected rare immigrant S **FW** 17-19mm. Forewing rather pointed, light or dark grey-brown or reddish brown, rather plain. Central cross-lines strongly converging to trailing edge. [Not illustrated.]

Latin *Callopistria juventina* Rare immigrant S **FW** 15-16mm. Forewing brown with fine whitish cross-lines, central ones thickly edged pink. Oval, kidney and veins pale. Irregular pale outer streaks and usually blotch near tip, whitish. Legs very hairy. **FS** In mainland Europe, June-July.

Double Kidney *Ipimorpha retusa* Local S,C **FW** 13-15mm. Similar to Olive. Forewing distinctly hooked, darker olive brown, often dusted grey anc tinged pink. Fine pale cross-lines roughly parallel, inner central often curved toward base in trailing half, outer central straight or slightly wavy. See Olive. **FS** Late July-early September. **Hab** BWd Wt.

Olive *Ipimorpha subtusa* Local S,C,(N,Ir) **FW** 14-16mm. Similar to Double Kidney. Forewing not or only slightly hooked, paler olive brown, nev pinkish. Inner central cross-line usually angled awa from base in trailing half, outer one curved. **FS** Late July-early September. **Hab** BWd Wt G.

Angle-striped Sallow *Enargia paleacea* Nb; suspected immigrant C,N,(Ir) **FW** 17-20mm. Forewing yellow or orange-yellow, sometimes slightly hooked. Cross-lines fine, dark brown, inne central strongly elbowed, outer central curved. Kidney with dark spot in trailing half. Hindwing yellowish white. Markings sometimes very faint (se Sallow). **FS** July-September. **Hab** BWd.

underside of hindwing

Copper Underwing
Amphipyra pyramidea

underside of hindwing

Svensson's Copper Underwing
Amphipyra berbera svenssoni

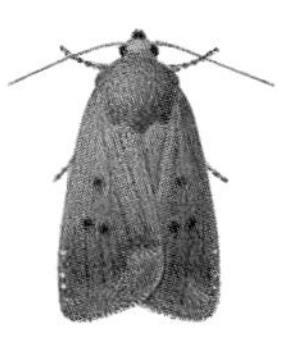

Mouse Moth
Amphipyra tragopoginis

Old Lady
Mormo maura

Bird's Wing
Dypterygia scabriuscula

♂

♀

Brown Rustic
Rusina ferruginea

Guernsey Underwing
Polyphaenis sericata

Straw Underwing
Thalpophila matura

Drache Moth
achea atriplicis

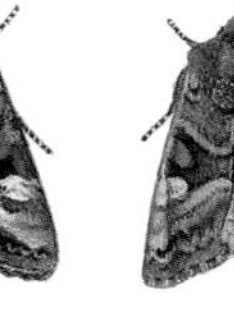

Small Angle Shades
Euplexia lucipara

Angle Shades
Phlogophora meticulosa

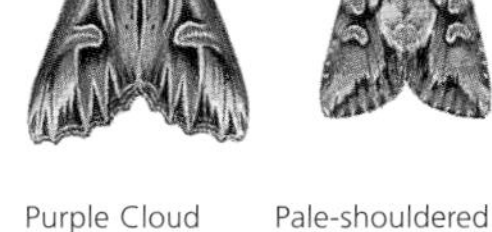

Purple Cloud
Actinotia polyodon

Pale-shouldered Cloud
Actinotia hyperici

Latin
oistria juventina

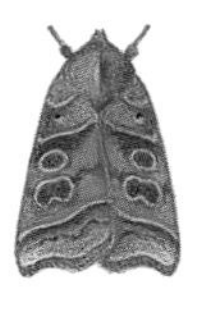

Double Kidney
Ipimorpha retusa

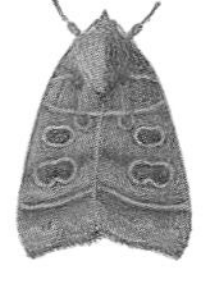

Olive
Ipimorpha subtusa

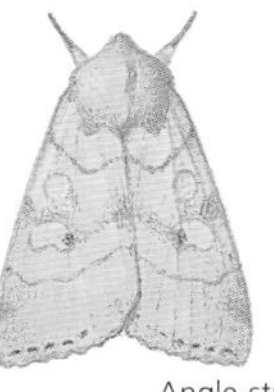

Angle-striped Sallow
Enargia paleacea

Suspected *Parastichtis suspecta* Local T **FW** 14-16mm. Rather slender. Forewing narrow at base, rather tapered. Rather plain greyish-, reddish- or purplish brown, or more variegated (especially in north and west) sometimes with yellowish brown. Very fine dark outer central cross-line, scalloped or formed by tiny black dots or dashes. If worn, see Common Rustic and Lesser Common Rustic (forewing tip blunt). **FS** July-August. **Hab** Wd A M Wt.

Dingy Shears *Parastichtis ypsillon* Local S,C,(N,Ir) **FW** 15-19mm. Forewing with leading edge gently curved. Rather plain soft grey-brown. Central tooth-mark and blackish edging on oval and kidney. Dog's Tooth (p.110) has outermost cross-line white, forming distinct central W. **FS** Late June-early August. **Hab** BWd Wt.

Heart Moth *Dicycla oo* RDB S **FW** 15-17mm. Forewing golden yellow, sometimes extensively clouded and banded reddish- or grey-brown. Markings reddish brown. Kidney broad, often heart-shaped. **FS** Late June-mid July. **Hab** BWd H.

Lesser-spotted Pinion *Cosmia affinis* Local S,(C) **FW** 12-16mm. Forewing reddish brown or dull grey-brown tinged reddish. Central cross-lines broader and white toward leading edge, especially strongly elbowed outer central one. Further small whitish blotch and blackish spot near tip, both sometimes faint. Hindwing inner half dark grey-brown, outer half blackish. Forewings held at steep angle at rest. See White-spotted and Lunar-spotted Pinions. **FS** Mid July-late August. **Hab** BWd H.

White-spotted Pinion *Cosmia diffinis* pRDB SE,(C) **FW** 14-16mm. Somewhat similar to Lesser-spotted Pinion and also rests with forewings steeply angled; forewing broader, richer reddish brown with large, bold white blotches on leading edge. Hindwing grey-brown. See also Lunar-spotted Pinion. **FS** Late July-late August. **Hab** BWd H.

Dun-bar *Cosmia trapezina* Common T **FW** 13-16mm. Forewing brown, grey-brown or reddish brown. Inner central cross-line very oblique, outer central curved or elbowed. Paler forms with black spot in trailing end of kidney. **FS** Mid July-mid September. **Hab** BWd H Sc G.

Lunar-spotted Pinion *Cosmia pyralina* Local S,(C) **FW** 13-16mm. Similar to Lesser-spotted Pinion and also rests with forewings steeply angled; forewing broader, richer pinkish brown. Diffuse white or white-outlined roughly half-moon shaped blotch toward tip on leading edge and black spot(s) near tip usually larger. Inner central cross-line not (or barely) edged white. Hindwing grey-brown. **FS** Early July-late August. **Hab** BWd H G.

Saxon *Hyppa rectilinea* Nb. N,(Ir) **FW** 16-19mm. Forewing base grey with 1-2 thick black bars, inner edge of darker central band very jagged in trailing half, outer edge strongly edged white in trailing half. Oval small, flattened. Thick black central bar. See Light Brocade (p.108). **FS** Late May-June. **Hab** M Sc Wd.

Dark Arches *Apamea monoglypha* Common T **FW** 19-26mm. Forewing rather tapered, grey-brown, pale greyish straw, dark brown or blackish (especially in north). Oval and kidney large. Outermost cross-line with central W. Thorax with dark V either side. See Northern Arches, Exile, Crescent Striped. **FS** June-August; (in south, September-November). **Hab** Ub.

Light Arches *Apamea lithoxylaea* Common T **FW** 18-23mm. Forewing rather tapered, light reddish straw, with fine dark streaks and dots. Short, dark, roughly scythe-shaped central mark (thickened in middle), two poorly defined brownish wedges, or smudges, on outer edge. See Reddish Light Arches. **FS** Late June-early August. **Hab** Gr Wd H G.

Reddish Light Arches *Apamea sublustris* Local S,(C,Ir) **FW** 18-21mm. Similar to Light Arches. Forewing generally darker, broader. Dark wedges on outer edge clearly defined; brown central mark usually shorter, thicker (or evenly thickened). **FS** June-July. **Hab** CGr Sd Sh.

Northern Arches *Apamea zeta* ssp. *assimilis* Na. N; **Exile** ssp. *marmorata* Shetland
Northern Arches: **FW** 17-19mm. Quite thickset, thorax deep-scaled, without well-defined crests. Forewing broad, blunt, usually rich dark brown or blackish, less often paler, more variegated. Pale markings sometimes pinkish brown. See Confused, Dark Arches, also Dusky and Dark Brocades (both with sharply defined double crest on thorax).
Exile: **FW** 19-20mm. More strongly marked and less reddish. Forewing honey-brown to blackish. **FS** July-August. **Hab** Up Gr.

Crescent Striped *Apamea oblonga* Nb. S,C,(Ir) **FW** 18-21mm. Forewing quite broad, grey-brown, smooth, silky, sometimes faintly marked. Kidney partly outlined whitish. Outermost cross-line with distinct central W, or broken. Sometimes a solid dark central bar. See White Colon (p.108), Dusky Brocade (smaller with more curved leading edge), Dark Arches, Confused, Large Nutmeg. All lack silky texture. **FS** Late June-early August. **Hab** Sm Gr Sd Wt.

Suspected
Parastichtis suspecta

Dingy Shears
Parastichtis ypsillon

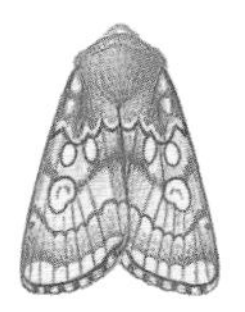
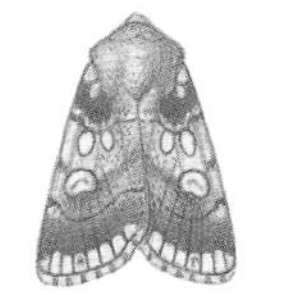

Heart Moth
Dicycla oo

Lesser-spotted Pinion
Cosmia affinis

White-spotted Pinion
Cosmia diffinis

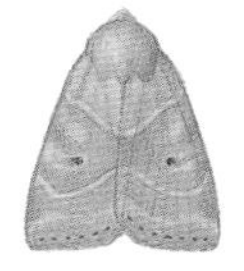

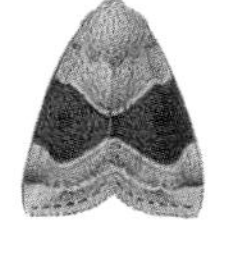
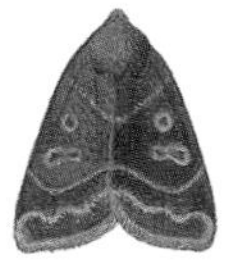

Dun-bar
Cosmia trapezina f. *badiofasciata*

Lunar-spotted Pinion
Cosmia pyralina

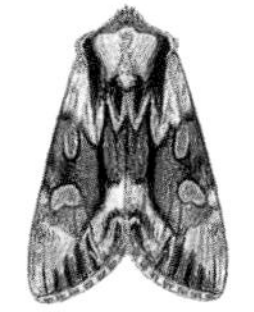

Saxon
Hyppa rectilinea

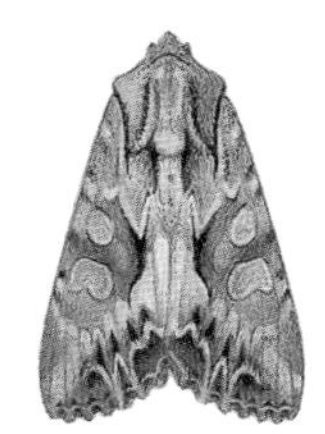

Dark Arches
Apamea monoglypha f. *aethiops*

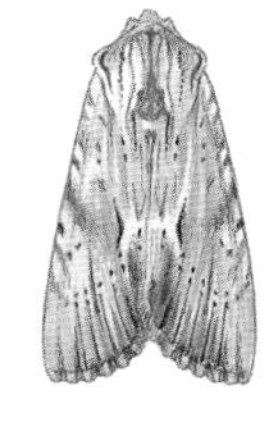

Light Arches
Apamea lithoxylaea

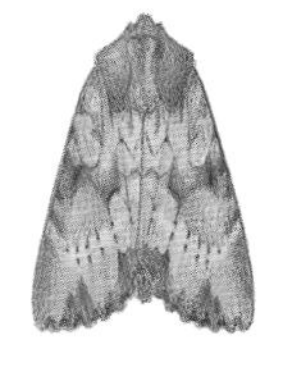

Reddish Light Arches
Apamea sublustris

orthern Arches
nea zeta assimilis

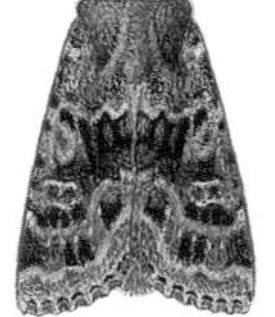

Exile
Apamea zeta marmorata

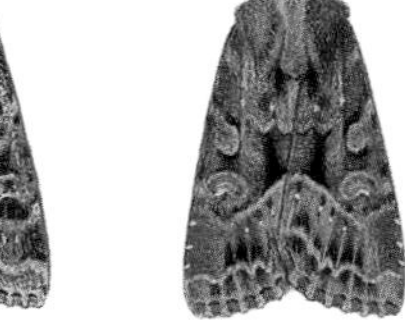

Crescent Striped
Apamea oblonga

Clouded-bordered Brindle *Apamea crenata* Common T **FW** 18-22mm. In one form forewing light yellowish, tinged red or grey, trailing half often white. Two reddish-brown wedges from outer edge, that near trailing edge long. F. *combusta* dark reddish brown, oval and kidney pale-outlined. See Clouded Brindle, Scarce Brindle. **FS** Late May-July. **Hab** Ub.

Clouded Brindle *Apamea epomidion* Common S,C,(N),Ir **FW** 17-20mm. Forewing from brown with pale brown marbling, to pale brown with darker marbling. Dark outer border wavy with two short, ill-defined dark wedges. Two short, thick, dark basal streaks. Oval and basal side of kidney outlined dark brown. See Clouded-bordered Brindle. **FS** June-July. **Hab** BWd Sc H G.

Scarce Brindle *Apamea lateritia* Immigrant S,(N) **FW** 19-24mm. Forewing rather plain, reddish-, yellowish-, greyish- or dull brown, or blackish. Usually very fine central cross-lines, the outer scalloped, or black dashes on veins. White dots on leading edge. Outer edge of kidney outlined chalky white. Oval indistinct. See Clouded-bordered Brindle (f. *combusta*), Pale Shining Brown (p.108). **FS** July-August.

Confused *Apamea furva* ssp. *britannica* Local N,W,(S,Ir) **FW** 16-19mm. Forewing dull grey-brown. Leading edge straight. Markings fine, often rather indistinct. Tuft of long scales near base of trailing edge. See Dusky Brocade f. *obscura* (forewing lacking scale tuft on trailing edge). See also Northern Arches, Crescent Striped, Nutmeg (p.108). **FS** July-September. **Hab** Up Cl Sd.

Dusky Brocade *Apamea remissa* Common T **FW** 17-19mm Forewing with leading edge curved. Outermost cross-line often with distinct central W. Brownish grey with markings inconspicuous (f. *obscura*), or markings stronger with central black bar and two basal streaks, or sometimes paler, brownish (f. *submissa*). See Confused, Dog's Tooth (p.110), Crescent Striped, White Colon (p.108), Dark Brocade (p.120), Large Nutmeg, Light Brocade, Pale-shouldered Brocade (p.110). **FS** June-July. **Hab** Gr.

Small Clouded Brindle *Apamea unanimis* Common S,C,(N),Ir **FW** 15-17mm. Forewing brownish. Kidney quite large, outlined chalky white. Two dark basal streaks. See Common and Lesser Common Rustics (rarely with two basal streaks, crescent on hindwing smaller and narrower). **FS** Late May-early July. **Hab** Wt Gr BWd.

Large Nutmeg *Apamea anceps* Local S,C **FW** 16-21mm. Forewing sandy, or grey-brown with sandy marbling. Central cross-lines very fine, dark; the inner jagged, the outer scalloped. Basal streak absent or brown, indistinct. See Dusky Brocade f. *obscura*, Rustic Shoulder-knot, Crescent Striped, Pale Shining Brown (p.108). **FS** June-July. **Hab** Gr Ar.

Rustic Shoulder-knot *Apamea sordens* Common T **FW** 16-19mm. Forewing quite broa rather plain sandy- or greyish brown (sometimes reddish-tinged). Black, slightly branched basal streak (sometimes reduced). See Large Nutmeg. **FS** May-July. **Hab** Gr Ar G.

Slender Brindle *Apamea scolopacina* Comm S,C,(Ir) **FW** 14-17mm. Forewing pale straw or orange-brown. Two very fine black scalloped cro lines. Kidney strongly outlined white. Thick dark basal streak on trailing edge and dark brown cre on thorax. **FS** Late June-mid August. **Hab** Wd.

Double Lobed *Apamea ophiogramma* Comm T **FW** 13-16mm. Forewing pale reddish brown, often tinged whitish, or dark brown. Large dark blotch in leading half. Kidney pale. Dark central **FS** June-August. **Hab** Wt Wd G.

Union Rustic *Eremobina pabulatricula* Former resident S,C,N; extinct Forewing whitish grey. Tw black basal streaks. Central cross-band in trailing narrowed, blackish. Reddish thoracic crest. See M Shoulder-knot (p.116). **FS** July-August. **Hab** Wd.

Marbled Minor *Oligia strigilis* Common T **FW** 11-13mm. Marbled, Rufous and Tawny Mar Minors are all variable (often blackish, obscurely marked), and are only reliably separable on geni differences. See also Rosy Minor. **FS** Late May-Ju **Hab** Ub.

Rufous Minor *Oligia versicolor* Local S,C,(N,Ir **FW** 11-12mm. See Marbled Minor. Also Rosy Mi **FS** June-July. **Hab** Wd A Gr Cl.

Tawny Marbled Minor *Oligia latruncula* Common S,C,(N) **FW** 11-13mm. See Marbled Minor. White-banded form is rare in Britain (frequent in Ireland). See also Rosy Minor. **FS** Late May-early August. **Hab** Ub.

Middle-barred Minor *Oligia fasciuncula* Common T **FW** 10-12mm. Quite thickset. Forew orange- or grey-brown. Dark central bar, each er edged white. Female Small Dotted Buff is slimme See also Cloaked and Least Minors. **FS** June-early August. **Hab** Gr Wt Wd G.

Cloaked Minor *Mesoligia furuncula* Common T **FW** 10-12mm. Rather slender. In one form, forewing basal half brown, outer half broadly whitish or grey. Sometimes a short dark central bar (see Rosy Minor – more thickset). Other form greyish white and brown, or almost unmarked straw (sometimes with long blackish trailing strea or brown. See also Least Minor, Small Dotted Bu **FS** Late July-early September. **Hab** Gr.

Rosy Minor *Mesoligia literosa* Common T **FW** 10-13mm. Forewing pinkish brown and grey, or brownish black. Central cross-lines strongly converging, with short dark central bar. See Cloak Minor. Other minors have central cross-lines less convergent. **FS** Mid July-late August. **Hab** Gr C G

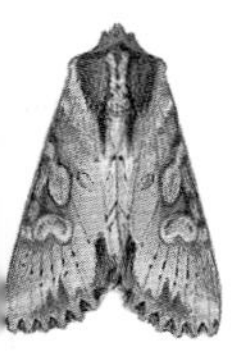

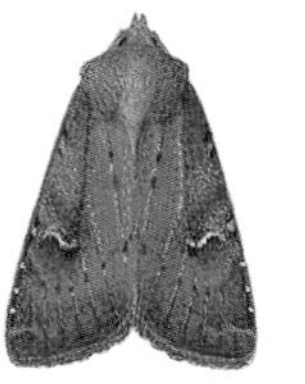

Clouded-bordered Brindle *Apamea crenata*

Clouded Brindle *Apamea epomidion*

Scarce Brindle *Apamea lateritia*

Confused *Apamea furva britannica*

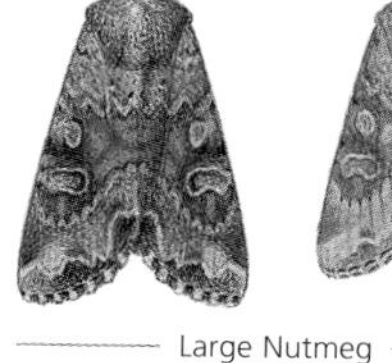

Dusky Brocade *Apamea remissa*

Small Clouded Brindle *Apamea unanimis*

Large Nutmeg *Apamea anceps*

Rustic Shoulder-knot *Apamea sordens*

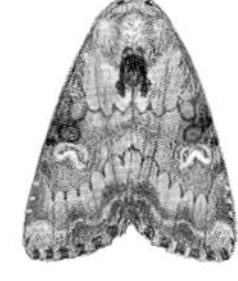

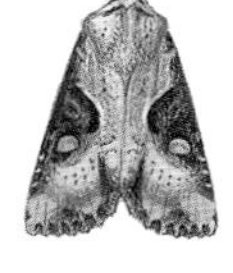
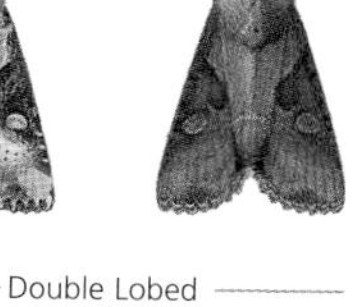

Slender Brindle *Apamea scolopacina*

Double Lobed *Apamea ophiogramma*

Union Rustic *Eremobina pabulatricula*

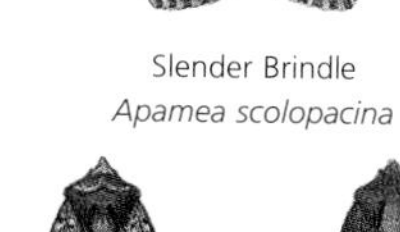

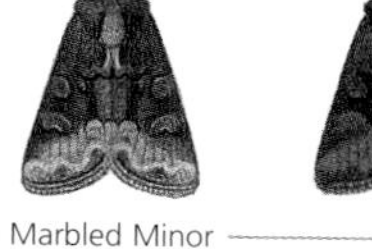

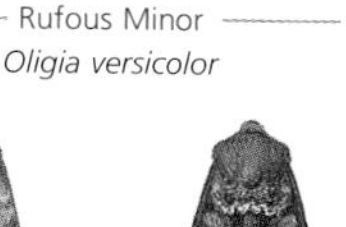

Marbled Minor *Oligia strigilis*

Rufous Minor *Oligia versicolor*

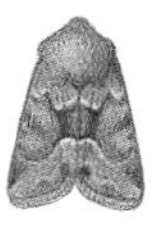

Tawny Marbled Minor *Oligia latruncula*

Burren, Co. Clare

Middle-barred Minor *Oligia fasciuncula*

f. *pallida*

f. *bicoloria*

Cloaked Minor *Mesoligia furuncula*

f. *latistriata*

Rosy Minor *Mesoligia literosa*

f. *aethalodes*

Common Rustic *Mesapamea secalis* Common T **FW** 12-16mm. Extremely variable. Forewing rather blunt. Yellowish-, greyish-, reddish-, blackish brown, or black. Kidney usually marked white. Sometimes a dark central bar. See Lesser Common Rustic and Remm's Rustic (separable only on differences in genitalia), Small Clouded Brindle. Crescent, ear moths and Suspected have sharp-tipped forewing. See also Oak Rustic. **FS** July-August. **Hab** Ub.

Lesser Common Rustic *Mesapamea didyma* Common T **FW** 11-16mm. Only separable from Common Rustic on differences in genitalia. Slightly smaller, on average. Black examples with chalky-white kidney are usually this species. **FS** July-August. **Hab** Ub.

Remm's Rustic *Mesapamea remmi* Local S,C,?N **FW** 11-16mm. Described on the basis of slight differences in genitalia and otherwise indistinguishable from Common Rustic and Lesser Common Rustic. [Not illustrated.]

Least Minor *Photedes captiuncula* ssp. *expolita* RDB C; ssp. *tincta* Ir **FW** 7-9mm. Ssp. *expolita* Forewing brownish. Cross-lines whitish, more pronounced in smaller female. Small examples of Cloaked Minor have forewing narrower, with outer central cross-line straighter. Ssp. *tincta* brighter orange-brown, with stronger white cross-lines. **FS** Mid June-early August. Male active by day. **Hab** CGr.

Small Dotted Buff *Photedes minima* Common T **FW** 11-14mm. Slender. Forewing pale straw, sometimes tinged reddish brown. Broad, rather plain in male. Central cross-lines or dots very fine, blackish. Triangular brown blotch near tip, sometimes a dark outer cross-band. Female smaller, forewing narrower, often with darker central white-edged cross-band. Cloaked Minor has central cross-lines strongly converging (cf. female). See also Middle-barred Minor. **FS** Late June-early August. **Hab** Gr Wd Wt.

Morris's Wainscot *Chortodes morrisii morrisii* RDB SW; **Bond's Wainscot** ssp. *bondii* RDB (probably extinct) SE **FW** 12-14mm. **Morris's Wainscot:** Rather slender, forewing quite broad, leading edge curved. White, very finely dusted blackish, especially near outer margin. Sometimes a curved outer central cross-line of black dots. Hindwing light grey, diffuse grey-brown outer band. **Bond's Wainscot:** Slightly larger, fore- and hindwing slightly darker, tinged brown. Forewing usually with outer central dots stronger. See Concolorous. **FS** Late June-mid July. **Hab** Cl.

Concolorous *Chortodes extrema* RDB S,(EC) **FW** 11-13mm. Forewing whitish. Curved outer row of black dots (may be faint) and sometimes inner dots. Kidney pale and very faint, or absent. Hindwing grey. See Mere (similar in shape), Small, Morris's and Bond's Wainscots. **FS** Mid May-mid July. **Hab** Wt Wd.

Lyme Grass *Chortodes elymi* Nb. SE,EC,NE **FW** 15-18mm. Forewing rather narrow, almost p light brown with faint row of outer dots, or hea streaked dark brown. Hindwing white. **FS** Mid Ju early August. **Hab** Sd.

Mere Wainscot *Chortodes fluxa* Nb. S,EC **FW** 12-15mm. Quite thickset. Forewing with leading edge almost straight. Creamy white to sandy or reddish brown. Rather plain with cross-lines faint or formed by tiny black dots, or with darker clouding. Kidney with grey spot in trailing half. Hindwing whitish or pale grey. See Concolorous. Also Small Wainscot (forewing narrower). **FS** July-mid August. **Hab** Wd Wt.

Small Wainscot *Chortodes pygmina* Commo **FW** 10-14mm. Quite thickset. Forewing rather li straw, pinkish straw, orange-, pinkish- or reddish brown. Usually with dark streaks and dusting and faint, curved, outer cross-line of dark dots. Kidney absent. Hindwing grey. See Mere Wainsc Concolorous, Small Rufous. **FS** August-Septemb **Hab** Wt Wd.

Fenn's Wainscot *Chortodes brevilinea* RDB E **FW** 14-17mm. Forewing rather broad, blunt. Sandy brown, extensively speckled and dusted blackish, cross-lines formed by black dots. Often short black basal streak (absent in f. *sinelinea*). S Brown-veined Wainscot (much smaller, forewing more rounded, with distinct kidney). See also Webb's and Rush Wainscots. **FS** Mid July-mid August. **Hab** Wt.

Dusky Sallow *Eremobia ochroleuca* Commor S,EC **FW** 14-16mm. Forewing marbled tawny o olive brown and straw. Broad, dark, whitish-edg central band, pinched centrally. Fringes chequere See Viper's Bugloss (p.110). **FS** Late July-early September. Sometimes active by day, often restir on flowers, especially knapweeds. **Hab** Gr.

Flounced Rustic *Luperina testacea* Common T **FW** 14-18mm. Rather thickset. Forewing usually coarse textured. Dull straw, light or dark brown, often dusted with grey, or blackish brow Sometimes a dark central bar. Hindwing usually whitish, tinged brown. See Sandhill and Dumeril Rustics. **FS** August-September. Does not feed. **Hab** Gr.

Sandhill Rustic *Luperina nickerlii* ssp. *demuth* Na. SE,E; ssp. *leechi* RDB SW; ssp. *gueneei* RDB WC; ssp. *knilli* Ir **FW** 15-18mm. Similar to some forms of Flounced Rustic. Forewing with oval ver small and round. Kidney outlined white. Hindwi usually silky white. Ssp. *leechi* forewing silvery w with darker grey central band. Ssp. *knilli* forewin brown. Ssp. *gueneei* forewing shades of light brown. Ssp. *demuthi* forewing straw to sandy re or dark brown, hindwing sometimes with brown margin. See also Dumeril's Rustic. **FS** Late July-la September. Rests on grass stems at night. **Hab** Sd Sm Cl.

Common Rustic
Mesapamea secalis

Lesser Common Rustic
Mesapamea didyma

Least Minor
Photedes captiuncula expolita
Photedes captiuncula tincta

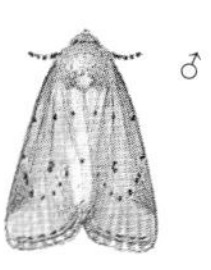
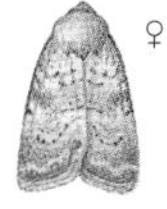
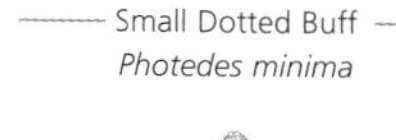

♂ ♀

Small Dotted Buff
Photedes minima

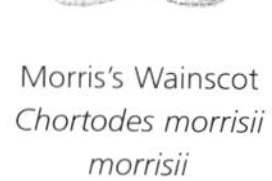

Morris's Wainscot
Chortodes morrisii morrisii

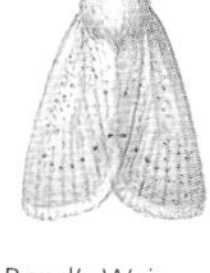

Bond's Wainscot
Chortodes morrisii bondii

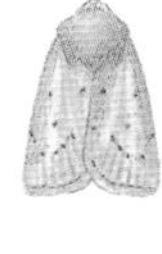

Concolorous
Chortodes extrema

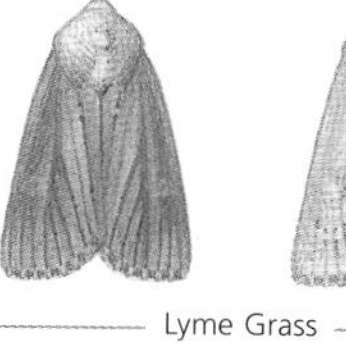

Lyme Grass
Chortodes elymi

Mere Wainscot
Chortodes fluxa

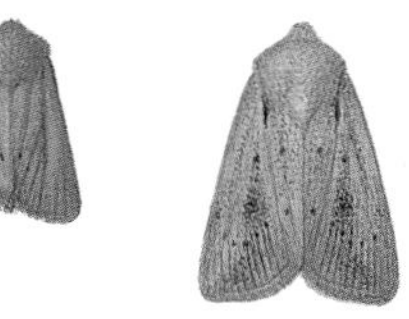

Small Wainscot
Chortodes pygmina

Fenn's Wainscot
Chortodes brevi-linea

Dusky Sallow
Eremobia ochroleuca

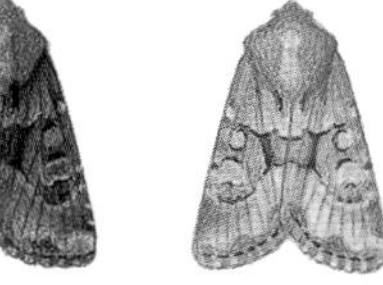

Flounced Rustic
Luperina testacea

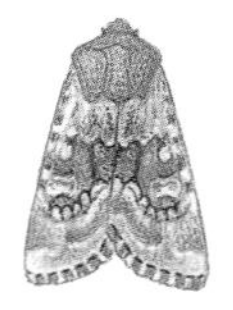
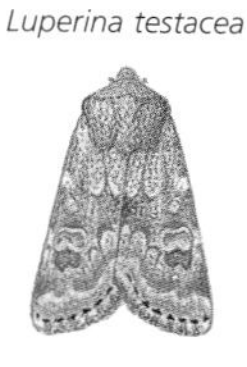

Sandhill Rustic

Luperina nickerlii demuthi

Luperina nickerlii leechi

Luperina nickerlii gueneei

Luperina nickerlii knilli

Dumeril's Rustic *Luperina dumerilii* Immigrant S **FW** 11-16mm. Variable. Forewing yellowish or straw, reddish brown or grey-brown. Often a broad, pale outer cross-band. Oval elongated, oblique. Outer central cross-line strongly oblique in trailing half. Central band often darker, with dark bar. In plainer forms, central veins often pale. See Flounced Rustic (forewing with coarse texture), Sandhill Rustic. **FS** August-September.

Scarce Arches *Luperina zollikoferi* Immigrant S,C,N **FW** 18-25mm. Forewing pale fawn. Kidney pale-outlined (sometimes indistinct) with dark spot in trailing half. In one form all markings weak. In f. *internigrata* forewing dusted blackish centrally with veins pale, blackish streak at base and on trailing edge, and dark outer wedges. See Bulrush Wainscot (broader, more rounded forewing), Large Wainscot (more pointed forewing, kidney absent or very faint). **FS** August-October.

Large Ear *Amphipoea lucens* Local SW,WC,N,Ir **FW** 14-17mm. The four species of ear moth are only reliably distinguishable on differences in their genitalia. All have forewing quite sharp-tipped or slightly hooked. Brown, reddish brown, or olive brown. Dark, wavy cross-lines. Kidney usually conspicuous, white or orange. Large moths with dark, strong cross-lines on the undersides of wings are most likely to be Large Ear. See also Crescent (lacks dark, wavy cross-lines), Common Rustic. **FS** August-September. **Hab** Wt M.

Saltern Ear *Amphipoea fucosa* ssp. *paludis* Local S,C,NW,(Ir) **FW** 14-16mm. See under Large Ear. Kidney often narrow. **FS** August-September. **Hab** Sd Sm Wt (in north).

Crinan Ear *Amphipoea crinanensis* Local W,C,N,Ir **FW** 13-15mm. See under Large Ear. Kidney and oval usually orange. **FS** August-September. **Hab** M Up Gr Sd.

Ear Moth *Amphipoea oculea* Common T **FW** 12-15mm. See under Large Ear. In southern lowland Britain away from the coasts, the most likely species, and not restricted to damp habitats. **FS** Late July-September. **Hab** Gr Wd Wt Sm.

Rosy Rustic *Hydraecia micacea* Common T **FW** 14-21mm. Forewing quite pointed, texture smooth and velvety (when fresh), pale to dark pinkish brown, purplish brown, less often dull brown. Usually a darker central cross-band, its outer edge oblique, gently curved or straight, sharply reflexed at leading edge. See Butterbur. **FS** August-October. **Hab** Ub.

Butterbur *Hydraecia petasitis* Local S,C,N **FW** 19-23mm. Not unlike Rosy Rustic, but forewin broader, leading edge usually more curved. Brown (not pinkish) and usually larger. Outermost cross-lir more jagged, usually forming a distinct W centrally **FS** August-early September. **Hab** Wt Gr.

Marsh Mallow Moth *Hydraecia osseola* ssp. *hucherardi* RDB SE **FW** 18-20mm. Forewing broad, quite pointed, straw coloured. Kidney pale-outlined, variably darkened internally. Usually dark outer cross-band. Hindwing whitish. **FS** Late August-September. **Hab** Gr Wt.

Frosted Orange *Gortyna flavago* Common T **FW** 16-19mm. Forewing broad, slightly hooked. Grey-brown, with broad striking golden yellow central cross-band, oval and kidney, outer band (sometimes faint) and basal blotch. See Fisher's Estuarine Moth. **FS** Late August-October. **Hab** Ub.

Fisher's Estuarine Moth *Gortyna borelii* ssp. *lunata* RDB (Protected) SE **FW** 21-24mm. Not unlike Frosted Orange, but larger. Oval and kidney white. Golden central cross-band with strong, fine scalloped cross-line near its outer edge (usually ve fine or faint in Frosted Orange). **FS** Early Septemb late October. **Hab** Gr.

Burren Green *Calamia tridens* ssp. *occidentalis* **FW** 17-18mm. Forewing green with whitish kidne and oval. Hindwing whitish. **FS** Late July-August. **Hab** CGr.

Haworth's Minor *Celaena haworthii* Local C,N,(S),Ir **FW** 10-14mm. Forewing blunt, reddish brown (sometimes pinkish) or dark purplish brown Kidney conspicuous, whitish with forked whitish veins extending outwards. Sometimes a pale diag- onal outer cross-band. See Crescent (especially ssp. *scotica*), forewing usually longer, more pointe and rarely flies by day. **FS** August-September. Mal active by day and at early dusk, also at night. **Hab** Wt M.

Crescent *Celaena leucostigma leucostigma* Loca S,C,N,Ir; ssp. *scotica* Local northern Scotland **FW** 14-17mm. Ssp. *leucostigma*: Forewing some- what pointed, dark chocolate- or reddish brown. Rather plain or with pale brown diagonal outer band and veins white near kidney. Kidney rather narrow, chalky white or pale buff. Ssp. *scotica*: Smaller, darker, more brightly marked. Irish moths are also dark, but not smaller. Ear moths have fin dark, wavy cross-lines. See also Haworth's Minor, Common and Lesser Common Rustics. **FS** Late Ju September. **Hab** Wt M.

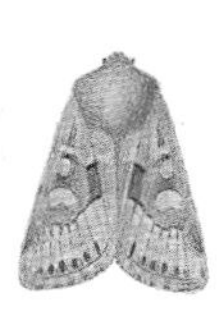

Dumeril's Rustic
Luperina dumerilii

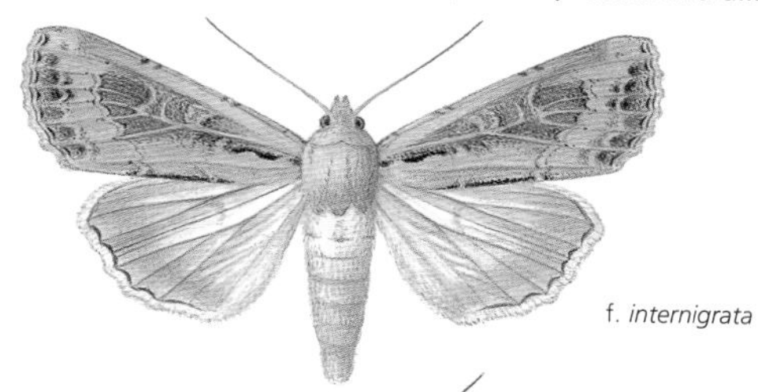

f. *internigrata*

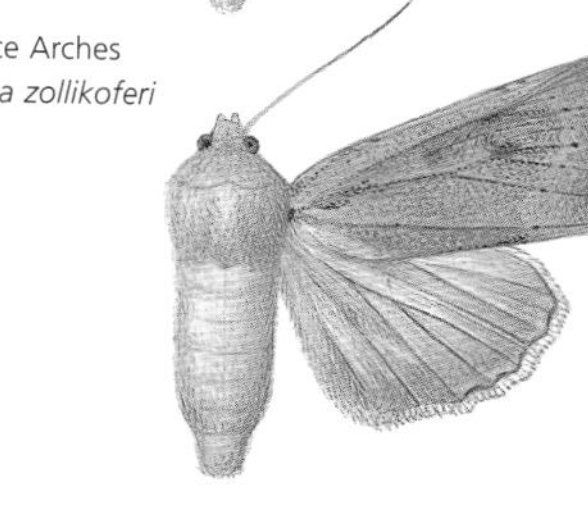

Scarce Arches
Luperina zollikoferi

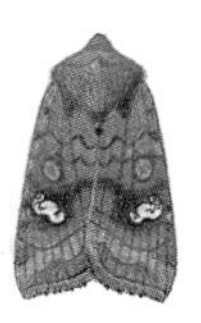

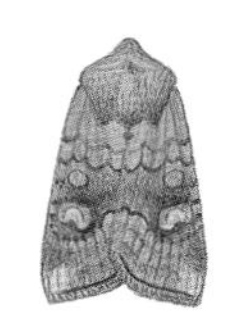

Large Ear
Amphipoea lucens

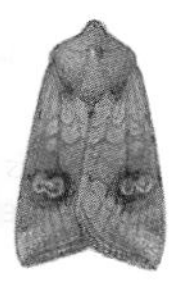
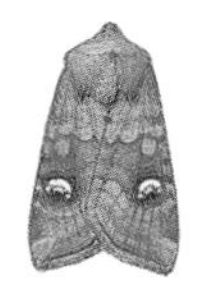

Saltern Ear
Amphipoea fucosa paludis

Crinan Ear
Amphipoea crinanensis

Ear Moth
Amphipoea oculea

Rosy Rustic
Hydraecia micacea

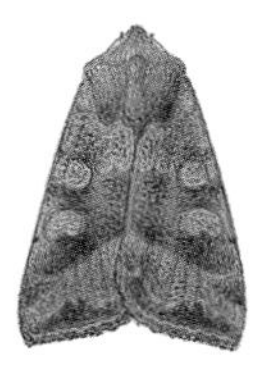

Butterbur
Hydraecia petasitis

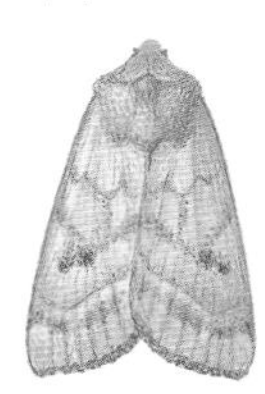

Marsh Mallow Moth
Hydraecia osseola hucherardi

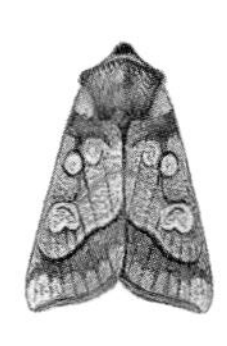

Frosted Orange
Gortyna flavago

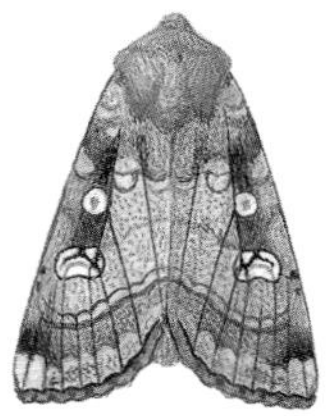

Fisher's Estuarine Moth
Gortyna borelii lunata

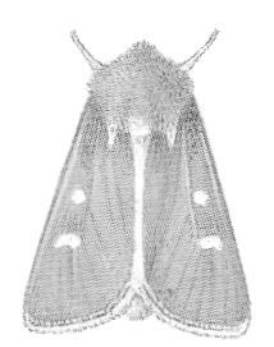

Burren Green
Calamia tridens occidentalis

Haworth's Minor
Celaena haworthii

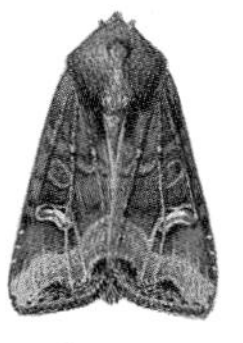

Crescent
Celaena leucostigma leucostigma
Celaena leucostigma scotica

Bulrush Wainscot *Nonagria typhae* Common S,C,(N),Ir **FW** 20-24mm. Forewing broad, rather blunt. Light and dark streaks and dots, and grey-white veins. Small, blackish dashes or crescents along outer edge and (usually) an outer cross-line of fine arrowheads. In male, light reddish brown, sometimes darker. Female light straw or darker greyish straw. Widespread f. *fraterna* is dark brown or blackish, with indistinct markings. See Large and Webb's Wainscots, Scarce Arches. **FS** Late July-late September. Does not feed. **Hab** Wt.

Twin-spotted Wainscot *Archanara geminipuncta* Local S,EC,(Ir) **FW** 11-16mm. Forewing broad, blunt. Light-, reddish-, greyish- or dark brown, or blackish. Rather plain. Central and outer veins sometimes blackish or whitish. Kidney narrow, often divided, sometimes faint, chalky white with dark edging or entirely dark. Brown-veined Wainscot (dark form) is more slender, forewing narrower near base, kidney usually broader. See also Rush Wainscot. **FS** Early August-mid September. Does not feed. **Hab** Wt.

Brown-veined Wainscot *Archanara dissoluta* Local S,C **FW** 12-15mm. Forewing broad and blunt in male, narrower and more pointed in female. Usually dull straw or reddish straw, dusted grey and black (female often greyer). Diffuse brown streak from base, in male broadening to outer edge, in female restricted to base. Kidney outlined white, most strongly in blackish trailing half, less often entirely dark-filled. Hindwing light grey. Central spot on underside of fore- and hindwing. Less frequent form dark or blackish brown. See White-mantled, Twin-spotted, Silky and Fenn's Wainscots. **FS** Late July-early September. **Hab** Wt.

White-mantled Wainscot *Archanara neurica* RDB SE **FW** 12-13mm. Similar to Brown-veined Wainscot, but more slender, with narrow white band on collar and lacking central spot on underside of fore- and hindwing. **FS** July-early August. **Hab** Wt.

Webb's Wainscot *Archanara sparganii* Nb. S,SE,SW,(Ir) **FW** 15-18mm. Forewing broad, rather blunt. Reddish brown or reddish straw to pale straw or whitish. Dark central streak (sometimes faint), variable streaking and dusting. Faint kidney with trailing half strongly edged or ringed black. Outer edge with row of black dots. Hindwing whitish, often streaked grey. See Rush and Bulrush Wainscots. **FS** August-early October. **Hab** Wt.

Rush Wainscot *Archanara algae* RDB SE,EC,Ir **FW** 14-18mm. Forewing broad, slightly hooked. In male orange-brown, in female straw or reddish straw. Diffuse narrow dark central streak and variable dark clouding, dusting and outer border. Outer edge with very fine dark line or dashes. Fai kidney filled grey at trailing end. Hindwing grey with rather faint dark central cross-line (stronger on underside). Irish moths are generally darker, and more heavily marked. See Webb's and Large Wainscots. **FS** August-September. **Hab** Wt.

Large Wainscot *Rhizedra lutosa* Common T **FW** 16-23mm. Very variable in size. Forewing pointed, often slightly hooked, light greyish straw reddish straw, lightly or (less often) heavily dusted and streaked black. Outer central curved cross-ro of fine dark dots, occasionally merged into a jagg cross-line. Hindwing whitish, lightly or (less often) heavily dusted grey, usually with central row of da dashes. See Blair's, Rush and Bulrush Wainscots, Scarce Arches. **FS** August-October. **Hab** Wt.

Blair's Wainscot *Sedina buettneri* RDB S **FW** 12-14mm. Forewing very pointed. Straw-coloured, with central grey streak and fine streaki and dusting. Hindwing dark grey with pale streak See Large Wainscot, also Reed Dagger (p.126) (larger, hindwing white). **FS** Late September-mid October. **Hab** Wt.

Fen Wainscot *Arenostola phragmitidis* Local S,EC,(WC) **FW** 14-16mm. Rather slender. Forewir broad, light or dull straw or light reddish brown. Plain, diffusely darker in outer third, fringe dark. Hindwing grey, fringe whitish. **FS** July-August. **Hab** Wt.

Brighton Wainscot *Oria musculosa* pRDB S **FW** 12-16mm. Forewing quite pointed, tip rounde leading edge straight. Sandy brown with broad creamy stripes. **FS** Late July-mid August. Has beer disturbed in large numbers by day during cereal harvesting. **Hab** Ar Gr.

Small Rufous *Coenobia rufa* Local S,C,(N,Ir) **FW** 10-12mm. Slender. Forewing rather rounded, straw-white, pinkish straw, pinkish-, reddish- or smoky brown, finely and variably dusted and streaked grey. Outer cross-line of dark dots. See Small Wainscot (much more thickset). **FS** July-August. Flies from an hour before dusk, and at night. **Hab** Wt.

Treble Lines *Charanyca trigrammica* Common S,C,Ir **FW** 15-17mm. Quite thickset. Forewing fairly broad, with three complete fairly straight da cross-lines. Pale to dark, rather milky greyish brow or orange-brown. Sometimes dark shading outsid central cross-line, less often extending to outer edge. Uncommon f. *obscura* dark grey-brown, cross-lines pale-edged. **FS** May-early July. **Hab** Ub

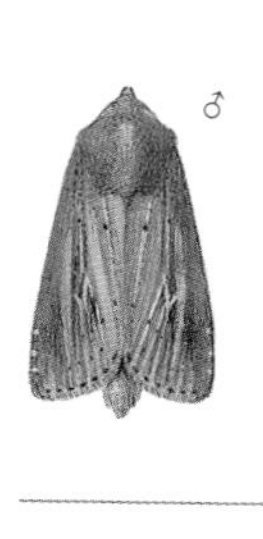

♂

f. *fraterna* ♂

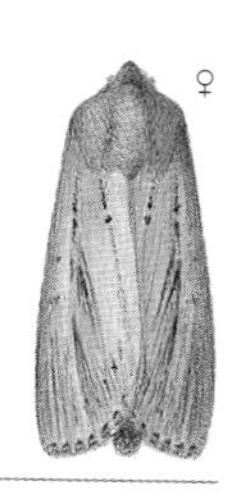

♀

Bulrush Wainscot
Nonagria typhae

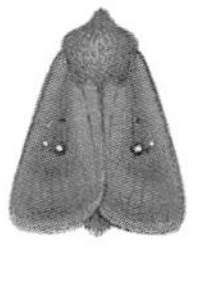

Twin-spotted Wainscot
Archanara geminipuncta

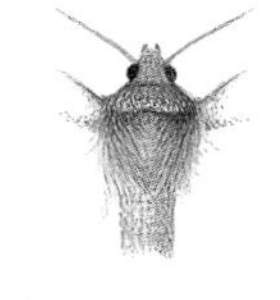

f. *arundineta*

Brown-veined Wainscot
Archanara dissoluta

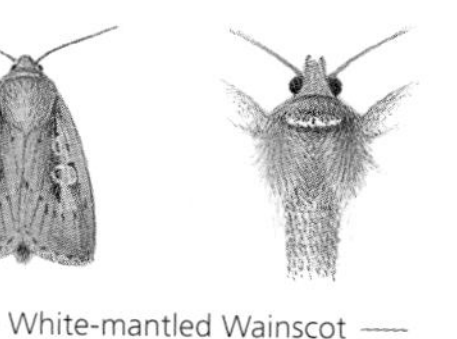

White-mantled Wainscot
Archanara neurica

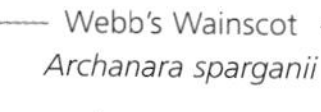

Webb's Wainscot
Archanara sparganii

♂ ♀

Rush Wainscot
Archanara algae

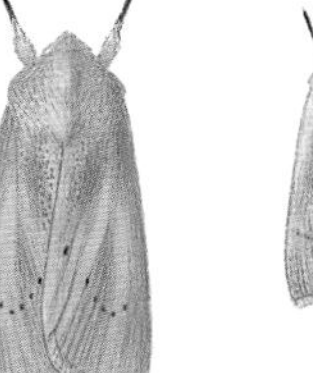

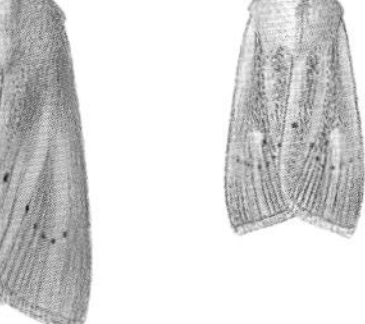

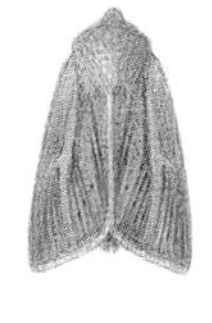

Large Wainscot
Rhizedra lutosa

Blair's Wainscot
Sedina buettneri

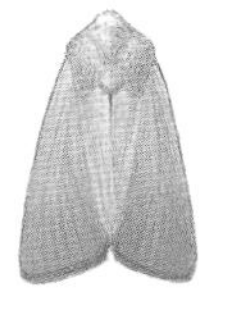

Fen Wainscot
Arenostola phragmitidis
f. *rufescens*

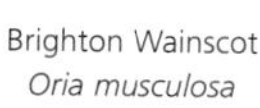

Brighton Wainscot
Oria musculosa

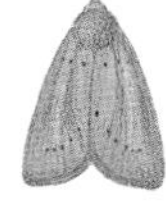

Small Rufous
Coenobia rufa

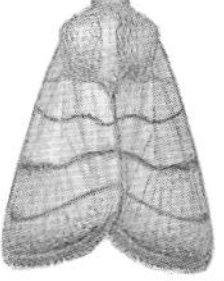

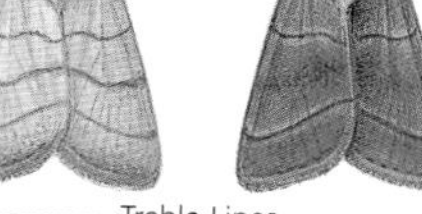

Treble Lines
Charanyca trigrammica

Uncertain *Hoplodrina alsines* Common S,C,(N),Ir **FW** 14-16mm. Forewing brown or tawny brown, sometimes dusted grey, especially along cross-lines. Oval and kidney pale-outlined. Dark, rather narrow central cross-band, sometimes indistinct. Hindwing in male grey-brown; darker, more uniformly grey-brown in female. See Rustic. Also Powdered, Vine's and Mottled Rustics. **FS** Mid June-mid August; (late autumn). **Hab** Ub.

Rustic *Hoplodrina blanda* Common T **FW** 13-16mm. Very similar to Uncertain, sometimes indistinguishable on external characters. Forewing usually greyer. Pale to dark grey-brown, heavily dusted grey, or almost blackish. Central band usually faint or absent. Outer central cross-lines often composed of dots. Hindwing greyish white to grey. See also Vine's, Mottled and Powdered Rustics. **FS** Late June-mid August; (in south, October). **Hab** Ub.

Powdered Rustic *Hoplodrina superstes* Rare immigrant S **FW** 13-15mm. Most similar to Vine's Rustic. Forewing pale grey-brown, with brown speckling (narrower, greyer, less speckled and more angular in Vine's). Uncertain and Rustic are browner, hindwing darker. **FS** June-August.

Vine's Rustic *Hoplodrina ambigua* Common S,(C,N,Ir) **FW** 13-15mm. Forewing rather angular, grey, tinged brown. Central cross-band usually faint, kidney and oval usually quite large. Hindwing whitish. See Rustic (slightly larger, forewing broader, slightly blunter, hindwing darker), also Common Quaker (p.112). **FS** May-July; August-September. **Hab** Ub.

Small Mottled Willow *Spodoptera exigua* Immigrant S,(T); resident Channel Islands **FW** 13-14mm. Forewing narrow, grey-brown. Oval and kidney pale pink or orange. Hindwing whitish. Rests with forewings held at steep angle close to body. See Dark Mottled Willow, Pale Mottled Willow. **FS** Mainly June-October.

Mediterranean Brocade *Spodoptera littoralis* Suspected rare immigrant S; import **FW** 14-19mm. Forewing rather narrow, marbled light and dark brown, often with violet tint. Veins whitish centrally. In male, diagonal cream flash through oval. Hindwing white. **FS** June, September, October.

Dark Mottled Willow *Spodoptera cilium* Rare immigrant SW **FW** 13mm. Forewing in male brown, in female darker, grey. Similar to Small Mottled Willow; forewing broader, kidney dark-filled, oval pale brown. See also Pale Mottled Willow. **FS** September-October.

Mottled Rustic *Caradrina morpheus* Common T **FW** 13-16mm. Rather slender. Forewing brown or dark brown, quite broad in male, slightly narrower and shorter in female. Distinctly silky when fresh. Kidney and oval broad, dark, not pale-outlined. Inner margin of outer cross-band well defined, smooth. Hindwing whitish. See Uncertain, Rustic, Vine's Rustic. **FS** June-August; (in south, October). **Hab** Ub.

Clancy's Rustic Pale Mottled Willow

Views of underside

Clancy's Rustic *Platyperigea kadenii* Immigrant and probable colonist S **FW** 13-15mm. Not unlike Pale Mottled Willow. Forewing rather pale grey or grey-brown, outermost area not or slightly darker. Narrow pale outer band edged brown only central with inward projection. Kidney noticeably dark. Oval very small, dark. Hindwing whitish. See also Lorimer's Rustic. **FS** June-July; September-October.

Lorimer's Rustic *Paradrina flavirena* Suspected rare immigrant S **FW** 13-15mm. Very similar to P Mottled Willow; rests with forewings held close t body. Confirmation by genitalia examination desir able. See also Clancy's Rustic. **FS** April-June; on the Continent, August-October.

Pale Mottled Willow *Paradrina clavipalpis* Common T **FW** 12-15mm. Rather slender. Forewing narrow at base. Grey-brown. Kidney darker, rather narrow, usually small white spots in outline. Oval small, dark. Narrow pale outer band edged tawny brown, outermost area distinctly darker. Four black dots on leading edge. Hindwin whitish. See Lorimer's, Clancy's, Vine's Rustics, Small Mottled Willow, Dark Mottled Willow. **FS** Mainly May-July; August-October. **Hab** Ub.

Silky Wainscot *Chilodes maritimus* Local S,C,(N,Ir) **FW** 13-15mm. Slender. Forewing narro light greyish straw, leading edge curved, hindwing silky-white. Usually rather plain, delicately streake grey, dusted black. Less often finely streaked blac or with black kidney, oval and/or central streak. S Brown-veined Wainscot (female), Levant Blacknec (p.150). Also micro-moth *Calamotropha paludella* (very long palps). **FS** Mid June-mid August. **Hab** V

Marsh Moth *Athetis pallustris* RDB EC **FW** M 15-16mm, F 9-11mm. Slender. Forewing in male fawn to brown, in female narrower, darker. Kidney and oval small, dark. Cross-lines dark. **FS** Late May-June. **Hab** Gr Wt.

Porter's Rustic *Proxenus hospes* Rare immigra SW **FW** 11-13mm. Forewing blunt, dull brown markings indistinct. Kidney and oval usually discer ible. Sometimes a reddish central streak. Hindwin white, with fine marginal line. **FS** In southern Europe, May-June; late August-September.

Reddish Buff *Acosmetia caliginosa* RDB (Protected) S **FW** M 13-15mm, F 9-12mm. Slende Forewing brick red, pinkish buff, grey or brown. Oval and kidney absent. Fine dark wavy or scallop cross-lines. See Small Dotted Buff (yellowish). **FS** May-June. **Hab** Gr.

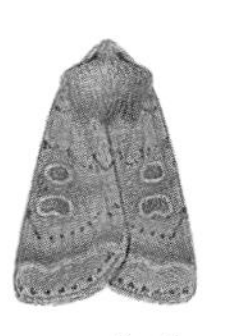

Uncertain
Hoplodrina alsines

Rustic
Hoplodrina blanda

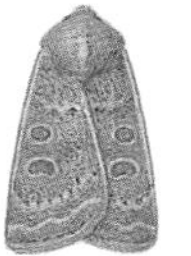
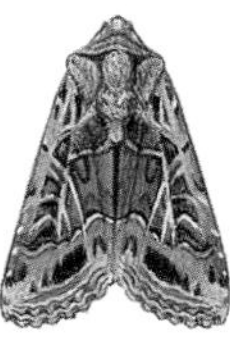

vdered Rustic
Hoplodrina superstes

Vine's Rustic
Hoplodrina ambigua

Small Mottled Willow
Spodoptera exigua

Mediterranean Brocade
Spodoptera littoralis

Dark Mottled Willow
Spodoptera cilium

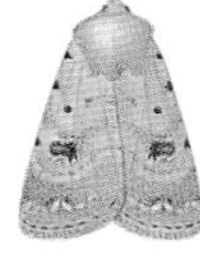

Mottled Rustic
Caradrina morpheus

Clancy's Rustic
Platyperigea kadenii

Lorimer's Rustic
Paradrina flavirena

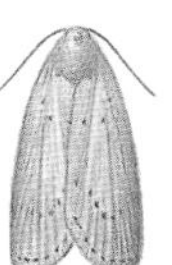
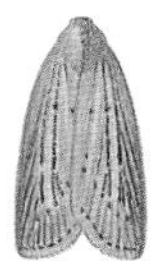
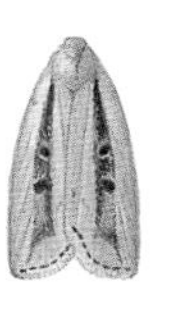
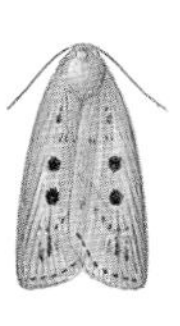

Pale Mottled Willow
Paradrina clavipalpis

Silky Wainscot
Chilodes maritimus
f. *nigristriata* f. *wismariensis* f. *bipunctata*

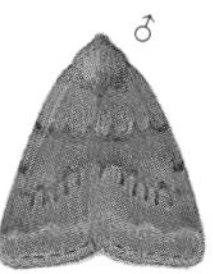

♂ ♀ ♂ ♀

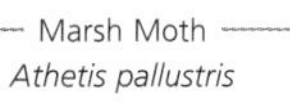

Marsh Moth
Athetis pallustris

Porter's Rustic
Proxenus hospes

Reddish Buff
Acosmetia caliginosa

Anomalous *Stilbia anomala* Local (S),SW,W,N,Ir **FW** 13-17mm. Slender. Forewing smooth, silky when fresh. Base narrow. Slate grey, blackish between oval and kidney and paler in trailing half. Forewing in female narrower, blackish grey, markings faint. **FS** August-September. **Hab** M Gr A Sd.

Rosy Marbled *Elaphria venustula* Nb. S **FW** 10-11mm. Forewing pinkish white, with pink stripe in leading half. Small, dark central block and roughly triangular brown blotches on trailing and outer edges. **FS** Late May-mid July. **Hab** BWd A Gr.

Stiriinae

Small Yellow Underwing *Panemeria tenebrata* Local S,C,(N,Ir) **FW** 8-10mm. Forewing dark brown (sometimes slightly reddish), dusted grey. Hindwing black with broad yellow band. **FS** May-early June. Flies only by day, in sunshine. **Hab** Gr.

Heliothinae

Pease Blossom *Periphanes delphinii* Former resident, immigrant or import S **FW** 14-15mm. Forewing with vivid purplish-pink shading. **FS** April-June. Often flies by day.

Bordered Sallow *Pyrrhia umbra* Local S,C,(N,Ir) **FW** 16-19mm. Forewing basal two-thirds orange to orange-yellow; pinkish brown from sharply angled cross-line beyond kidney. **FS** June-July. **Hab** CGr Sd Sh Wd.

Scarce Bordered Straw (Old World Bollworm) *Helicoverpa armigera* Immigrant S,(T) **FW** 16-19mm. Forewing dark purplish- to pale brown, darker markings varying in intensity and clarity. Black dots on outer edge rather faint. See Eastern Bordered Straw, Bordered Straw. **FS** Most frequent September-October.

Marbled Clover *Heliothis viriplaca* RDB; suspected immigrant S,(EC) **FW** 13-15mm. Forewing yellow-brown, with fairly straight dark central cross-band. See Shoulder-striped Clover. **FS** Mid June-July; (late July-August). Flies by day and at night, visiting flowers. **Hab** Gr Sh Ar Wd.

Shoulder-striped Clover *Heliothis maritima* ssp. *warneckei* RDB S; ssp. *bulgarica* Rare immigrant SE **FW** 13-17mm. Similar to Marbled Clover. Forewing with dark streak at base and dark central cross-band more angulated. Ssp. *bulgarica* lacks distinct basal streak. **FS** June-July. Flies by day and night, visiting flowers. **Hab** A.

Bordered Straw *Heliothis peltigera* Immigrant S,(T) **FW** 16-19mm. Forewing straw yellow to orange-brown. Bold grey kidney with diffuse, sometimes faint, brown blotch adjacent on leading edge. On outer edge, black dot at trailing corner only. See Scarce Bordered Straw, Eastern Bordered Straw. **FS** Most frequent June-August.

Eastern Bordered Straw *Heliothis nubigera* Rare immigrant S **FW** 16-20mm. Similar to Scarce Bordered Straw and Bordered Straw. Forewing with at least three bold, black dots in leading half of outer edge and distinct central notch in dark outermost cross-band.

Spotted Clover *Schinia scutosa* Immigrant T **FW** 15-16mm. Forewing whitish. Veins whitish. Large kidney, oval and other blotches brown. **FS** May-September. Flies by day and night.

Eustrotiinae

Purple Marbled *Eublemma ostrina* Immigrant S,(T) **FW** 8-9mm. Forewing rather pointed. Pale brown, streaked and clouded darker brown, with purple in outer half; or whitish with brown markings. See Small Marbled. **Beautiful Marbled** *Eublemma purpurina*, a recent immigrant (not illustrated) is larger, with outer half of forewing usually bright purple, the demarcation clear, acutely angled. **FS** May-October. Flies by day and at night.

Small Marbled *Eublemma parva* Immigrant S,(T) **FW** 7-8mm. Forewing yellowish white, with fairly straight, brown, white-edge central cross-line, and fine cross-line beyond middle forming question-mark. See Purple Marbled (larger, lacks central cross-line) and Scarce Marbled. **FS** March-October.

Scarce Marbled *Eublemma minutata* Suspected rare immigrant S **FW** 7-8mm. Similar to Small Marbled, but on forewing dark outer cross-band with central inward V-shaped kink. [Not illustrated.]

Marbled White Spot *Protodeltote pygarga* Common S,(C,Ir) **FW** 11-12mm. Forewing dark grey-brown with incomplete whitish outer cross-band, occasionally reduced. See Pretty Marbled. **FS** Late May-July. **Hab** Wd A Gr M.

Pretty Marbled *Deltote deceptoria* Immigrant; transitory resident S **FW** 12-13mm. Forewing dark grey-brown, extensively marbled white, including base. See Marbled White Spot. **FS** May-June.

Silver Hook *Deltote uncula* Local S,C,NW,Ir **FW** 11-12mm. Forewing olive brown. Creamy white streak in leading half, with white kidney forming projection. **FS** May-July. **Hab** Wt A M.

Silver Barred *Deltote bankiana* RDB S,Ir; immigrant S,C **FW** 10-12mm. Forewing brown. Two roughly parallel silvery white cross-bands. **FS** May-July. Easily disturbed by day. Active from dusk. **Hab** Wt.

Acontiinae

Spotted Sulphur *Emmelia trabealis* Presumed extinct S **FW** 10-11mm. Forewing yellowish cream with dark brown spots and stripes. **FS** June-July. Easily disturbed by day. Flies in late afternoon and at night. **Hab** Gr F.

Pale Shoulder *Acontia lucida* Immigrant S; resident Jersey **FW** 12-15mm. Most like Four-spotted (p.150), but basal third of forewing white or greyish white. Hindwing white with broad black marginal band and blackish basal streaks. **FS** June-August. Visits flowers by day and flies at night.

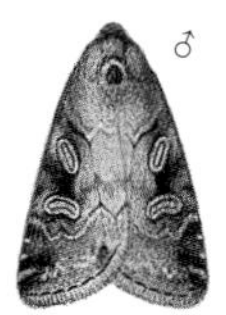

♂ ♀

Anomalous
Stilbia anomala

Rosy Marbled
Elaphria venustula

Small Yellow Underwing
Panemeria tenebrata

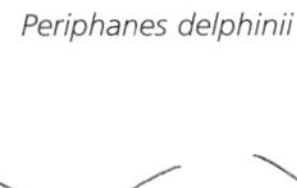

Pease Blossom
Periphanes delphinii

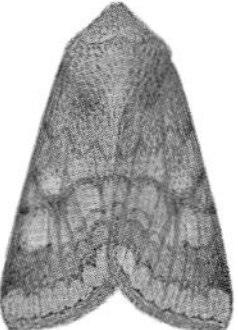

Bordered Sallow
Pyrrhia umbra

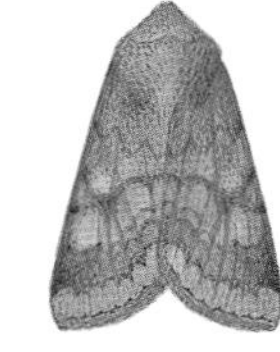

Scarce Bordered Straw
Helicoverpa armigera

arbled Clover
eliothis viriplaca

Shoulder-striped Clover
Heliothis maritima warneckei

Bordered Straw
Heliothis peltigera

Eastern Bordered Straw
Heliothis nubigera

Spotted Clover
Schinia scutosa

Purple Marbled
Eublemma ostrina

f. *carthami*

Small Marbled
Eublemma parva

Marbled White Spot
Protodeltote pygarga

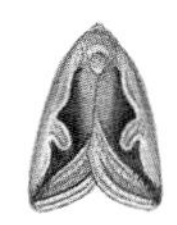

Pretty Marbled
Deltote deceptoria

Silver Hook
Deltote uncula

Silver Barred
Deltote bankiana

Spotted Sulphur
Emmelia trabealis

Pale Shoulder
Acontia lucida

Eariadinae

Cream-bordered Green Pea *Earias clorana* Nb. S,EC,Ir **FW** 10-12mm. Forewing green. Leading edge curved, with white stripe; fringes usually whitish. Hindwing white. When fully at rest, holds wings at steep angle. Rarely, forewing brownish green with brown fringes. See Spiny Bollworm, Egyptian Bollworm. Green Oak Tortrix *Tortrix viridana* has plain green forewing, grey hindwing, rests with wings flat. **FS** Late May-July; (August onwards). **Hab** Wt Wd Sh.

Spiny Bollworm *Earias biplaga* Rare immigrant/import S **FW** 11-12mm. Forewing green or yellowish green. Faint darker cross-lines. Fringes brown. Sometimes a large central purplish-brown blotch on trailing edge. See Cream-bordered Green Pea (forewing more pointed, cross-lines absent, leading edge more curved), Egyptian Bollworm. **FS** July-September.

Egyptian Bollworm *Earias insulana* Suspected rare immigrant S; import **FW** 10-11mm. Forewing green or brown, with darker cross-lines. See Spiny Bollworm. Should be retained for confirmation. See also Cream-bordered Green Pea. **FS** July-October.

Chloephorinae

Scarce Silver-lines *Bena bicolorana* Local S,C **FW** 19-23mm. Forewing broad, leading edge curved. Bright green, with two fine, diagonal yellowish-white cross-lines. Front appendages pink. **FS** June-July. **Hab** BWd.

Green Silver-lines *Pseudoips prasinana* ssp. *britannica* Common S,C,(N),Ir **FW** 16-19mm. Forewing green. Usually three diagonal white cross-lines, the first sharply angled at leading edge. Fringes pinkish brown in male, greenish in female. Antennae orange-pink, palps and front legs pink. **FS** May-July; (August-September). **Hab** BWd.

Oak Nycteoline *Nycteola revayana* Local S,(C,N,Ir) **FW** 11-13mm. Forewing narrow, leading edge steeply arched at base, then straight or slightly concave. Grey, brown or blackish, or a combination thereof, with dark wavy cross-lines or bands, often black spots and dark central roughly triangular blotch on leading edge. More rarely, broad tawny band along leading edge and long, branched, blackish central streak. Hindwing grey. See Sallow Nycteoline, Eastern Nycteoline, Grey Square. *Acleris cristana* and *A. hastiana* (family Tortricidae, micro-moths) are usually smaller, with raised scales on forewing and shorter palps. **FS** In southern England and Scilly, late June-July; September-May. Elsewhere, August-early June. **Hab** BWd.

Eastern Nycteoline *Nycteola asiatica* Rare immigrant S,C **FW** 11-13mm. Very similar to Oak Nycteoline. Forewing generally broader, leading edge much less steeply-arched at base. Glossy grey, fine dark wavy central cross-lines. Brownish central spot, often a diffuse cross-band or blotch. Suspected examples should be retained for confirmation. **FS** Recorded in September. [Not illustrated.]

Sallow Nycteoline *Nycteola degenerana* Rare immigrant/import S **FW** 12-13mm. Forewing dark grey and brown, often extensively marbled white. Sometimes a broad dark central cross-band. Head and palps usually white. Suspected examples should be retained for confirmation.

Grey Square *Pardasena virgulana* Suspected import S **FW** 8-12mm. Somewhat like Oak Nycteoline. Forewing relatively broad, predominantly grey, leading edge curved, not concave. Variable. Often fine blackish cross-lines, basal slightly curved, central wavy, often a dark central bar. Hindwing white, sometimes with dark marginal band. Suspected examples should be retained for confirmation.

Pantheinae

Nut-tree Tussock *Colocasia coryli* Common T **FW** 14-17mm. Furry, rather thickset. Antennae feathered in male. Forewing broad, usually dark grey-brown in basal half (grey at very base) and light grey or white in outer half. Sometimes more uniformly grey. F. *melanotica* is dark brownish grey or blackish (southern England). **FS** In south, late April-mid June; late July-early September. In north, May-early July. **Hab** BWd.

Plusiinae Silver and golden Ys, gems, brasses and allies

Forewings held at a steep angle, usually with metallic marks, and conspicuous tufts on body.

Golden Twin-spot *Chrysodeixis chalcites* Immigrant; import S,(C,N) **FW** 15-18mm. Forewing dark pinkish brown with metallic gold blotches, largest in central area (best seen from in front or above). Two central silver spots, sometimes joined. In male, tufts on underside of abdomen tip black. See Tunbridge Wells Gem. **FS** July-November, mainly August-October.

Tunbridge Wells Gem *Chrysodeixis acuta* Rare immigrant S,(C) **FW** 14-18mm. Very similar to Golden Twin-spot, but with black crescent mark near forewing tip. In male, abdomen tufts brown. **FS** May; September-November.

Scar Bank Gem *Ctenoplusia limbirena* Immigrant S **FW** 15-18mm. Forewing brown to blackish, often tinged purplish. Small purple, pinkish or red-brown ellipse or tear-drop mark near centre of outer edge. Central silver spots usually fused (see Ni Moth). Forewing more ornate than Silver Y. **FS** June-October.

Accent Gem *Ctenoplusia accentifera* Suspected rare immigrant SE (one record) **FW** 11-14mm. Forewing reddish- or greyish brown. Central mark silver, narrow, sock-shaped, strongly outlined in gold on outer edge. Black bar near base of trailing edge and small black wedge near outer edge. **FS** Recorded in September.

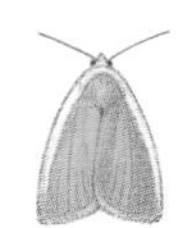

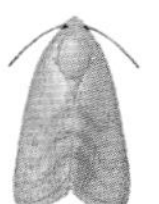
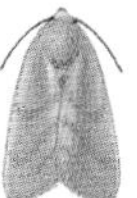

Cream-bordered Green Pea *Earias clorana*

Spiny Bollworm *Earias biplaga*

Egyptian Bollworm *Earias insulana*

Scarce Silver-lines *Bena bicolorana*

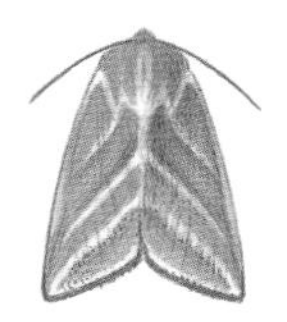

Green Silver-lines *Pseudoips prasinana britannica*

Oak Nycteoline *Nycteola revayana*

f. *ramosana* f. *notata* f. *lichenodes* f. *rosea* f. *undulana*

Sallow Nycteoline *Nycteola degenerana*

♀

Grey Square *Pardasena virgulana*

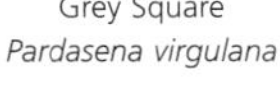

Nut-tree Tussock *Colocasia coryli*

f. *medionigra* f. *avellana* f. *melanotica*

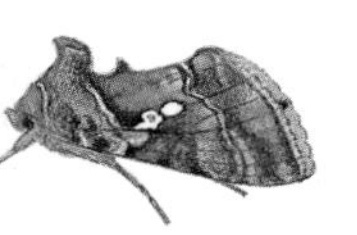
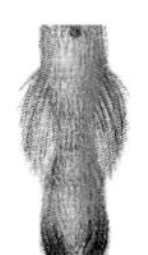

♂ abdomen

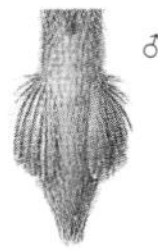

♂ abdomen

Golden Twin-spot *Chrysodeixis chalcites*

Tunbridge Wells Gem *Chrysodeixis acuta*

Scar Bank Gem *Ctenoplusia limbirena*

Accent Gem *Ctenoplusia accentifera*

Ni Moth *Trichoplusia ni* Immigrant S,(C,Ir) **FW** 15-17mm. Resembles Silver Y but forewing more ornate, light grey-brown. Central silver marks usually separate, inner forming an 'n'. Usually a whitish spot in trailing corner. See also Scar Bank Gem. **FS** May-October.

Streaked Plusia *Trichoplusia vittata* Suspected rare immigrant S **FW** 15-18mm. Forewing grey, not metallic. Long, fairly straight whitish central streak.

Slender Burnished Brass *Thysanoplusia orichalcea* Immigrant S,(C,Ir); import **FW** 17-20mm. Forewing brown. Large brassy blotch tapering towards base. **FS** Mainly August-October.

Burnished Brass *Diachrysia chrysitis* Common T **FW** 16-19mm. Forewing broad, hooked. Brassy cross-bands, sometimes joined centrally. **FS** June-July; (in south, August-September). **Hab** Ub.

Scarce Burnished Brass *Diachrysia chryson* Na. S,WC **FW** 20-24mm. Forewing broad, hooked, reddish brown, with large brassy blotch near tip. **FS** July-August. **Hab** Wt Wd Cl.

Dewick's Plusia *Macdunnoughia confusa* Immigrant S,(C,N) **FW** 12-17mm. Forewing brownish, trailing two-thirds of central area bronze or gold. Quite large central metallic silver dog-leg mark, extending as thin line to trailing edge. See Golden Twin-spot, Tunbridge Wells Gem. **FS** May; July-October.

Golden Plusia *Polychrysia moneta* Common S,C,(N,Ir) **FW** 17-20mm. Forewing broad, golden-yellow and grey. Kidney large, silvery white. Thorax with large fan-like crest. **FS** Late June-early August; (in south, September). **Hab** G.

Purple-shaded Gem *Euchalcia variabilis* Probable import **FW** 17-19mm. Forewing brown, with white cross-lines, pink cross-bands and clouding.

Gold Spot *Plusia festucae* Common T **FW** 14-19mm. Forewing reddish brown or rich brown, with gold blotches. Outermost central silvery white blotch smaller, elliptical or tear-shaped. Elongated gold and silvery white marks near tip. See Lempke's Gold Spot. **FS** In south, June-July; August-September. Elsewhere, late June-mid August. **Hab** Wt A M Gr Wd.

Lempke's Gold Spot *Plusia putnami* ssp. *gracilis* Local C,(N,S,Ir) **FW** 14-15mm. Very similar to Gold Spot. Forewing usually orange-brown, fine brown cross-lines usually more distinct, longest elongated silvery mark near tip usually ends more bluntly. Both species vary, so examination of genitalia may be necessary. **FS** July-August. **Hab** Wt Up.

Silver Y *Autographa gamma* Immigrant T **FW** 13-21mm. Forewing dull metallic grey or brown, sometimes purplish tinged, rarely black. Central silver spots fused to form clear Y-mark, rarely broken or enlarged. See Scarce Silver Y, Plain Golden Y, Beautiful Golden Y, Ni Moth, Scar Bank Gem, Essex Y. **FS** All year, most frequent May-September. Active by day and night. **Hab** Ub.

Beautiful Golden Y *Autographa pulchrina* Common T **FW** 17-20mm. Forewing dark reddis or purplish brown, extensively marbled with pinki or light purplish brown. Metallic bronzy-green blotch near outer edge. Kidney sharply pinched, finely edged in gold. Central gold marks usually a V and an oval spot, sometimes fused to form a Y, sometimes reduced. See Plain Golden Y, Silver Y. **FS** In south, late May-late July. In north, late June early September. **Hab** Ub.

Plain Golden Y *Autographa jota* Common T **FW** 17-21mm. Similar to Beautiful Golden Y, but less ornate. Kidney not gold-edged, indistinct. Forewing light to dark reddish brown, softly marbled pink or pinkish brown. Y-mark usually broken, sometimes reduced. See also Silver Y. **FS** In south, June-early August. In north, mid July August. **Hab** Ub.

Gold Spangle *Autographa bractea* Common W,N,(S),Ir **FW** 18-21mm. Forewing rather plain, dark reddish brown, clouded with dull pinkish brown and sometimes greyish brown. Central metallic mark large, broad, golden. **FS** Early July-early August. **Hab** Ub.

Stephens' Gem *Megalographa biloba* Suspect rare immigrant S **FW** 15-18mm. Forewing with large double-lobed central silver mark.

Scarce Silver Y *Syngrapha interrogationis* Loca C,N,Ir; immigrant S,C,N **FW** 15-18mm. Forewing blackish, extensively marbled and clouded silvery grey (sometimes with darker grey or mauve-tinge Central mark split into a V or an 'n' and an oval, sometimes forming a Y or a meandering blotch, or thin and reduced. Most immigrant examples are small, marked with dull grey, and have paler hindwing. See Ni Moth, Silver Y. **FS** Late June-mic August. Immigrants late July-August. Sometimes active by day. **Hab** M.

Essex Y *Cornutiplusia circumflexa* Suspected rar immigrant S **FW** 16-21mm. Similar to Silver Y, bu forewing less metallic, more ornate, often tinged lilac or violet when fresh. Central silver mark like oblique, distorted U.

Dark Spectacle *Abrostola triplasia* Common W,(T),Ir **FW** 14-18mm. Similar to Spectacle. Forewing ground-colour brownish black, basal area dull straw or reddish brown, cross-lines edge reddish brown. Outer cross-banding and blotches dull straw. **FS** June-July; (in south, late August-September). **Hab** Ub.

Spectacle *Abrostola tripartita* Common T **FW** 15-17mm. Tufts on thorax resemble spectacle from front. Forewing grey or dark grey, sometime tinged lilac or pink. Broad blackish central band. Large oval and kidney blackish-outlined. Oval fuse with second central oval. Basal area and outer cross-band lighter grey. See Dark Spectacle. **FS** La May-mid July; (in south, late July-early September **Hab** Ub.

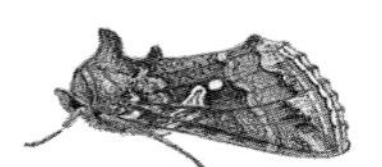

Ni Moth
Trichoplusia ni

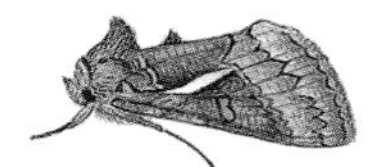

Streaked Plusia
Trichoplusia vittata

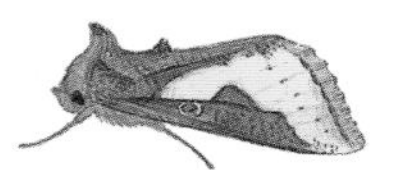

Slender Burnished Brass
Thysanoplusia orichalcea

Burnished Brass
Diachrysia chrysitis
f. *juncta* — f. *aurea*

Scarce Burnished Brass
Diachrysia chryson

Dewick's Plusia
Macdunnoughia confusa

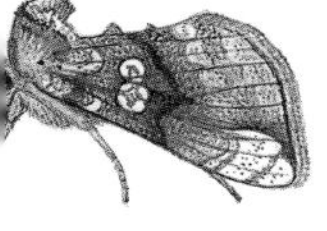

Golden Plusia
Polychrysia moneta

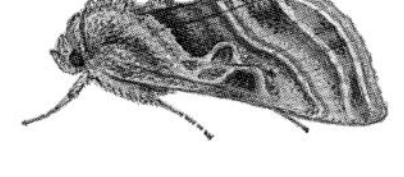

Purple-shaded Gem
Euchalcia variabilis

Gold Spot
Plusia festucae

Lempke's Gold Spot
Plusia putnami gracilis

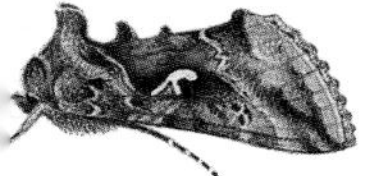

Silver Y
Autographa gamma
f. *gammina* — f. *nigricans*

Beautiful Golden Y
Autographa pulchrina

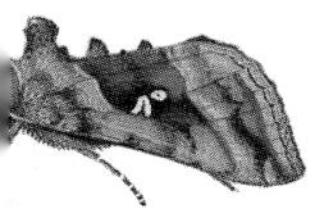

Plain Golden Y
Autographa jota

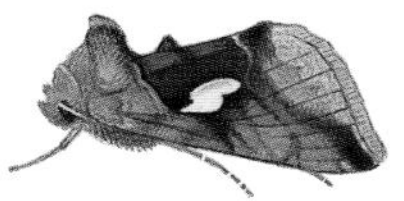

Gold Spangle
Autographa bractea

Stephens' Gem
Megalographa biloba

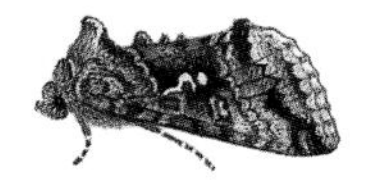

Scarce Silver Y
Syngrapha interrogationis

Essex Y
Cornutiplusia circumflexa

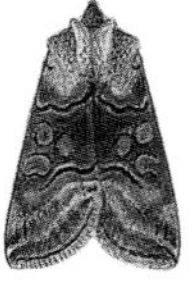

Dark Spectacle
Abrostola triplasia

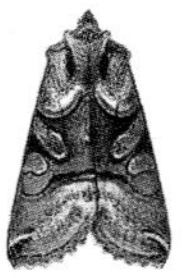

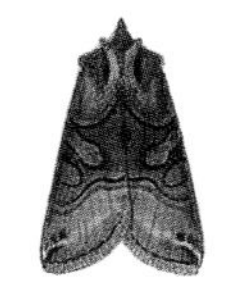

head-on view showing 'spectacles'

Spectacle
Abrostola tripartita
f. *plumbea*

Catocalinae
Red underwings and allies

Clifden Nonpareil *Catocala fraxini* Immigrant S,E,(T); extinct transitory resident SE **FW** 41-48mm. Forewing grey. Pale central blotch, zigzagged outer central and undulating inner central cross-lines. Hindwing black with broad curved violet-blue central cross-band, scalloped outer margin and broad white fringe. Larger and greyer than related species. **FS** August-October. **Hab** BWd.

Red Underwing *Catocala nupta* Common S,C **FW** 33-40mm. Forewing grey with irregular jagged cross-lines and bands and obscurely marbled with brownish grey. Hindwing red (very rarely dark brown), with black marginal band, scalloped margin and white fringe. Central band strongly elbowed, and pinched in leading half. Underside of fore- and hindwings black with bold white bands, which show up strikingly in flight. See Rosy Underwing, French Red Underwing. **FS** Early August-October. Occasionally active by day. **Hab** Wd G H Wt.

Rosy Underwing *Catocala electa* Rare immigrant S **FW** 33-39mm. Similar to Red Underwing, but forewing paler, greyer, plainer and smoother-looking. Outer jagged cross-line dark and much more noticeable, with strong double outward projection in leading half. Red on hindwing tends to rosy pink. **FS** July-September.

French Red Underwing *Catocala elocata* Rare immigrant Jersey **FW** 39-43mm. Very similar to Red Underwing but with generally more indistinct forewing markings, and usually larger. On hindwing, black central cross-band gently curved, of even thickness in leading half and gradually tapering in trailing half. [Not illustrated.]

Light Crimson Underwing *Catocala promiss* RDB S **FW** 26-32mm. Forewing grey-brown with irregular dark cross-lines and bands and variably variegated whitish, usually extensively. Hindwing crimson with central black cross-band gently wavy **FS** Mid July-early September. Occasionally active by day, flying around the oak canopy in afternoon sunshine. **Hab** BWd.

Dark Crimson Underwing *Catocala sponsa* RDB S **FW** 29-34mm. Similar to Light Crimson Underwing, but on hindwing central cross-band contorted into a deep W-shape. Also generally larger, forewing browner, darker and less variegated. **FS** Late July-early September, occasionally October, especially as a possible immigrant. Recen observed active by day, investigating sap runs and sugary baits. **Hab** BWd.

Minsmere Crimson Underwing *Catocala conjuncta* Rare immigrant E Very similar to Dark and Light Crimson Underwings, but on hindwing central black cross-band gently curved, not wavy. On forewing, dark outer central cross-line projecti outwards very strongly in leading half, degree of variegation variable. [Not illustrated.]

Oak Yellow Underwing *Catocala nymphagoga* Suspected rare immigrant S **FW**17-21mm. Rather like a miniature Crimson Underwing specie but with yellow hindwing. Forewing mottled with various shades of grey and brown, and often variegated with whitish. On hindwing, central black central cross-band elbowed roughly at right-angle in trailing half. One of several European *Catocala* species with yellow hindwings. **FS** July-August.

Clifden Nonpareil
Catocala fraxini

f. *brunnescens*

Red Underwing
Catocala nupta

Rosy Underwing
Catocala electa

Light Crimson Underwing
Catocala promissa

Oak Yellow Underwing
Catocala nymphagoga

Dark Crimson Underwing
Catocala sponsa

Lunar Double-stripe *Minucia lunaris* Immigrant S,(C,Ir); transitory resident S **FW** 23-26mm. Forewing warm brown to grey-brown, with darker brown shading, especially towards outer edge. Central cross-lines cream, fairly straight or gently curved. Kidney prominent, darker; oval very small. Hindwing brown with golden sheen, diffuse darker central band, basal third paler. **FS** May-June. Easily disturbed by day from leaf-litter. **Hab** BWd.

Passenger *Dysgonia algira* Immigrant S **FW** 17-23mm. Forewing broad, brown with waisted, greyish- or brownish white central cross-band and prominent dark marks at tip. Hindwing brown with diffuse, narrow whitish central cross-band. See Geometrician. **FS** August-September.

Geometrician *Prodotis stolida* Rare immigrant S **FW** 14-16mm. Forewing dark brown, with straight, cream inner central cross-band. Wavy outer central cream cross-band, thickly edged brown. Hindwing dark brown, gently curved white inner central cross band, fringe white with dark section beyond middle and white spot nearby. **FS** September.

Mother Shipton *Callistege mi* Common S,C,(N),Ir **FW** 13-16mm. Forewing dark brown, dusted and marked greyish yellow. Large, irregular cream-edged dark brown central blotch resembles caricature of an old hag. **FS** May-July. Active only by day. **Hab** Gr.

Burnet Companion *Euclidia glyphica* Common S,C,(N),Ir **FW** 13-15mm. Forewing warm dark grey-brown, with dark brown cross-bands and dark blotch near tip. Hindwing with basal half dark brown, outer half orange-yellow, with dark veins and band. **FS** May-July. Active only by day. **Hab** Gr.

Ophiderinae

Alchymist *Catephia alchymista* Immigrant S **FW** 19-21mm. Forewing black, marked with pale brown and whitish near outer edge. Hindwing blackish, basal third white, fringes with black and white sections. **FS** June-September. **Hab** Wd Sc.

Four-spotted *Tyta luctuosa* Na. S,EC,(SW); suspected immigrant S,C,E **FW** 12-13mm. Forewing blackish, large white blotch in leading half at two-thirds. Hindwing blackish with broad white central cross-band. See Pale Shoulder (p.142). **FS** May-early July; late July-late August. Active by day and at night. **Hab** Gr.

Blackneck *Lygephila pastinum* Local S,C **FW** 18-21mm. Top of head and collar blackish brown. Forewing light pastel grey, sometimes darker, with very fine wavy brown pencilling. Kidney narrow, solidly dark brown with one or two adjacent dark spots, oval very small. **FS** June-July. Easily disturbed by day. **Hab** Gr Wt Wd.

Scarce Blackneck *Lygephila craccae* RDB SW **FW** 18-20mm. Similar to Blackneck. Forewing narrower, generally darker. Veins often prominently pale. Four dark spots on leading edge up to two-thirds. Kidney with dark spots. No other central marks. **FS** July-August. **Hab** Cl.

Levant Blackneck *Tathorhynchus exsiccata* Rare immigrant S,SW **FW** 13-18mm. Forewing narrow and rather blunt, grey-brown. Black streak at base and between small, pale oval and kidney. Whitish zigzagged outer cross-line, sometimes fai Hindwing whitish with broad, dark grey-brown marginal band. See Silky Wainscot (p.140). **FS** February-March, June, September-November.

Herald *Scoliopteryx libatrix* Common T **FW** 19-23mm. Forewing broad, grey-brown, strongly hooked, with outer edge deeply indented and scalloped. White cross-lines and frosting, central and basal orange blotches. **FS** In southern England, July; September-November, reappearing April-June. Elsewhere, August-November, reappearing April-June. **Hab** Ub.

Small Purple-barred *Phytometra viridaria* Local T **FW** 9-11mm. Fore- and hindwings dull brown or olive brown. In one form, two magenta outer cross-bands on forewing (sometimes with pale narrow band between), and sometimes one c hindwing. Day-flying micro-moth *Pyrausta despica* has narrower forewing with oval and kidney, and pale thin central cross-band on hindwing. **FS** May-August. Mainly active by day. **Hab** CGr A M Wd S

Rivulinae

Lesser Belle *Colobochyla salicalis* Rare immigrar extinct resident S,SE **FW** 13-15mm. Forewing pointed, grey with three brown, pale-edge cross-lines, outermost curving to wing tip. **FS** May-July. Easily disturbed by day. **Hab** BWd.

Beautiful Hook-tip *Laspeyria flexula* Local S,(C **FW** 13-15mm. Forewing strongly hooked, outer edge with blunt central projection. Warm grey-brown, often lilac-tinted, rusty brown towards out edge. Two small dark central dots and two fine, fairly straight, dark-edged yellowish brown cross-lines, angled at leading edge, and one on hindwing. See Scalloped Hook-tip (p.18). **FS** June-early August; (in south, September-October). **Hab** BWd Sc H O.

Straw Dot *Rivula sericealis* Common S,C,NW,Ir **FW** 13-15mm. Forewing straw yellow, yellowish brown or light brown. Outer edge and fringe brown. Kidney prominent, dark. Sometimes fine dark cross-lines. **FS** June-July; in south, August-September. Easily disturbed by day. **Hab** Gr Wt.

Waved Black *Parascotia fuliginaria* Nb. S,(C); suspected immigrant SE **FW** 11-14 mm. Fore- anc hindwings charcoal grey, with wavy creamy-white cross-bands, outer central sometimes thickened in blotches in outer area, especially in trailing half. Rests with wings flat and widely spread. **FS** June-July. May be disturbed by day. **Hab** BWd.

Lunar Double-stripe
Minucia lunaris

Passenger
Dysgonia algira

Geometrician
Prodotis stolida

Mother Shipton
Callistege mi

Burnet Companion
Euclidia glyphica

hindwing

Alchymist
Catephia alchymista

Four-spotted
Tyta luctuosa

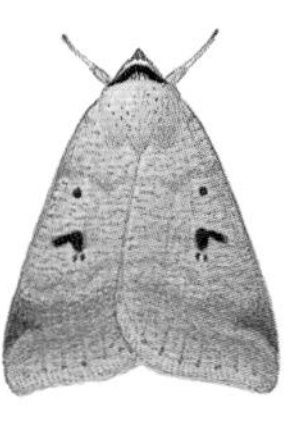

Blackneck
Lygephila pastinum

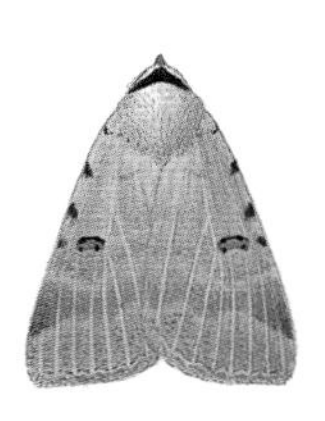

Scarce Blackneck
Lygephila craccae

Levant Blackneck
Tathorhynchus exsiccata

Herald
Scoliopteryx libatrix

f. *fusca*

Small Purple-barred
Phytometra viridaria

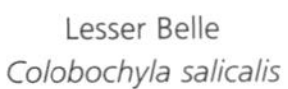

Lesser Belle
Colobochyla salicalis

Beautiful Hook-tip
Laspeyria flexula

Straw Dot
Rivula sericealis

Waved Black
Parascotia fuliginaria

Hypeninae Snouts

Beautiful Snout *Hypena crassalis* Local S,WC,(EC,Ir) **FW** 14-16mm. Forewing with extensive dark brown blotch (paler in female). In male, rest of wing grey, brown and white, in female mainly whitish. **FS** May-August. Easily disturbed by day. **Hab** Wd M A.

Snout *Hypena proboscidalis* Common T **FW** 15-19mm. Forewing very broad, slightly hooked. Brown, dull greyish- or purplish brown, cross-lines distinct, solid brown. Bloxworth and Paignton Snouts lack clear solid brown cross-lines. See also Buttoned Snout. **FS** In south, June-early August; late August-October. From Midlands northwards and in Ireland, June-August. Easily disturbed by day. **Hab** Ub.

Bloxworth Snout *Hypena obsitalis* RDB SW **FW** 15-17mm. Forewing variegated white and brown, to rather plain brown. Fine irregular outer central cross-line; often dark central blotch in leading half. See Paignton Snout, Snout. **FS** July-August; September-October, reappears May-June. **Hab** Cl.

Paignton Snout *Hypena obesalis* Rare immigrant S **FW** 18-22mm. Not unlike Bloxworth Snout, but larger with forewing more strongly tapered. **FS** August-October.

Buttoned Snout *Hypena rostralis* Nb. S **FW** 13-15mm. Forewing rather narrow, leading edge slightly curved, light to dark grey-brown, sometimes streaked pale brown. Central marks often like a button-hole, but may be reduced. **FS** August-October, reappears April-June. **Hab** H G Sc Wd.

Strepsimaninae

White-line Snout *Schrankia taenialis* Nb. S,(Ir) **FW** 9-11mm. Forewing brown. Outer central cross-line distinct, fine, dark, white-edged, slightly kinked. Kidney clear, small, dark, sometimes with short streak but rarely reaching outer central cross-line. See Pinion-streaked Snout, Marsh Oblique-barred. **FS** July-August; (September-October). **Hab** Wd M H.

Pinion-streaked Snout *Schrankia costaestrigalis* Local S,C,(NW,Ir) **FW** 9-11mm. Forewing narrow, dull straw or brown. Thick dark streak obscures kidney and reaches rather faint, strongly kinked outer central cross-line. Markings sometimes reduced or unclear. See White-line Snout (broader forewing). **FS** June-August; (in south, August-October). **Hab** Wd Wt A M.

Marsh Oblique-barred *Hypenodes humidalis* Nb. T **FW** 6-8mm. Forewing pale brown. Cross-lines fine, dark, oblique, outermost extending to tip. See also Small Marbled (p.142). **FS** June-August. Active by day and at dusk. **Hab** M A Wt.

Herminiinae Fan-foots

Common Fan-foot *Pechipogo strigilata* Na. S **FW** 14-16mm. Forewing whitish- or greyish fawn, dusted grey. Cross-lines brown, slightly diffuse, outermost straight, weakly pale-edged. Kidney narrow, rather faint. Hindwing whitish. Similar species have richer brown forewing with clearer cross-lines, and grey-brown hindwing. **FS** Late Ma early July. **Hab** BWd.

Plumed Fan-foot *Pechipogo plumigeralis* Rare immigrant; probable resident SE **FW** 13-15mm. Forewing warm brown, quite pointed. Kidney rath elongated, brown-centred. Central cross-lines fine irregular or jagged; outermost pale, fairly straight, dark-edged. Antennae in male feathered. See Dus Fan-foot. **FS** July-August.

Fan-foot *Zanclognatha tarsipennalis* Common S,C,(N),Ir **FW** 13-16mm. Forewing brown, sometimes yellowish brown (W Scotland, Ireland). Kidne narrow, curved. Cross-lines dark; inner central gen curved, outer central like question mark, outermos almost straight, weakly pale-edged, reaching leadi edge. Very fine dark dashes along outer edge. In male, antenna with small, roughly central bulge. See Shaded, Small and Jubilee Fan-foots. **FS** June-August. Easily disturbed by day. **Hab** BWd H G.

Jubilee Fan-foot *Zanclognatha lunalis* Rare immigrant S **FW** 14-17mm. Similar to Fan-foot b slightly larger, kidney bolder, more curved. Forewi light brown to red-brown, often purplish-tinged. Outer central cross-line finely scalloped. See also Dusky and Shaded Fan-foots. **FS** July-August.

Dusky Fan-foot *Zanclognatha zelleralis* Rare immigrant S **FW** 14-17mm. Forewing brown, rough-textured. Kidney broad, brown-centred. Central cross-lines finely scalloped, outermost pale fairly straight, dark-edged. See Plumed and Jubilee Fan-foots. **FS** June-July.

Shaded Fan-foot *Herminia tarsicrinalis* RDB SE **FW** 12-14mm. Similar to Fan-foot. Slightly smaller with diffuse dark central forewing cross-band, fine dark unbroken line along outer edge, antenna without bulge in male. See also Small Fan-foot. **FS** June-July. **Hab** BWd Sc.

Small Fan-foot *Herminia grisealis* Common T **FW** 11-13mm. Forewing with outermost cross-line curved, extending to tip. **FS** June-August. **Hab** BW Sc H G.

Dotted Fan-foot *Macrochilo cribrumalis* Nb. SE,S **FW** 13-14mm. Forewing pointed, whitish fawn. Two cross-rows of dark dots, central dark d Hindwing whitish. Antenna slightly feathered in male. **FS** June-August. **Hab** Wt.

Clay Fan-foot *Paracolax tristalis* Na.; immigrant SE **FW** 14-16mm. Fore- and hindwings warm sandy brown, cross-lines and kidney fine, dark. On forewing, outer central cross-line strongly curved in leading half. See Olive Crescent. *Ebulea croceal* (micro) is smaller, hindwing white. **FS** Late June-early August. Easily disturbed by day. **Hab** BWd

Olive Crescent *Trisateles emortualis* RDB; suspected immigrant SE,S **FW** 14mm. Fore- and hindwings light fawn to sandy brown. Cross-lines pale, yellowish, almost straight. Single cross-line on hindwing. See Clay Fan-foot. **FS** June-July. **Hab** BW

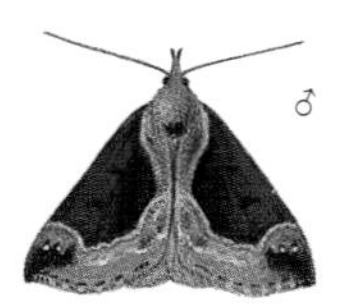

Beautiful Snout
Hypena crassalis

Snout
Hypena proboscidalis

Bloxworth Snout
Hypena obsitalis

Paignton Snout
Hypena obesalis

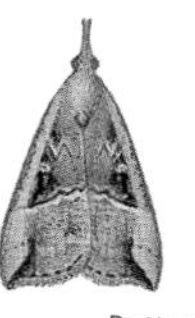

Buttoned Snout
Hypena rostralis
f. *unicolor*

/hite-line
Snout
ıkia taenialis*

Pinion-streaked Snout
Schrankia costaestrigalis

Marsh
Oblique-barred
Hypenodes humidalis

White-line Snout

Pinion-streaked Snout

Marsh Oblique-barred

Details of Strepsimaninae forewing markings

Common Fan-foot
Pechipogo strigilata

Plumed Fan-foot
Pechipogo plumigeralis

Fan-foot
Zanclognatha tarsipennalis

ɔilee Fan-foot
ılognatha lunalis

Dusky Fan-foot
Zanclognatha zelleralis

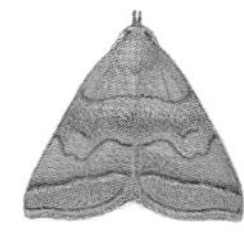

Shaded Fan-foot
Herminia tarsicrinalis

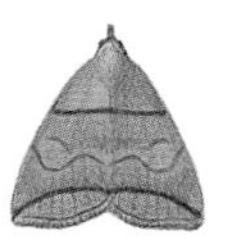

Small Fan-foot
Herminia grisealis

Dotted Fan-foot
Macrochilo cribrumalis

Clay Fan-foot
Paracolax tristalis

Olive Crescent
Trisateles emortualis

Further reading

Bradley, J 2000 *Checklist of Lepidoptera recorded from the British Isles.* (2nd ed.) D Bradley, Fordingbridge

Fry, R, & Waring, P 2001 *A guide to moth traps and their use. Amateur Entomologist 24.* (2nd ed.) Amateur Entomologists' Society, London

Leverton, R 2001 *Enjoying moths.* Poyser, London

Porter, J 1997 *The colour identification guide to caterpillars of the British Isles.* Viking, London

Skinner, B 1998 *The colour identification guide to moths of the British Isles.* Viking, London

Waring, P, Townsend, M, & Lewington, R 2003 *Field Guide to the Moths of Great Britain and Ireland.* British Wildlife Publishing

Young, M R 1997 *The natural history of moths.* Poyser, London

Organisations

Amateur Entomologists' Society Ideal for beginners, but retains many members for life! Publishes the *AES Bulletin*. Contact: AES, PO Box 8774, London SW7 5ZG (www.theaes.org).

British Entomological & Natural History Society The national society for the field entomologist. Publishes *British Journal of Entomology & Natural History*. Contact: BENHS Secretary, c/o Dinton Pastures Country Park, Davis Street, Hurst, Reading Berks RG10 0TH (www.benhs.org.uk).

Butterfly Conservation Despite the name, involved in conservation of moths as well as butterflies. Lead Partner on moths for UK Biodiversity Action Plan and National Moth Recording Network. Publishes *Butterfly*. Contact: Butterfly Conservation, Manor Yard, East Lulworth, Wareham, Dorset BH20 5QP (www.butterfly-conservation.org).

Index of scientific names